Basic Practice of
Chemical Engineering

Basic Practice of Chemical Engineering

Esber I. Shaheen

Institute of Gas Technology,
Gas Developments Corporation,
and Illinois Institute of Technology

Houghton Mifflin Company · Boston
Atlanta · Dallas · Geneva, Illinois · Hopewell, New Jersey · Palo Alto · London

Printed in the U.S.A.

Library of Congress Catalog Card Number: 74-14499

ISBN: 0-395-17645-X

Cover photograph courtesy of Mobil Oil Corporation.

Contents

5. Energy Balances in Physical and Thermochemical Processes

Preface

The broad discipline of chemical engineering, which interacts with the other technological professions, requires an effective introductory course. An overall study of chemical engineering practice has been prepared, reflecting the current demand for generalized education and stressing the solution to practical and current problems in the chemical process industries. The aim is to serve both students in chemical and petroleum engineering and others who are involved in the chemical industry and need educational training in this discipline.

Chapter 1 serves to inform and enlighten the reader about the chemical engineering profession. My experience has been that beginners are at a loss as to what chemical engineers do and what their relation is to other engineers. The old practice has been to ignore this important factor and to plunge directly into dimensions and units. In Chapter 2, a primary emphasis has been placed on dimensions and units from a broad and practical point of view. The examples and the problems at the end of this chapter have been chosen to convey ideas about basic equations and chemical engineering fundamentals. While the sutdent is learning dimensions, units, and definitions, he becomes acquainted with relationships which he will encounter later in his career.

Gases, liquids, and humidity are covered in Chapter 3. The treatment is clear and concise, but with sufficient coverage of fundamental concepts; unnecessary details are eliminated so that the basic principles are not buried with superfluous material. The student is gaining experience and is now better prepared to tackle the material balances in Chapter 4. Numerous examples of current practice are used to facilitate assimilation of subject material. The student or engineer is prepared to solve not only the small-scale problems, but also those dealing with full-scale plants. Unsteady state problems are included here for the purpose of preserving continuity. The use of computers is illustrated at the end of Chapter 4, from which the student should get a direct "feel" for the effectiveness of computers in solving certain material balance problems. This is presented on a moderate basis so that the attention of the student is not detracted from the main task of learning the material balances.

Energy balances are presented in Chapter 5 in a comprehensive and progressive manner. Simultaneous use of material and energy balances in flow situations is described, and the mechanical energy equation is introduced, giving the student a necessary understanding of the overall picture of balances. While real problems are used and the applied approach is stressed, theoretical analysis is given its due weight, and some elements of thermodynamics are offered for consideration.

The two major issues facing the world today—energy and environment—are both depicted in problems and descriptive material in the text. Chapter 5, which covers energy balances in physical and thermochemical processes, includes a special section on material and energy interaction in pollution control.

Numerous problems at the end of each chapter (except Chapter 1) have been titled and categorized to enable the instructor to utilize them most effectively. The answers to these problems are supplied in an accompanying Solutions Manual. A mathematical review, certain derivations, and necessary data are included in the Appendices.

The author expresses his sincere appreciation to Dr. W. M. Langdon whose broad industrial experience helped in strengthening the applied touch in this book.

Students at various universities, especially at Illinois Institute of Technology, were indeed very helpful during classroom trials. In this regard, specific thanks are given to Richard J. Lowery, Robert E. Clute, R. C. B. Poon, W. Chantarasorn, M. Abul-Hamayel, and Remon Dihu. Drs. L. L. Tavlarides, R. E. Peck, and R. C. Kintner offered many encouraging and constructive comments. Dr. H. F. Johnson of the University of Tennessee, and Dean R. G. Griskey of the University of Wisconsin were a genuine source of guidance, wisdom, and inspiration. The eagerness to help manifested by Mrs. W. Bachman and Mr. Al Avadian is certainly appreciated.

Special acknowledgment is made to Dr. Glenn A. Atwood, University of Akron; Dr. R. F. Blanks, Michigan State University; Dr. Paul W. Murrill, Louisiana State University; Dr. Thomas G. Smith, University of Notre Dame; Dr. J. R. Thygeson, Drexel University; and Dr. Robert Torrest, University of New Hampshire. Their reviews, constructive criticism and help gave a unique contribution to the book, and their efforts are most sincerely appreciated.

The family of the author was a source of strength and determination. The deepest appreciation is expressed to my wife, Shirley, for her constant encouragement, her valuable suggestions, organization, and numerous typings of the ever reviewed and revised manuscript.

ESBER I. SHAHEEN

1.
Chemical Engineering Practice

Engineering is a noble profession in which knowledge of mathematics and natural laws is applied to the use of materials and forces of nature for the welfare of humanity. Man walking on the moon, jets touring the globe, a superhighway sweeping across a mammoth suspension bridge, a maze of chemical complexes making products for a brighter tomorrow—all attest to the ingenuity and skill of the engineer. As a creative and dynamic profession, engineering combines initiative, imagination, and good judgment—along with art and science.

1.1 THE ART AND SCIENCE OF ENGINEERING

In many respects engineering is an art and not a science. It includes many factors arising from safety considerations and set precedents. A good engineer can treat this art as a science for obtaining more useful products. To do so, he must have a real and intuitive understanding of his profession, along with continual and extensive practice. Observing the rules in every case may be correct, but it is not good engineering. Inevitably, good engineering means making some mistakes, but not the same ones and not too many.

The most difficult task is to treat engineering factors with the respect they deserve. Suppose we are designing a heat exchanger for an average duty of 10^6 Btu/hr. The question comes up about safety, or overdesign, factors; some organizations automatically add 10 to 50% overage. Company policy can take all the engineering decisions out of a job, but without professional judgment, there is no engineering. It is a good idea to design for the exact requirements and have an overage factor only if cost or other conditions require it.

1.2   PRODUCING A USEFUL RESULT

The engineer should employ methods of calculation that lead to the best results in the most efficient manner. Moreover the result must be communicated to the user. The engineer should be able to choose and use optimum conditions, and he should be able to recognize when he has obtained the right answer.

The availability of computers makes almost any type of calculation an easy accomplishment. However, this is not entirely advantageous, since the calculation can become routine and the practitioner may lose the sense and feeling for what he is producing. The best guideline is to exercise *good judgment*.

1.3   THE CHEMICAL ENGINEERING PROFESSION AND THE ENGINEER

In today's complicated and sophisticated technology, the various engineering disciplines—mechanical, chemical, metallurgical, environmental, sanitary, and others—overlap in many areas. These include fluid mechanics, heat transfer, thermodynamics, and so on. The new trend toward general education puts the accent on fundamentals and requires specialization in certain areas. This specialization is reflected in a wide spectrum of engineering functions, as shown in Figures 1.1, 1.2, 1.3, and 1.4.

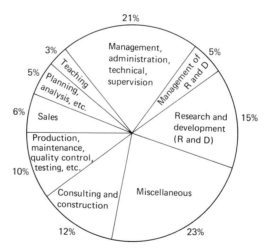

Figure 1.1   Occupational distribution of all engineers (1). (Numbers in parentheses are keyed to references at the end of this chapter.)

Chemical engineering is a profession dedicated to the service of humanity through research and development, and, through the design, construction, and operation of plants, to making chemical products at a profit. It is unique in its strong dependence on chemistry as well as on the basic sciences of physics and mathematics.

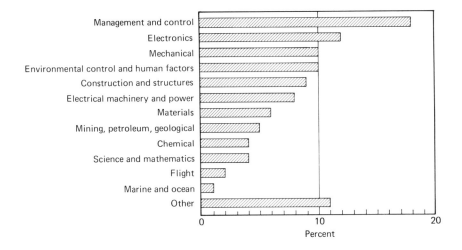

Figure 1.2   Employed area of technology (1).

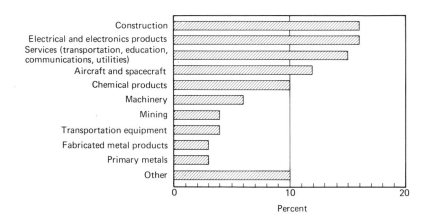

Figure 1.3   Employment product or services (1).

There is a basic distinction between a chemist and a chemical engineer. The chemist discovers and makes products in ounces on laboratory benches, while the chemical engineer discovers products and makes them in tons in a large plant designed and built through his ingenuity. You can imagine a myriad of problems in going from laboratory scale to full-plant scale. In discovering nylon, the chemist did not worry about economics or about the translation of this discovery to fit basic needs of humanity. The chemical engineer studies the economics of a process; he designs reactors, special pumps, extruders, spinnerets; he draws on his vast knowledge of fluid flow, heat transfer, thermodynamics, mass transfer, and kinetics. Then comes the final product: strong fibers to clothe an exploded population and to provide fabrics with a new "feel." The chemist is not an engineer at all, for he does not have the basic engineering fundamentals nor the strong dose of mathematics usually acquired by engineers.

Almost every facet of industry employs chemical engineers, and their contributions to mankind include: life support systems in other environments, peaceful use of atomic energy, synthetic rubber, textiles, petrochemicals, and many more. Many achievements in biomedical engineering also depend heavily on the genius of the chemical engineer. Two prime examples are the artificial kidney and the heart pump.

What are the functions of chemical engineers? We will look at some of them in the next section.

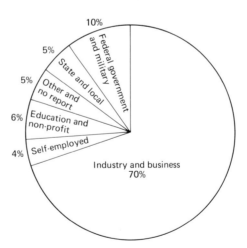

Figure 1.4   Type of employer (1).

1.4 CHEMICAL ENGINEERING JOBS

Management

Management in one form or another is a very common function for 21% of all engineers, and especially for the chemical engineer. It includes project managers, leaders of small teams, supervisors of operating units, and administrators of various areas.

Research and Development

In this field, the chemical engineer develops new ideas and improves old processes and products. The importance of the field is attested to by the large number of engineers engaged in it (20%, according to Figure 1.1). More than 50% of all present chemical products and processes were unknown 10 years ago. In research and development the chemical engineer today is engaged in finding ways to de-salinate sea water on a large scale, maintaining life in both outer space and under-sea explorations, solving our environmental problems, and increasing food re-sources for the undernourished peoples of the world.

Design

In design work, the engineer combines scientific principles with practical ex-perience. In order to design a chemical process, for example, the engineer must have a good understanding of equipment design. Most equipment is specified on a custom basis, and this task requires a common understanding between the designer and the manufacturer. Figures 1.5 and 1.6 show two simple process designs; the chemical engineer should be able to design the equipment used in these processes.

Project Engineering

The project engineer supervises all the steps involved in carrying a new idea from research to production. Obviously this kind of work encompasses a general prac-tice of all chemical engineering functions. In fact, project engineering is a gener-ality of the field and is a favorite stepping stone into management.

Consulting

The chemical process industry customarily employs outside firms or individuals to furnish professional services in their specialty. The chemical engineer can do

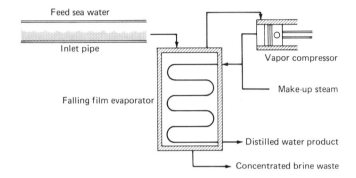

Figure 1.5 Vapor-compression process for making fresh water from sea water.

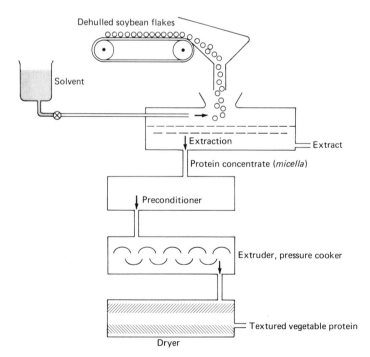

Figure 1.6 The extrusion cooking process for making meat substitutes.

consulting as an individual, as an associate of an engineering group, or as a full-time employee of a consulting firm. Part-time consulting is often done by university professors. Consulting nominally covers only the giving of professional advice. In reality it usually includes making detailed design specifications and plans, supervisory tests, and so on. Thus the activities of a consultant can involve every facet of chemical engineering.

Production

Each major operating unit of a plant is usually the responsibility of one or two engineers. Production engineers have the dual responsibility of operating the units safely at optimum efficiency and of exercising leadership and good social judgment when dealing with the working force. Some production engineers must be prepared to trouble-shoot their own equipment when the need arises.

Sales Engineering

This kind of work deals mainly with customer service and includes the coordination of customer needs with plant production. Such service, along with the sale of final products, requires a high order of general engineering knowledge. Personality, tact, and other social skills are necessary for a successful sales career.

Planning

The tremendous pace at which changes take place in the chemical industry requires that some chemical engineers be continually engaged in planning for what the needs may be three, five, or ten years from now.

Academic Careers

The teaching profession makes the Ph.D. degree almost a must for those wishing to pursue an academic career. It also involves research, development, publications, and consulting. The various levels of academic training and their distribution in several disciplines are shown in Figures 1.7 and 1.8.

Others

There are many other areas where chemical engineers fit: patent law, insurance adjustment, safety, lubrication, air conditioning, nuclear engineering, and so on.

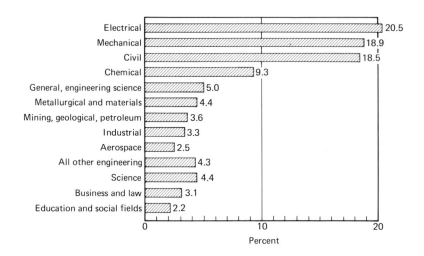

Figure 1.7   Distribution of engineers according to field of interest (1).

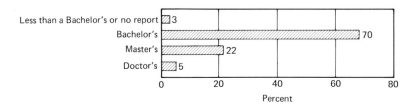

Figure 1.8   Degree distribution for all engineers (1).

A number of new disciplines and industries have emerged. Leading these are environmental engineering, biomedical engineering, new food technologies, space exploration, desalination, and ocean floor exploitation. The chemical engineer is playing a leading role in all these areas.

1.5   INTERESTING STATISTICS ABOUT ENGINEERS AND CHEMICAL ENGINEERS

Many interesting figures about the engineering profession have been compiled by the Engineers Joint Council (1). Data were obtained through National Register Questionnaire. These data indicate that the engineer has a median age of 43 years (Figure 1.9). Seventy percent of all engineers work for industry (Figure 1.4).

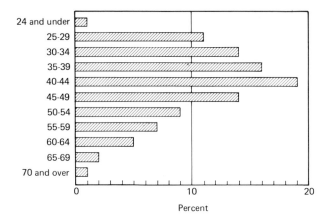

Figure 1.9   Age distribution of engineers (1).

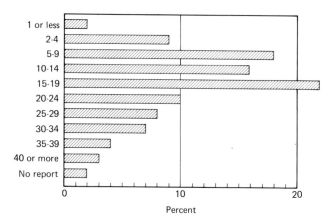

Figure 1.10   Years of professional experience (1).

Seventy percent have only a bachelor's degree (Figure 1.8). Sixty percent of all engineers are electrical, mechanical, and civil (Figure 1.7), rather evenly divided among the three disciplines, and 9% are chemical engineers. The average engineer has 15 to 19 years of experience (Figure 1.10). This survey, taken from professional societies, membership, does not reflect recent graduates who are not affiliated with technical organizations.

A major problem arises from fast-changing technology, and there is considerable discussion among engineers on the issue of general versus specialized training.

The opinion of chemical engineers (4) shown in Figures 1.11 and 1.12 favors specialized engineering, management engineering, and higher education through the master's degree.

The need for engineers and chemical engineers through the years is projected in Figure 1.13.

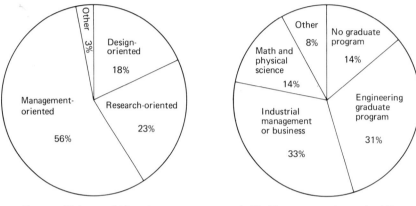

a. If you could choose, which graduate engineering program would you take?

b. Would you go to graduate school if you could do your education over again?

Figure 1.11   Two replies indicate the chemical engineer's high regard for graduate work and business courses (5).

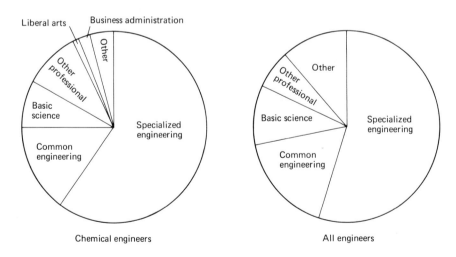

Chemical engineers

All engineers

Figure 1.12   How engineers would choose if they could repeat their undergraduate education (5).

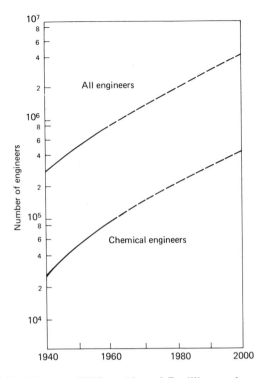

**Figure 1.13 The year 2000 could see 4.7 million engineers at work
in the U.S.; 10% should be chemical engineers (5).**

1.6 SALARIES

The salary compensation for different engineering categories is illustrated in
Table 1.1 for the years 1967, 1976, and 1984.

**Table 1.1 ESTIMATED SALARIES FOR ENGINEERS
IN THE YEARS AHEAD (2)**

Position	Salary increase rate (%)	Salary 1967 ($/yr)	Salary 1976 ($/yr)	Salary 1984 ($/yr)
Plant manager	3	25,000	32,000	41,000
Senior scientist	7	24,000	40,000	70,000
Senior industrial engineer	3	20,000	25,000	33,000
Design engineer, 10-yr experience	4	15,000	21,000	31,000

1.7 CONCLUDING COMMENTS

Engineering in general and chemical engineering in particular are at a crossroads of history, in the midst of change and extensive debate. The social and environmental challenges of today and of the years to come will ultimately reshape the profession. In the process of reasserting their status and importance to society, chemical engineers will play a pioneering role in shaping the future. Who knows? Perhaps this world could use some engineers in its political machine; they have never been very active in politics.

REFERENCES

1. Anonymous. The engineering profession in new profile. *Engineer,* March-April 1969, pp. 24-31.

2. Anonymous. What will it be like in 1984? *Chemical Engineering Progress* 64(10):29 (October 1968).

3. American Institute of Chemical Engineers. *Will you be a chemical engineer?* New York.

4. American Society for Engineering Education. 1964. *Chemical engineering education.*

5. Ellwood, Peter. Educating tomorrow's chemical engineer. *Chemical Engineering,* 26 September 1966.

6. Hughson, R. V. Salaries: Watch out—the new grads are catching up. *Chemical Engineering,* 26 August 1968.

7. Lawton, R. W. Staying alive in spacecraft. *Chemical Engineering,* 4 July 1966.

8. Manufacturing Chemists Association. *Careers ahead in the chemical industry.* Washington, D.C.

9. Scrimgeour, R. B. Engineering salaries continue upward. *Chemical Engineering Progress* 65(8):17-24 (August 1969).

10. University of Tennessee, Department of Chemical and Metallurgical Engineering Publications. 1964. *The field of the chemical engineer.* Knoxville, Tennessee.

QUESTIONS FOR DISCUSSION

1. How would you design a process for recycling air in an undersea laboratory?

2. In your opinion, what are the most important assets of a "successful" engineer, aside from the knowledge of his particular field of engineering?

3. Does the public pay for the engineers' overdesign, or "fudge," factor?

4. The text describes a wide spectrum of engineering careers. Name six of the job functions mentioned in the text.

5. According to the text, what percentage of all engineers are chemical engineers?

6. What must an engineer do to assure himself of a firm background in business and economics?

7. Describe a possible process for the manufacture of synthetic detergent flakes.

8. What is chemical engineering?

9. If you were to take a graduate engineering course, what would it be?

10. Describe a manufacturing process for sugar.

11. In what respects may chemical engineering be thought of as an art rather than a science?

12. Pollution has become a major problem of our times. In view of this, the chemical engineer must be aware of the ecological dangers that might arise in an industrial plant. Atomic energy is considered a clean method for producing electricity. However, there are always ecological dangers. Describe a few of these when producing electricity by atomic energy.

13. When designing an industrial system, the chemical engineer must be aware of all the factors making up the system. For example, consider a unit that cools a high temperature gas by passing water over pipe coils of the gas. What factors must be taken into consideration when designing this unit?

14. If you were to build a chemical plant, what type of engineers would you choose?

15. Do you think that there will be specialization in a major field of engineering? If so, why?

16. What salary could a 1978 chemical engineering student expect upon graduation?

17. Why must there be a certain feeling or intuitive understanding for any given engineering problem?

18. A company manufactures a useful product; but during the processing of this product, SO_2 gas is given off. What could the factory do to reduce the amount of this pollutant that is emitted to the air?

19. Suggest a process for making fresh water from sea water.

20. Suggest an ideal plant for waste disposal.

21. What role does a chemical engineer's judgment play in the practice of his profession?

22. Describe a simple process for making skim milk in a powdered form. Recover butter as a by-product.

23. What possible effect might the requirement of more business and administration courses by schools in their engineering programs have on the occupational distribution of engineers?

24. Why does a successful chemical engineer need to have common sense and good judgment as well as a general knowledge of engineering?

25. What is the difference between *research* and *development*?

26. A manufacturer wishes to produce a certain new product. Explain how the different job functions of various chemical engineers could contribute to the development of this product.

27. Acetylene (C_2H_2) can be made by adding water to calcium carbide. Draw a simple flow diagram for the reaction.

28. Your boss is happy with your method for making acetylene, but being economy-minded, he wants to know what can be done with all the $Ca(OH)_2$ you are making. Any suggestions?

29. Describe three different processes for energy conversion.

30. Discuss the factors involved in designing a self-contained life support system for use on lengthy space voyages.

31. How would you design a process for the manufacture of animal glue?

32. Discuss a process for purifying water.

33. Describe a unit for recycling scrap metal.

2.
Dimensions, Units, and Definitions

The chemical engineer will discover that data are usually expressed in many different ways that are sometimes inconsistent and not clearly defined. Acquaintance with these various ways is essential, and one should be able to convert readily from one system to another. The conversion of units via handbook is simple, convenient, and correct. However, in practice it is better to be able to convert units by using logical procedures, and to keep track of the units.

This chapter covers systems of dimensions, units, and auxiliary properties that are necessary in chemical engineering practice. The latter portion of the chapter contains examples to illustrate the manipulation of units, using the various systems interchangeably.

2.1 DIMENSIONS AND UNITS

Physical quantities are identified by dimensions and units. *Mass, length,* and *time* are basic physical concepts referred to as *dimensions.* Thus dimension is a general term for our basic concepts of measurement. A dimension is quantitatively expressed in a unit. For example, the dimension of temperature may be in units of degrees Fahrenheit or of degrees centigrade (Celsius*); the dimension of length may be expressed in centimeters, feet, inches, and so on. However, long distances in outer space are expressed in units of light years (the distance light travels in one year; the velocity of light is 3×10^8 m/sec).

---

*This is now the standard term, but engineers invariably use *centigrade* instead of *Celsius*. It should be realized that *centigrade* and *Celsius* refer to the same scale.

Basically, there are two systems of units, the *international* or *metric system* (SI) and the *English system*. The latter is used in two versions, the *customary English* and the *American engineering system* (AES).

There is continual effort to change to the international (metric) system. Nearly all nations of the world are adopting it. However, United States engineering work will use American engineering units for a few more years to come. The conversion to the metric system is moving progressively, despite claims that the conversion process is expensive.

International (Metric) System

Historically the idea of the metric system was initiated in France in the year 1670. It was then proposed to have a standard unit based on a permanent measure provided by nature. For length, the choice was the ten millionth portion of the distance from the pole to the equator along the meridian passing through Paris. This unit of length was called the meter.* The unit of mass, the gram, was based on this dimension expressed as a volume of water; namely, $(1 \text{ m} \times 10^{-2})^3$ or 1 cm^3 has a mass of 1 gram at maximum density 4°C. The international or metric system has two subsystems.

1. CGS system (centimeter-gram-second).   It includes the following basic units.

Dimension	Symbol	Unit
Length	L	centimeter (cm)
Mass	M	gram (g)
Time	θ	second (sec)
Temperature	T	degrees Kelvin (°K)

The unit of force is defined by

$$1 \text{ dyne} = 1 \text{ g} \times 1 \text{ cm/sec}^2$$

Now consider Newton's law of motion:

$$F = k_n \cdot m \cdot a \tag{2.1}$$

*Present definitions of units employ more accurate and reproducible quantities. For example, 1 m $= 1.65076373 \times 10^6$ times the wavelength of krypton-86.

where

$$F = \text{force}$$

$$k_n = \text{Newton's proportionality constant}$$

$$m = \text{mass}$$

$$a = \text{acceleration}$$

The value of the constant of proportionality is determined solely by the units chosen for F, m, and a. Thus in the cgs system, one gram mass with an acceleration of 1 cm/sec^2, that is, one dyne, will make $k_n = 1$. An equivalent expression is

$$k_n = \frac{F}{ma} = \frac{1 \text{ g} \times 1 \text{ cm/sec}^2}{1 \text{ g} \times 1 \text{ cm/sec}^2} = 1$$

2. MKS system (meter-kilogram-second). The unit of force is the newton. A newton is defined as

$$1 \text{ newton} = 1 \text{ kg} \times 1 \text{ m/sec}^2$$

and the value of k_n is one.

Table 2.1 contains the common prefixes used to express multiples of units. For example, multiples of meter may be expressed as kilometer, decameter, centimeter, decimeter, etc. A *deci-* is one tenth of a basic unit, and a *kilo-* is equal to

Table 2.1   PREFIXES FOR MULTIPLE UNITS

Common prefix	Meaning
Femto-	10^{-15}
Pico-	10^{-12}
Nano-	10^{-9}
Micro-	10^{-6}
Milli-	10^{-3}
Centi-	10^{-2}
Deci-	10^{-1}
Deca-	10^{1}
Hecto-	10^{2}
Kilo-	10^{3}
Mega-	10^{6}
Giga-	10^{9}

one thousand basic units (for example, 1 kilogram = 1000 grams; 1 kilometer = 1000 meters).

English System

The English system is a legacy of the Roman occupation of Britain. In modern times it is stated in the three forms described below.

1. FPS (English absolute) system. It includes the following units.

Dimension	Symbol	Unit
Length	L	foot (ft)
Mass	M	pound mas (lb_m)
Time	θ	second (sec)
Temperature	T	degrees Rankine (°R)

The unit of force is the poundal, defined as

$$1 \text{ pdl} = 1 \text{ poundal} = 1 \text{ lb}_m \times 1 \text{ ft/sec}^2$$

which, as in the metric system, gives $k_n = 1$.

2. Gravitational system. This system has two versions, the British engineering and the American engineering.

British engineering system. The basic units in this system are as follows.

Dimension	Symbol	Unit
Length	L	foot (ft)
Force	F	pound weight (lb_w) or pound force (lb_f)
Time	θ	second (sec)
Temperature	T	degrees Rankine (°R)

The *pound weight* is the force exerted by the earth's gravitational attraction on one pound mass. The unit of mass, known as the *slug*, is defined as

$$1 \text{ slug} = \frac{1 \text{ lb}_w \text{ or } lb_f}{1 \text{ ft/sec}^2}$$

while

$$lb_m = \frac{1\ lb_f}{32.2\ ft/sec^2}$$

and from

$$F = k_n\, m\, a \qquad\qquad (2.1)$$

$$k_n = F/m\, a = 1$$

In other words, 1 slug = 32.2 lb_m = 32.2 lb_w at the surface of the earth. In this system, there is no mention of lb_m.

American engineering system (AES). In the AES, *pound mass and pound force are considered equivalent* since the variation of gravitational acceleration is negligible on the surface of the earth (Table 2.2).

Table 2.2 VARIATION OF GRAVITATIONAL ACCELERATION (g) WITH LOCATION

$g\left(\dfrac{g\text{-cm}}{sec^2}\right)$	Station	Latitude	Longitude	Elevation (meters)
979.192*	Yavapai, Arizona	36°, 3.9'	112°, 7.1'	2179
982.192	St. Michael, Alaska	63°, 28.5'	162°, 2.4'	1
980.278	Chicago, Illinois	41°, 47.4'	87°, 36.1'	182
980.112	Washington, D. C.	38°, 53.2'	77°, 0.5'	14
978.165	Monrovia, Liberia	6°, 9'	10°, 48.8'	41
981.188	Greenwich, England	51°, 28.6'	0.0	0.048
978.331	Bahia, Brazil	12°, 58.5'	38°, 31'	4

*The standard international value is 980.665.

From Newton's law we have

$$lb_f = k_n \times lb_m \times g$$

or

$$k_n = \frac{lb_f}{lb_m}\left(\frac{1}{32.174}\ \frac{sec^2}{ft}\right)$$

$$k_n = \frac{1}{32.174} \frac{\text{lb}_f}{\text{lb}_m} \times \frac{\text{sec}^2}{\text{ft}} = \frac{1}{g_c}$$

and

$$g_c = 32.174 \simeq 32.2 \; \frac{\text{lb}_m}{\text{lb}_f} \times \frac{\text{ft}}{\text{sec}^2}$$

This quantity, g_c, is a constant conversion factor that must be distinguished from the gravitational acceleration g. If you are on the surface of the moon, g_c is 32.2 numerically and g is 32.2/5, since the gravitational acceleration on the moon is approximately 6 ft/sec^2.

In the English system, the following equivalents should be mentioned:

$$1 \; \text{lb}_f = 1 \; \text{lb}_w = 32.2 \; \text{poundals}$$

$$= 32.2 \; \text{lb}_m \times 1 \; \text{ft/sec}^2$$

$$1 \; \text{slug} = 32.2 \; \text{lb}_m$$

These various systems are summarized in Table 2.3.

Table 2.3   DIMENSIONS AND UNITS IN VARIOUS SYSTEMS

System		Length	Mass	Time	Force
International (metric)	cgs	cm	g	sec	dyne
	mks	m	kg	sec	newton
English absolute	fps	ft	lb_m	sec	poundal
BES British engineering (gravitational)		ft	slug	sec	lb_w or lb_f
AES American engineering (gravitational)		ft	lb_m	sec	lb_f

Dimensional Consistency

Every physical relationship expressed in the form of an equation must be dimensionally consistent; i.e., all the units should be equivalent on both sides of the equation. Problems often arise from incomplete definition of dimensional constants.

From basic dimensions, we can derive net dimensions for many properties in chemical engineering. Let us consider the two systems: $ML\theta T$ or mass, length, time, and temperature, and the $ML\theta TFH$ or mass, length, time, temperature, force, and heat. Table 2.4 lists some useful properties with their dimensions expressed in general form. The use of these units and dimensions is illustrated in the following examples.

Table 2.4 DIMENSIONS OF VARIOUS QUANTITIES

Quantity	Dimension	
	$ML\theta TFH$	$ML\theta T$
Velocity	L/θ	L/θ
Mass flow rate	M/θ	M/θ
Pressure	F/L^2	$M/L\theta^2$
Viscosity	$M/L\theta$	$M/L\theta$
Density	M/L^3	M/L^3
Surface tension	F/L	M/θ^2
$DV\rho/\mu$ = Reynolds number	None	None
Mass flux	$M/L^2\theta$	$M/L^2\theta$
Temperature	T	T
Heat transfer coefficient	$H/\theta L^2 T$	$M/\theta^3 T$
Thermal diffusivity	L^2/θ	L^2/θ
Mass diffusivity	L^2/θ	L^2/θ
Kinematic viscosity	L^2/θ	L^2/θ
Thermal conductivity	$H/L\theta T$	$ML/\theta^3 T$
Heat	H	ML^2/θ^2
Rate of heat transfer	H/θ	ML^2/θ^3
Specific heat	H/MT	$L^2/\theta^2 T$
Enthalpy	H/M	L^2/θ^2

Example 2.1   Conversion of length units

The moon is 240,000 miles from the earth. Express this distance in

1. Kilometers
2. Light-years

given that the velocity of light in free space is

$$c = 3 \times 10^8 \text{ m/sec} = 186,000 \text{ mi/sec}$$

and that 1 light-year is the distance traveled by light in 1 year.

Solution

1. Distance $= 240{,}000$ mi $\times 1.61$ km/mi $= 386{,}400$ km ◁

2. Distance traveled $=$ speed $\times$ time

$$1 \text{ light-year} = 186{,}000 \text{ mi/sec} \times 1 \text{ yr}$$

$$= 186{,}000 \, \frac{\text{mi-yr}}{\text{sec}} \times \frac{365.25 \text{ days}}{\text{yr}} \times \frac{24 \text{ hr}}{\text{day}} \times \frac{60 \text{ min}}{\text{hr}} \times \frac{60 \text{ sec}}{\text{min}}$$

$$= 5.87 \times 10^{12} \text{ mi}$$

$$\text{Distance} = 240{,}000 \text{ mi} \times \frac{1 \text{ light-year}}{5.87 \times 10^{12} \text{ mi}}$$

$$= 4.90 \times 10^{-8} \text{ light-year} \quad ◁$$

Example 2.2   Relationship between g and g_c

Determine whether or not g and g_c are numerically equal in each of the following systems of units:

1. cgs system

2. American engineering system

3. Poundal, lb_m, ft, sec

4. lb_f, slug, ft, sec

Solution

From Newton's second law, $F = k_n ma$, we can determine g_c as the reciprocal of the constant k_n:

$$g_c = \frac{1}{k_n} = \frac{ma}{F}$$

1. In the cgs system,

$$g_c = \frac{1 \text{ gram} \times 1 \text{ cm/sec}^2}{1 \text{ dyne}} = 1 \quad ◁$$

2. In the American engineering system, the mass (in lb_m) is numerically equal to the weight (in lb_f). Therefore,

$$g_c = \frac{m}{F} \times g = \frac{1 \text{ lb}_m}{1 \text{ lb}_f} \times 32.2 \frac{\text{ft}}{\text{sec}^2} = 32.2 \frac{\text{lb}_m \text{ ft}}{\text{lb}_f \text{ sec}^2}$$

3. In the English absolute (fps) system,

$$g_c = \frac{1 \text{ lb}_m \times 1 \text{ ft/sec}^2}{1 \text{ poundal}} = 1$$

4. In the British engineering system,

$$g_c = \frac{1 \text{ slug} \times 1 \text{ ft/sec}^2}{1 \text{ lb}_f} = 1$$

Therefore, only in the American engineering system is g_c numerically equal to g, near the surface of the earth.

Example 2.3   Use of g_c

1. Gravitational acceleration at the moon's surface is $1/5\, g$ (at the earth's surface, $g = 32.2$ ft/sec^2). What is the weight of a body on the moon's surface if its mass is 5000 lb$_m$?

2. Find the kinetic energy of 100 lb$_m$ moving at 5 ft/sec on

   a. The moon's surface

   b. The earth's surface

Solution

1. $$F = \frac{1}{g_c} ma = \frac{1}{32.2 \frac{\text{lb}_m\text{-ft}}{\text{lb}_f\text{-sec}^2}} \times 5000 \text{ lb}_m \times \frac{32.2 \text{ ft/sec}^2}{5}$$

    $$F = \text{weight} = 1000 \text{ lb}_f$$

2. Kinetic energy is independent of weight, as expressed by the equation

$$\text{K.E.} = \frac{1}{2} mv^2 \times \frac{1}{g_c}$$

Therefore, the kinetic energy at both the earth's surface and the moon's is

$$\text{K.E.} = \frac{1}{2} \times 100 \text{ lb}_m \times (5 \tfrac{\text{ft}}{\text{sec}})^2 \times \cfrac{1}{32.2 \cfrac{\text{lb}_m\text{-ft}}{\text{lb}_f\text{-sec}^2}} = 38.9 \text{ ft-lb}_f$$

Example 2.4 Dimensional analysis and g_c

Some chemical engineering textbooks define the friction factor for fluid flow in tubes by the relationship

$$f = \frac{D(-\Delta P)}{2\rho v^2 \Sigma L}$$

where

f = friction factor (dimensionless)

D = tube diameter, ft

ΔP = pressure drop in the tube, lb_f/ft^2

ρ = fluid density, lb_m/ft^3

v = average fluid velocity over a cross section, ft/sec

ΣL = total effective length of the tube, ft

What is needed to make this equation dimensionally constant? Prove your result.

Solution

Using only the units of the expression

$$\frac{D\Delta P}{\rho v^2 \Sigma L} = \cfrac{\text{ft} \times \cfrac{\text{lb}_f}{\text{ft}^2}}{\cfrac{\text{lb}_m}{\text{ft}^3} \times \cfrac{\text{ft}^2}{\text{sec}^2} \times \text{ft}} = \text{lb}_f \times \frac{\text{sec}^2}{\text{lb}_m\text{-ft}}$$

multiply by g_c:

$$\text{lb}_f \times \frac{\text{sec}^2}{\text{lb}_m\text{-ft}} \times 32.2 \frac{\text{lb}_m}{\text{lb}_f} \frac{\text{ft}}{\text{sec}^2} = \text{dimensionless}$$

Therefore, the equation is dimensionally consistent with the right side if multiplied by g_c:

$$f = \frac{g_c D(-\Delta P)}{2\rho v^2 \Sigma L}$$

(Isn't g_c wonderful?)

Example 2.5 Values of g_c and relative magnitude of force units

1. Find the value and units of g_c in the mks and the AES systems.
2. List in order of decreasing magnitude the following forces.

   a. 1 lb_f

   b. 1 poundal

   c. 1 dyne

   d. 1 newton

Solution

1. In the mks system,

$$g_c = \frac{ma}{F} = \frac{1 \text{ kg} \times 1 \text{ m/sec}^2}{1 \text{ newton}} = 1$$

since 1 newton = 1 kg $\times$ 1 m/sec^2. Then because mass (in lb_m) is numerically equal to weight (in lb_f) in the American engineering system,

$$g_c = \frac{mg}{w} = \frac{1 \text{ lb}_m \times 32.2 \text{ ft/sec}^2}{1 \text{ lb}_f} = 32.2 \frac{\text{lb}_m\text{-ft}}{\text{lb}_f\text{-sec}^2}$$

2. To compare relative magnitudes of various forces, we must first express them in the same system of units. Let this system be the cgs.

a. $\quad 1 \text{ lb}_f = 32.2 \frac{\text{lb}_m\text{-ft}}{\text{sec}^2} \times \frac{454 \text{ g}}{\text{lb}_m} \times \frac{12 \text{ in.}}{\text{ft}} \times \frac{2.54 \text{ cm}}{\text{in.}} = 446,000 \frac{\text{g-cm}}{\text{sec}^2}$

b. 1 poundal $= 1 \frac{\text{lb}_m\text{-ft}}{\text{sec}^2} \times \frac{454 \text{ g}}{\text{lb}_m} \times \frac{12 \text{ in.}}{\text{ft}} \times \frac{2.54 \text{ cm}}{\text{in.}} = 13,838 \frac{\text{g-cm}}{\text{sec}^2}$

c. $1 \text{ dyne} = 1 \dfrac{\text{g-cm}}{\text{sec}^2}$

d. $1 \text{ newton} = 1 \dfrac{\text{kg-m}}{\text{sec}^2} \times \dfrac{1000 \text{ g}}{\text{kg}} \times \dfrac{100 \text{ cm}}{\text{m}} = 100,000 \dfrac{\text{g-cm}}{\text{sec}^2}$

Therefore, the list of forces in decreasing magnitude is:

1. lb_f 2. Newton   3. Poundal   4. Dyne

Example 2.6   Viscosity of molten lead

Molten lead has the viscous properties shown in the following table. Determine the viscosity of lead in lb_m/ft-sec at 600°C.

Temperature (°C)	Viscosity (cp)
411	2.116
551	1.700
844	1.185

Solution

A plot of the given data will allow a relatively accurate value of viscosity by interpolation.

Therefore, the viscosity at 600°C is approximately 1.575 cp.

$$\mu = 1.575 \text{ cp} \times \frac{.01 \text{ poise}}{\text{centipoise}} \times \frac{1 \text{ g/cm-sec}}{1 \text{ poise}} \times \frac{1 \text{ lb}_m}{454 \text{ g}} \times \frac{2.54 \text{ cm}}{\text{in.}} \times \frac{12 \text{ in.}}{\text{ft}}$$

$$\mu = 1.06 \times 10^{-3} \text{ lb}_m/\text{ft-sec}$$

Example 2.7 Steel consumption of paper clips

During World War II the production of paper clips was curtailed to conserve steel for more essential purposes. Estimate the tons of steel saved per day assuming that

1. Population was 150,000,000.
2. Usage was 1 clip per day per person.
3. Density of the steel used was 7.81 g/cm^3.
4. Dimensions of the paper clip were:
   a. 1/32″ in diameter
   b. First loop: 1/4 in. × 1 in.
   c. Second loop: 1/4 in. × 1 1/4 in.

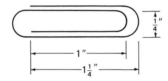

Solution

To determine the approximate length of the wire, treat the curved parts as straight.

$$\text{Length} = 2 \times 1 \text{ in.} + 2 \times 1\ 1/4 \text{ in.} + 3 \times 1/4 \text{ in.} = 5.25 \text{ in.}$$

$$\text{Volume} = \pi \times \left(\tfrac{1}{2} \times \tfrac{1}{32} \text{ in.}\right)^2 \times 5.25 \text{ in.} = 4.03 \times 10^{-3} \text{ in}^3$$

$$\text{Mass} = 4.03 \times 10^{-3}\frac{\text{in.}^3}{\text{clip}} \times \left(\frac{2.54 \text{ cm}}{\text{in.}}\right)^3 \times \frac{7.81 \text{ g}}{\text{cm}^3} \times \frac{\text{lb}_m}{454 \text{ g}}$$

$$\times \frac{\text{ton}}{2000 \text{ lb}_m} \times 1\frac{\text{clip}}{\text{person-day}} \times 1.5 \times 10^8 \text{ persons}$$

$$= 85.2 \text{ tons/day}$$

Example 2.8 Atmospheric temperature vs. altitude

Atmospheric temperature varies with altitude as shown in the accompanying table. Prepare a plot of temperature in °F versus distance in miles.

Distance from earth's surface (km)	Temperature ($^\circ$F)
0	59
1.6	36
3.2	24
4.8	0.6
6.4	−22
8.0	−35
9.6	−57
11.2	−70

Solution

If the conversion factor for kilometers to miles is forgotten, it can be found by converting centimeters to inches:

$$\frac{1 \text{ km}}{10^5 \text{ cm}} \times \frac{2.54 \text{ cm}}{\text{in.}} \times \frac{12 \text{ in.}}{\text{ft}} \times \frac{5280 \text{ ft}}{\text{mi}} = \frac{1.61 \text{ km}}{\text{mi}}$$

Distance	km	0	1.6	3.2	4.8	6.4	8.0	9.6	11.2
	mi	0	1.0	2.0	3.0	4.0	5.0	6.0	7.0

Using the converted values of distance, a plot can be constructed.

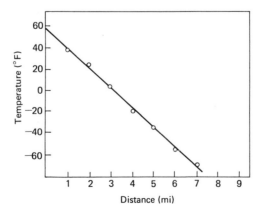

2.2 DEFINITIONS OF INTEREST

The Mole

A mole is a quantity of material whose weight is numerically equal to molecular weight. In the case of some solids such as iodine, sulfur, and carbon, the atomic weight is arbitrarily specified as molecular weight. Scientifically, the present basis is that carbon with an atomic number of 6 and mass number 12 has an atomic weight of exactly 12.000000 (specified as 12 atomic mass units).

Molecular quantities represent simple ratios of reacting substances and are universally used in chemical computations. In the American engineering system, we use the pound-mole (lb-mole), and if we speak of one molecular weight of CO_2, we would be considering

$$\frac{44 \text{ lb of } CO_2}{\text{lb-mole}}$$

In brief,

$$\text{g-moles} = \frac{\text{gram of substance}}{\text{molecular weight}} \qquad (2.2)$$

$$\text{lb-moles} = \frac{\text{pound mass of substance}}{\text{molecular weight}} \qquad (2.3)$$

$$1 \text{ lb-mole} = 454 \text{ (1 g-mole)}$$

$$= 454 \,(6.02 \times 10^{23}) \text{ molecules}$$

The number 6.02×10^{23} molecules (1 g-mole of any ideal substance) is known as *Avogadro's number.*

Molar Volume

The molar volume of an ideal gas is the volume occupied by one mole of the gas at standard temperature and pressure (STP). Thus 1 g-mole of CO_2 at zero $^\circ$C and one atmosphere occupies a volume approximately equal to 22.4 liters. Also, 1 lb-mole of an ideal gas at STP occupies a volume of 359 ft^3. These conclusions follow from Avogadro's law, namely, that at the same temperature and pressure, equal volumes of ideal gases contain the same number of molecules.

Mole and Mass Fractions

Given a mixture of n_A moles of substance A and n_B moles of substance B, the fractions of A and B are, respectively,

$$\text{Mole fraction of } A = \frac{\text{moles of } A}{\text{moles of } A + \text{moles of } B} = \frac{n_A}{n_A + n_B} \tag{2.4}$$

$$\text{Mole fraction of } B = \frac{n_B}{n_A + n_B} \tag{2.5}$$

And

$$\text{Mass fraction of } A = \frac{(n_A)(\text{molecular weight of } A)}{(n_A)(\text{molecular weight of } A) + (n_B)(\text{molecular weight of } B)} \tag{2.6}$$

$$= \frac{\text{mass of } A}{\text{mass of } A + \text{mass of } B} \tag{2.7}$$

Density and Specific Gravity

Density. The density of a substance is the mass per unit volume:

$$\rho = \frac{\text{mass}}{\text{volume}} = \frac{M}{V} \tag{2.8}$$

Thus the density of water at $4°C$* and one atmosphere is 62.4 lb_m/ft^3 or 1 g/cm^3. The density of mercury is 13.6 g/cm^3, or

$$13.6 \frac{g}{cm^3} \times \frac{lb_m}{454 \text{ g}} \times \left(\frac{30.48 \text{ cm}}{ft}\right)^3 = 13.6 \times 62.4 \frac{lb_m}{ft^3}$$

Thus, in order to convert density from g/cm^3 to lb_m/ft^3, all you have to do is multiply by the density of water, 62.4 lb_m/ft^3.

For ideal gases at STP,

$$\rho = \frac{\text{molecular weight}}{\text{molar volume}} \tag{2.9}$$

Thus,

$$\rho O_2 = \frac{32 \text{ g}}{22,400 \text{ cm}^3}$$

*The temperature for maximum density.

Specific gravity. In general, the specific gravity of a substance is the ratio of the density of that substance to the density of a reference substance at specified temperature and pressure. For liquids and solids this reference substance is the density of water taken at $4°C$, $25°C$, or $70°F$, and one atmosphere. For gases the reference substance is usually air, but at times H_2, N_2, or O_2 is used as a reference. In brief,

$$s = \text{specific gravity} = \frac{\rho_A}{\rho_R} = \frac{(\text{lb/ft}^3)_A}{(\text{lb/ft}^3)_R} \tag{2.10}$$

where

$$\rho_A = \text{density of substance } A$$

$$\rho_R = \text{density of reference substance}$$

For gases at the same temperature and pressure,

$$s = \frac{M_A}{M_R} = \frac{\text{molecular weight of } A}{\text{molecular weight of } R} \tag{2.11}$$

Many scales are used in general practice. Some of the following scales are used in various industries.

Degree Baumé

$$°\text{Bé}_{l\,60}^{\;60*} = \frac{140}{s} - 130 \quad \text{(lighter than water)} \tag{2.12}$$

$$°\text{Bé}_{h\,60}^{\;60} = 145 - \frac{145}{s} \quad \text{(heavier than water)} \tag{2.13}$$

Degree American Petroleum Institute

$$°\text{API}_{\;60}^{70} = \frac{141.5}{s} - 131.5 \quad \text{(lighter than water)} \tag{2.14}$$

Degree Twadell (used in England)

*Upper and lower numbers refer to temperature of measured and reference substances, respectively.

$$^{\circ}TW^{60}_{60} = 200\,(s - 1) \quad \text{(heavier than water)} \tag{2.15}$$

Degree Brix

$$^{\circ}Bx_{l}{}^{60}_{60} = \frac{400}{s} - 400 \quad \text{(lighter than water)} \tag{2.16}$$

$$^{\circ}Bx_{h}{}^{60}_{60} = \text{arbitrary scale} \quad \text{(heavier than water)}$$
$$1 \text{ division} = 1 \text{ wt \% sugar} \tag{2.17}$$

Specific Volume

This property is merely the reciprocal of density. The specific volume of water at $4^{\circ}C$ and one atmosphere is $1/62.4$ ft^3/lb$_m$; and for air at STP the specific volume is $359/29 = 12.38$ ft^3/lb$_m$. Other units may be used, for example: ft^3/g-mole, ft^3/lb-mole, liter/kg, cm^3/g, and so on.

Concentration

Concentration is the term used for the quantity of matter in a given volume. It is expressed in many ways, such as the following.

Common expressions. These include g/cm^3, moles/liter, and ppm (parts per million), used for very dilute concentrations. For example, the oxygen concentration in a water sample is 12 ppm:

$$\text{Concentration of } O_2 = \frac{12 \text{ lb } O_2}{10^6 \text{ lb } H_2O}$$

Molarity. This is the number of gram-moles of solute dissolved in 1 liter of solution.

$$\text{Molarity} = M = \frac{\text{g-moles of solute}}{1 \text{ liter of solution}} \tag{2.18}$$

A one molar (1 M) solution of alcohol C_2H_5OH would contain 46 g of alcohol dissolved in enough water to make 1 liter of solution.

Molality. This is the number of gram-moles of solute dissolved in 1000 g of solvent.

$$\text{Molality} = M' = \frac{\text{g-moles of solute}}{1000 \text{ g of solvent}} \qquad (2.19)$$

Molarity is more frequently used than molality.

Normality. Concentration expressed in mole equivalents of solute per liter of solution is called normality; equivalents depend on the type of reaction (oxidation, reduction, neutralization, and so on).

$$\text{Normality} = N = \frac{\text{g-mole equivalents}}{1 \text{ liter of solution}}$$

The equivalent weight of an acid is that amount which will yield one g-mole of acidic hydrogen, and for a base it is the quantity of base which will yield one g-mole of hydroxyl. For example,

$$\text{Equivalent weight of HCl} = \text{g-molecular weight}/1 = 36.5$$

$$\text{Equivalent weight of } H_2SO_4 = 98/2 = 49$$

$$\text{Equivalent weight of Ba(OH)}_2 = 171.38/2 = 85.7$$

To make 1 liter of 1 N solution of H_2SO_4, it is necessary to have 49 g of H_2SO_4. The normal solution is made up by adding the 49 g of acid* to about 500 g of water, cooling the mixture to room temperature and then adding sufficient water for the mixture to be 1 liter. Normal solutions of salts and bases are dealt with by extending the H^+ and OH^- concept. As an example, 1 N potassium phosphate K_3PO_4 is 212.3/3 = 70.77 g, since this quantity represents one equivalent of either the phosphate radical or potassium.

*Concentrated H_2SO_4 is available as 96% acid.

Pressure and Fluid Statics

Pressure is defined as force per unit area. The standard atmospheric pressure can be expressed in any of the following ways:

1 atmosphere (atm)

760 mm Hg

29.92 in. Hg

33.91 ft H_2O

14.7 psia (pound per square inch absolute)

1.013×10^6 dynes/cm^2

1.013×10^6 bars

In engineering, pressure is generally measured as gauge pressure relative to the actual barometric pressure. When one has 25 pounds pressure, it means 25 pounds per square inch gauge, and in absence of a barometric reading, this is equal to 39.7 or 40 psia. The general expression is

$$\text{Absolute pressure} = \text{gauge pressure} + \text{barometric pressure} \qquad (2.20)$$

The barometric pressure is generally taken to be 14.7 psia.

While the standard measure is the height of a column of mercury in an evacuated tube (Figure 2.1) the absolute pressure is usually measured by the movement of an evacuated diaphragm (aneroid barometer, Figure 2.2).

Manometers are often used to measure moderate pressures (Figures 2.3 and 2.4). For better understanding of the pressures given by manometers, an intro-

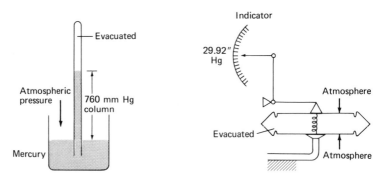

Figure 2.1. Mercury barometer   Figure 2.2. Aneroid barometer

duction to fluid statics is essential. As the name indicates, in fluid statics, there is no fluid motion. Without motions between fluid elements, there are no shear stresses, and viscosity does not enter into the formulation.

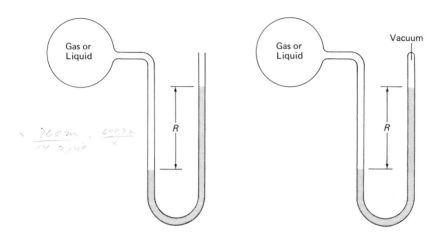

Figure 2.3. U-tube manometer,   Figure 2.4. Absolute pressure
              open-ended   manometer

Pressure at a given depth in a static fluid. Consider a vertical cylinder containing fluid at rest. The object is to develop an expression for the pressure exerted on a fluid element located at any desired height. Let such an element have a thickness dh as shown below.

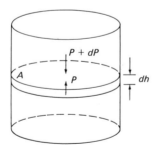

The fluid element is at equilibrium, and the forces acting downward must be equal to the forces acting upward. The downward forces are the pressure force $(P + dP)\, A$, and the weight of the element is $\rho\, g/g_c\, dh\, A$. The upward pressure force is PA, and the force balance is:

$$(P + dP) A + \rho \frac{g}{g_c} \, dh \, A = PA \tag{2.20a}$$

or

$$PA + dP \, A + \rho \frac{g}{g_c} \, dh \, A - PA = 0 \tag{2.20b}$$

and

$$dP = -\rho \frac{g}{g_c} \, dh \tag{2.20c}$$

Integrate both sides:

$$\int dP = - \int \rho \frac{g}{g_c} \, dh = P_2 - P_1 \tag{2.20d}$$

For constant density, the above equation reduces to

$$P_2 - P_1 = \rho (h_1 - h_2) \frac{g}{g_c} \tag{2.20e}$$

This equation gives the mathematical expression for hydrostatic equilibrium. From this relationship, we find the pressure at the bottom of a tank of height h as

$$P = \rho h \frac{g}{g_c} \tag{2.20f}$$

When a manometer reading is given by R, as shown in Figures 2.3 and 2.4, the equivalent pressure is

$$P = \rho R \frac{g}{g_c} \tag{2.20g}$$

The inclined manometer of Figure 2.5 is more sensitive than the usual manometer because of the inclination angle α. A vertical reading of h will be $R \sin \alpha$ for the inclined manometer. The pressure is found by the expression

$$P_2 - P_1 = R \sin \alpha \tag{2.20h}$$

To develop a relationship between pressures P_1 and P_2 exerted on the two ends of any configuration of manometers, it is recommended that you choose a datum plane, say O-O as shown in Figure 2.6. The existence of equilibrium tells us that the sum of downward forces exerted on the left side of the manometer is equal to the sum of downward forces exerted on the right, and at the same datum plane O-O. The equivalent force corresponding to the height of each fluid is solved for; the equality is set, and $P_1 - P_2$ is solved for.

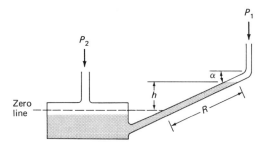

Figure 2.5.   Inclined-tube manometer for increased sensitivity

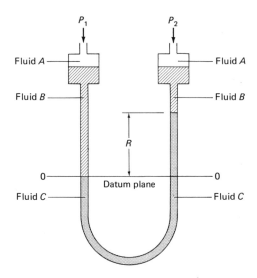

Figure 2.6.   Two-fluid manometer for increased sensitivity

For applied work requiring ruggedness and reliability, the Bourdon (Figure 2.7) and diaphragm (Figure 2.8) gages are most prevalent.

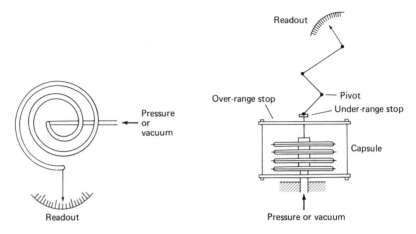

Figure 2.7. Spiral-type Bourdon gauge   **Figure 2.8. Diaphragm gauge**

Temperature

The concept of temperature in the AES is based on the difference between the melting and boiling points of water at 760 mm Hg absolute. These correspond to $0°$ and $100°$ in the centigrade scale, and $32°$ and $212°$ in the Fahrenheit scale (Figure 2.9). Conversion is done by using the number of degrees given, relative to a common reference temperature such as $0°C$ or $32°F$. The relationships for converting temperature measurements from one system to another are:

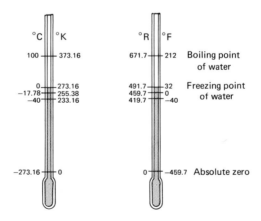

Figure 2.9. Common temperature scales

$$°C = \frac{(°F - 32)}{1.8} \qquad (2.21)$$

or

$$°F = 1.8 \, (°C) + 32 \qquad (2.22)$$

A more fundamental definition of temperature is that the volume change (ΔV) of an ideal gas at constant pressure is 1/273.16 or 1/492 part for a temperature difference of 1°C and 1°F, respectively, at the freezing point of water. Conversion of °C or °F to the absolute scales is done by using these expressions:

$$\text{Degree Kelvin} = °K = °C + 273 \qquad (2.23)$$

$$\text{Degree Rankine} = °R = °F + 460 \qquad (2.24)$$

and

$$\Delta(°R) = 1.8 \, \Delta(°K) \qquad \Delta(°F) = 1.8 \, \Delta(°C) \qquad (2.25)$$

To illustrate the conversion of 25°C to °F, consider

$$°F = 1.8 \, (25) + 32 = 77$$

In many cases, only temperature differences are involved. An example is heat capacity, which is numerically the same in both cgs and AES units:

$$7 \, \frac{\text{cal}}{\text{g-}°C} \times \frac{1 \, \text{Btu}}{252 \, \text{cal}} \times \frac{1}{\dfrac{1 \, \text{lb}_m}{454 \, \text{g}} \times \dfrac{1.8 \, (°F)}{(°C)}} = 7 \, \frac{\text{Btu}}{\text{lb}_m\text{-}°F}$$

The basic measures of temperature and the instruments used are listed below.

1. Thermal expansion (thermometers)

   a. Gas (Figure 2.10)

   b. Liquid

   c. Solid (Figure 2.11)

2. Electrical measures

   a. Thermocouples (Figure 2.12), based on the emf (electromotive force) developed between the hot and cold junctions of two dissimilar metals.

   b. Thermistors and platinum resistors, based on the change of electrical resistance with temperature.

3. Optical measures

    a. Pyrometer (Figure 2.13), based on color matching of object and a standard filament heated by an adjustable electric current.

    b. Thermopile, a series of thermocouples receiving radiant energy.

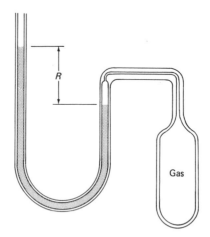

Figure 2.10.   Constant volume gas thermometer

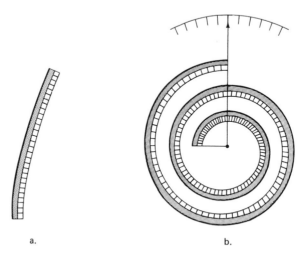

Figure 2.11.   (a) Bimetallic strip curved by change in temperature and (b) Bimetal thermometer

Figure 2.14 is an overall survey of temperature ranges covered by the various measuring instruments.

The examples below illustrate the use of some of the definitions mentioned previously.

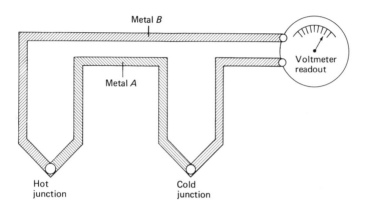

Figure 2.12. Temperature measurement by thermocouple

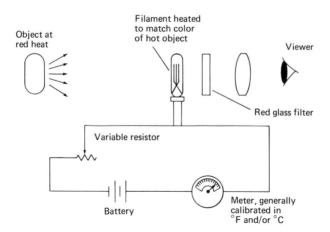

Figure 2.13. Optical pyrometer

42

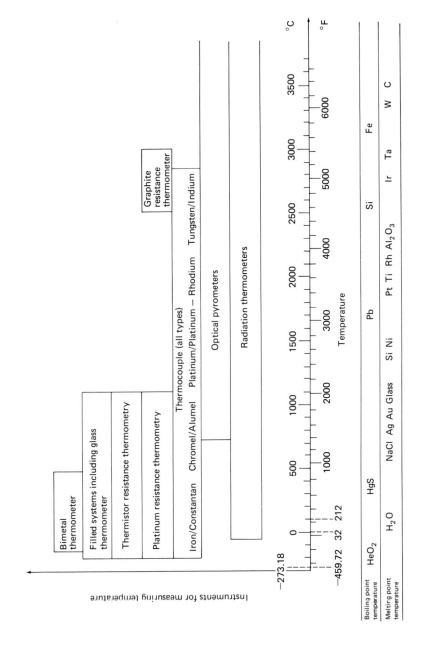

Figure 2.14. Survey of temperature-measuring instruments (4)

Example 2.9   Mass and mole fractions

Determine the mass and mole fractions of chlorine in the following substances:

$$1.\ Ca(ClO)_2 \qquad 2.\ KClO_4 \qquad 3.\ Zn(ClO_3)_2$$

Solution

Basis: 1 lb-mole of the compound.

1.

Component	lb-mole	Molecular weight	lb_m
Ca	1.0	40.1	40.1
Cl_2	1.0	70.9	70.9
O_2	1.0	32.0	32.0
	3.0		143.0

Mass fraction $Cl_2 = 70.9/143.0 = 0.496$

Mole fraction $Cl_2 = 1/3 = 0.333$

2.

Component	lb-mole	Molecular weight	lb_m
K	1.0	39.1	39.1
Cl_2	0.5	70.9	35.5
O_2	2.0	32.0	64.0
	3.5		138.6

Mass fraction $Cl_2 = 35.5/138.6 = 0.256$

Mole fraction $Cl_2 = 0.5/3.5 = 0.143$

3.

Component	lb-mole	Molecular weight	lb_m
Zn	1.0	65.4	65.4
Cl_2	1.0	70.9	70.9
O_2	3.0	32.0	96.0
	5.0		232.3

Mass fraction $Cl_2 = 70.9/232.3 = 0.306$

Mole fraction $Cl_2 = 1/5 = 0.2$

Example 2.10 Molecules of H_2O and sand particles

Compare the number of molecules in a glass of water (200 ml) with the estimated number of particles of sand on a beach, where

$$\text{Apparent density of sand} = 118 \text{ lb}_m/\text{ft}^3$$

$$\text{Absolute density of sand} = 3.44 \text{ g/cm}^3$$

$$\text{Particle diameter} = 0.5 \text{ mm}$$

$$\text{Length of beach} = 3 \text{ mi}$$

$$\text{Width of beach} = 100 \text{ ft}$$

$$\text{Depth of sand} = 4 \text{ ft}$$

Solution

$$\text{Molecules of water} = 200 \text{ ml} \times \frac{1 \text{ g}}{\text{ml}} \times \frac{1 \text{ g-mole}}{18 \text{ g}} \times 6.023 \times 10^{23} \frac{\text{molecules}}{\text{g-mole}}$$

$$= 6.7 \times 10^{24}$$

Part of the apparent volume of sand on the beach is space between particles.

$$\text{Volume of sand} = 4 \text{ ft} \times 100 \text{ ft} \times 3 \text{ mi} \times \frac{5280 \text{ ft}}{\text{mi}} \times 118 \frac{\text{lb}_m}{\text{ft}^3} \times \frac{1}{3.44 \text{ g/cm}^3}$$

$$\times \frac{454 \text{ g}}{\text{lb}_m} \times \left(\frac{1 \text{ ft}}{30.48 \text{ cm}}\right)^3 = 3.48 \times 10^6 \text{ ft}^3$$

$$\text{Sand particles} = 3.48 \times 10^6 \text{ ft}^3 \times \frac{1 \text{ particle}}{\frac{4}{3}\pi\left(\frac{0.5 \text{ mm}}{2}\right)^3} \times \left(\frac{25.4 \text{ mm}}{\text{in.}}\right)^3 \times \left(\frac{12 \text{ in.}}{\text{ft}}\right)^3$$

$$= 1.50 \times 10^{15} \text{ particles}$$

Thus there are

$$\frac{6.7 \times 10^{24}}{1.50 \times 10^{15}} = 4.5 \text{ billion} \quad \triangleleft$$

times as many molecules in the glass of water as there are sand particles on the beach.

Example 2.11   Specific gravity of H_2SO_4 solution

Chemically pure sulfuric acid is available in the chemical storeroom as 96 wt % material. Determine

1. Specific gravity at 15°C (4°C is temperature of the reference substance)
2. Specific gravity at 60°F (reference substance is 60°F)
3. Density in standard °Bé
4. Mole % water

The density of the material is 1.8355 g/cm³ at 20°C, and it decreases by 0.0010 g/cm³ for a change from 15° to 20°C.

Solution

Assume that the density of the material changes linearly from 15° to 20°C.

1.   Specific gravity $\frac{15°C}{4°C} = \frac{(1.8355 + 0.0010) \text{ g/cm}^3}{1.0000 \text{ g/cm}^3} = 1.8365$ ◁

2. The density of water at 60°F (15.5°C) is 0.99905 g/cm³.

$$\text{Specific gravity } \frac{60°F}{60°F} = \frac{(1.8355 + (4.5/5) \times 0.0010) \text{ g/cm}^3}{0.9990 \text{ g/cm}^3} = 1.8382 ◁$$

3. $°Bé = 145 - \frac{145}{1.8382} = 66$ ◁

4. Basis: 100 lb$_m$ material.

Component	lb$_m$	Molecular weight	lb-mole
H_2SO_4	96	98	0.980
H_2O	4	18	0.222
			1.202

$$\text{Mole \% } H_2O = \frac{0.222}{1.202} = 18.47\% ◁$$

Example 2.12   Buoyancy exerted on a human body by a "body" of water

1. What is the approximate average density of water in

   a. Lake Michigan with 70 ppm of salt?

   b. The Mediterranean with 35,000 ppm of salt?

2. Assume that a person swimming is completely submerged in a "body" of water. What is his/her buoyancy in Lake Michigan and in the Mediterranean if he/she weights 115 lb and has a density of 0.98 g/cm^3? The salt density is about 2.165 g/cm^3 and the average temperature is 75°F in both bodies of water.

Archimedes' principle states that (1) a body immersed in a fluid is buoyed upward by a force equal to the weight of the fluid displaced by the body, and (2) a floating body displaces its own weight of the fluid in which it floats.

Solution

Assume that the solution of salt in water does not change the volume of the solution. Basis: 10^6 lb_m of H_2O.

1a.
$$\text{Density} = \frac{\text{mass}}{\text{volume}}$$

$$\begin{matrix}\text{Total mass of sample}\\ \text{from Lake Michigan}\end{matrix} = 10^6 \ lb_m \ H_2O + 70 \ lb_m \ \text{salt}$$

$$\text{Total volume} = \frac{10^6 \ lb_m}{62.4 \ lb_m/ft^3} + \frac{70}{2.165 \times 62.4} \ ft^3$$

$$\begin{matrix}\text{Density of water}\\ \text{in Lake Michigan}\end{matrix} = \frac{10^6 + 70}{10^6/62.4 + 70/(2.165 \times 62.4)}$$

$$\approx 62.4 \ lb_m/ft^3 \quad \triangleleft$$

1b.
$$\begin{matrix}\text{Density of water}\\ \text{in the Mediterranean}\end{matrix} = \frac{10^6 + 35,000}{10^6/62.4 + 35,000/(2.165 \times 62.4)}$$

$$\approx 63.6 \ lb_m/ft^3 \quad \triangleleft$$

2. By Archimedes' principle, the buoyant force is equal to the weight of displaced water; or equivalently, it is equal to the volume immersed multiplied by the density of the fluid.

$$\text{Volume of human body} = 115 \text{ lb}_m \times \frac{1}{0.98 \text{ g/cm}^3} \times \frac{1 \text{ g/cm}^3}{62.4 \text{ lb}_m/\text{ft}^3} = 1.88 \text{ ft}^3$$

$$\begin{matrix} \text{Buoyant force} \\ \text{in Lake Michigan} \end{matrix} = 1.88 \text{ ft}^3 \times 62.4 \text{ lb}_m/\text{ft}^3 \times g/g_c$$

$$= 117 \text{ lb}_f$$

$$\begin{matrix} \text{Buoyant force} \\ \text{in the Mediterranean} \end{matrix} = 1.88 \text{ ft}^3 \times 63.6 \text{ lb}_m/\text{ft}^3 \times g/g_c$$

$$= 119.6 \text{ lb}_f$$

Example 2.13 Pressure and force on a submarine

A modern submarine can travel 1000 ft below sea level. If a submarine can be considered a cylinder 35 ft in diameter and 200 ft long, what is the average pressure and total force exerted on the submarine? The average density of the sea water is 1.04 g/cm^3.

Solution

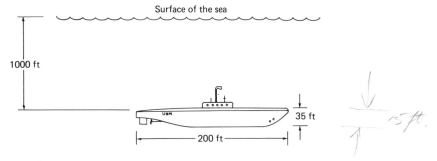

To determine the average pressure without a calculus approach, an approximation can be obtained if we calculate the pressure on the top of the submarine (1000 ft deep), add this to the pressure on the bottom of the submarine (1035 ft deep), and finally divide by two.

$$P_{top} = P_{atm} + \frac{\rho h_1 g}{g_c}$$

$$= 14.7 \frac{lb_f}{in.^2} + \left(1.04 \frac{g}{cm^3}\right)\left(\frac{lb_m}{454\ g}\right)\left(\frac{2.54\ cm}{in.}\right)^3$$

$$(1000\ ft)\left(\frac{12\ in.}{1\ ft}\right)\left(32.2 \frac{ft}{sec^2}\right)\left(\frac{1\ lb_f\text{-}sec^2}{32.2\ lb_m\text{-}ft}\right)$$

$$P_{top} = 14.7\ lb_f/in.^2 + 450.5\ lb_f/in.^2$$

$$= 465.2\ psia \quad \lhd$$

$$P_{bottom} = P_{atm} + \frac{\rho h_2 g}{g_c}$$

$$= 14.7\ lb_f/in.^2 + \left(1.04 \frac{g}{cm^3}\right)\left(\frac{1\ lb_m}{454\ g}\right)\left(\frac{2.54\ cm}{in.}\right)^3$$

$$(1035\ ft)\left(\frac{12\ in.}{ft}\right)\left(32.2 \frac{ft}{sec^2}\right)\left(\frac{1\ lb_f\text{-}sec^2}{32.2\ lb_m\text{-}ft}\right)$$

$$P_{bottom} = 14.7\ lb_f/in.^2 + 466.2\ lb_f/in.^2$$

$$= 480.9\ psia \quad \lhd$$

$$P_{avg} = \frac{P_{top} + P_{bottom}}{2}$$

$$= \frac{465.2\ psia + 480.9\ psia}{2}$$

$$= 473.0\ psia \quad \lhd$$

$$\text{Total force} = P_{avg} A_L = \left(473.0 \frac{lb_f}{in.^2}\right)\left(\frac{144\ in.^2}{ft^2}\right)(2\pi)\left(\frac{35\ ft}{2}\right)(200\ ft)$$

$$= 1.50 \times 10^9\ lb_f \quad \lhd$$

Example 2.14 Normality of aqueous solution

Find the normality of the following solutions.

1. 2 M sulfuric acid
2. 0.5 M phosphoric acid
3. 37 wt % nitric acid
4. 96 wt % H_2SO_4

Solution

In general, the normality of a solution is given by

$$\text{Normality} = \frac{\text{(weight of compound per liter of solution)}}{\text{(equivalent weight of the compound)}}$$

1. For H_2SO_4, the molecular weight is 98. Therefore, for a 2 M solution,

$$\text{Weight per liter} = \frac{2 \text{ g-mole } H_2SO_4}{1 \text{ liter solution}} \times \frac{98 \text{ g } H_2SO_4}{1 \text{ g-mole } H_2SO_4}$$

$$= 196 \frac{\text{g } H_2SO_4}{\text{liter solution}}$$

$$\text{Equivalent weight} = \left(\frac{98 \text{ g } H_2SO_4}{1 \text{ g-mole } H_2SO_4}\right) \bigg/ \left(\frac{2 \text{ g-atom H}}{1 \text{ g-mole } H_2SO_4}\right)$$

$$= 49 \frac{\text{g } H_2SO_4}{\text{g-atom H}}$$

$$\text{Normality} = \frac{196 \text{ g } H_2SO_4/\text{liter solution}}{49 \text{ g } H_2SO_4/\text{g-atom H}} = 4 \frac{\text{g-atom H}}{\text{liter solution}}$$

$$= 4 \ N \quad \triangleleft$$

2. Similarly for H_3PO_4 of molecular weight 98 in 0.5 M solution:

Normality =

$$\left(\frac{0.5 \text{ g-mole H}_3\text{PO}_4}{1 \text{ liter solution}} \times \frac{98 \text{ g H}_3\text{PO}_4}{1 \text{ g-mole H}_3\text{PO}_4}\right) \Big/ \left(\frac{98 \text{ g H}_3\text{PO}_4}{1 \text{ g-mole H}_3\text{PO}_4} \div \frac{3 \text{ g-atom H}}{1 \text{ g-mole H}_3\text{PO}_4}\right)$$

$$= 1.5 \, N \quad \triangleleft$$

For a concentration given in weight percent, the numerator of the general equation is found in a different manner.

3. For a 37 wt % HNO_3 solution, the denstiy at 20°C is 1.227 g/cm³.

Normality =

$$\left(\frac{1227 \text{ g solvent}}{1 \text{ liter solution}} \times \frac{37 \text{ g HNO}_3}{100 \text{ g solution}}\right) \Big/ \left(\frac{63 \text{ g HNO}_3}{1 \text{ g-mole HNO}_3} \div \frac{1 \text{ g-atom H}}{1 \text{ g-mole HNO}_3}\right)$$

$$= 7.2 \, N \quad \triangleleft$$

4. Similarly, for a 96 wt % H_2SO_4 solution whose density is 1.835 g/cm³ at 20°C,

Normality =

$$\left(\frac{1835 \text{ g solvent}}{1 \text{ liter solution}} \times \frac{96 \text{ g H}_2\text{SO}_4}{100 \text{ g solution}}\right) \Big/ \left(\frac{98 \text{ g H}_2\text{SO}_4}{1 \text{ g-mole H}_2\text{SO}_4} \div \frac{2 \text{ g-atom H}}{1 \text{ g-mole H}_2\text{SO}_4}\right)$$

$$= 36 \, N \quad \triangleleft$$

Example 2.15   Normality

10 ml of KOH solution requires 40 ml of 0.2 N HCl for neutralization to occur. What is the normality of the KOH?

Solution

$$V_A \cdot N_A = V_B \cdot N_B$$

$$(40 \text{ ml})(0.2 \, N) = (10 \text{ ml})(N_B)$$

$$N_B = \frac{(40 \text{ ml})(0.2 \text{ } N)}{10 \text{ ml}}$$

$$N_B = \text{normality of KOH} = 0.8 \text{ } N \quad \triangleleft$$

Example 2.16 Pressure units conversion

Convert 20 psia to:

1. lb_f/ft^2
2. Atmospheres
3. Inches of water
4. Inches of mercury

Solution

1. $\quad 20 \text{ psia} = 20 \text{ } lb_f/in.^2 \times 144 \text{ in.}^2/ft^2 = 2880 \text{ } lb_f/ft^2 \quad \triangleleft$

2. $\quad 20 \text{ psia} \times 1 \text{ atm}/14.7 \text{ psia} = 1.36 \text{ atm} \quad \triangleleft$

3. $\quad 20 \text{ psia} \times \dfrac{33.91 \text{ ft } H_2O}{14.7 \text{ psia}} \times \dfrac{12 \text{ in.}}{ft} = 553.6 \text{ in. } H_2O \quad \triangleleft$

4. $\quad 20 \text{ psia} \times \dfrac{29.92 \text{ in. Hg}}{14.7 \text{ psia}} = 40.7 \text{ in. Hg} \quad \triangleleft$

Example 2.17 Leakage from a water tank

The bottom of a water tank leaks at a rate given by

$$Q = 0.61 \text{ } S \sqrt{(2 \text{ } g_c \Delta P)/\rho}$$

where

$Q = $ rate of leakage, ft^3/sec

$S = $ cross-sectional area of the leak $= 1 \times 10^{-5} \text{ } ft^2$

$\Delta P = $ driving pressure across the leak, lb_f/ft^2

$\rho = $ fluid density, lb_m/ft^3

If the water level in the tank is 40 ft above the bottom, what is the rate of leakage in gallons per day?

Solution

$$\Delta P = \frac{\rho h g}{g_c} = 62.4 \, \frac{\text{lb}_m}{\text{ft}^3} \times 32.2 \, \frac{\text{ft}}{\text{sec}^2} \times 40 \text{ ft} \times \frac{1}{g_c}$$

$$= 2500 \, \text{lb}_f/\text{ft}^2$$

$$Q = 0.61 \times 10^{-5} \text{ ft}^2 \sqrt{\frac{2 \times (32.2 \, \text{lb}_m\text{-ft}/\text{lb}_f\text{-sec}^2) \times (2500 \, \text{lb}_f/\text{ft}^2)}{62.4 \, \text{lb}_m/\text{ft}^3}}$$

$$\times \frac{7.48 \text{ gal}}{\text{ft}^3} \times \frac{3600 \text{ sec}}{\text{hr}} \times \frac{24 \text{ hr}}{\text{day}}$$

$$= 200 \text{ gal/day} \quad \triangleleft$$

Example 2.18 Temperature conversion

Convert 200°C to:

1. °F   2. °R   3. °K

Solution

1.
$$°F = 1.8°C + 32$$
$$°F = 1.8 \, (200) + 32$$
$$= 392°F \quad \triangleleft$$

2.
$$°R = °F + 460 = 392°F + 460 = 852°R \quad \triangleleft$$

3.
$$°K = °C + 273 = 200°C + 273 = 473°K \quad \triangleleft$$

NOMENCLATURE

Symbol	Meaning
A	Surface area, ft^2
a	Acceleration, ft/sec^2

Symbol	Meaning
$^\circ$API	Degree American Petroleum Institute for measuring specific gravity
$^\circ$Bé$_l$	Degree Baumé for material lighter than water
$^\circ$Bé$_h$	Degree Baumé for material heavier than water
$^\circ$Bx$_l$	Degree Brix for material lighter than water
$^\circ$Bx$_h$	Degree Brix for material heavier than water
C	Velocity of light in free space, 3×10^8 m/sec
$^\circ$C	Degree centigrade
D	Tube diameter, ft
F	Force, lb$_f$ or lb$_w$
$^\circ$F	Degree Fahrenheit
f	Friction factor, dimensionless
g	Gravitational acceleration, ft/sec^2
g_c	32.2 (lb$_m$/lb$_f$) (ft/sec^2)
H	Heat, Btu/mole
h	Head of inclined tube manometer, ft
K.E.	Kinetic energy, ft-lb$_f$
$^\circ$K	Degree Kelvin
k_n	Newton's proportionality constant
L	Length, ft or cm
M	Mass, lb$_m$ or g
M	Molarity, moles/liter
M'	Molality, moles/1000 g of solvent
m	Mass, lb$_m$ or g
N	Normality, gram equivalent weight/liter
n_A	Moles of substance A
n_B	Moles of substance B
P	Pressure, lb$_f$/ft^2
P_1	Pressure at point 1, lb$_f$/ft^2
P_2	Pressure at point 2, lb$_f$/ft^2
ΔP	Pressure drop, lb$_f$/ft^2

Symbol	Meaning
Q	Volumetric flow rate, ft^3/sec
R	Manometer head, ft
$^\circ$R	Degree Rankine
S	Cross sectional area, ft^2
s	Specific gravity, dimensionless
T	Temperature, $^\circ$K or $^\circ$R
$^\circ$T$_w$	Degree Twadell, for specific gravity
t_c	Temperature, $^\circ$C
t_f	Temperature, $^\circ$F
V	Volume, ft^3
v	Average velocity, ft/sec
W	Weight, lb$_f$

Greek letters	Meaning
α	Angle of inclination of inclined tube manometer, degrees
θ	Time, sec
μ	Viscosity, centipoise
ρ	Density, lb$_m$/ft^3
ρ_A	Density of substance A, lb$_m$/ft^3
ρ_R	Density of reference substance, lb$_m$/ft^3

REFERENCES

1. Chisholm, L. J. 1967. *Units of weight and measure: International (metric) and U.S. customary.* Washington: National Bureau of Standards.

2. Green, M. H. 1961. *International and metric units of measurement.* New York: Chemical Publishing Co.

3. Henley, E. J., and Rosen, E. M. 1969. *Material and energy balance computations.* New York: John Wiley.

4. Himmelblau, D. M. 1962. *Basic principles and calculations in chemical engineering.* Englewood Cliffs, N.J.: Prentice-Hall.

5. Hodgman, C. D.; Weast, R. C.; Selby, S. M. 1968. *Handbook of chemistry and physics.* Cleveland: Chemical Rubber Publishing Co.

6. Hoistendahl, H.S. 1964. *Engineering units and physical quantities.* London: Macmillan.

7. Hougen, O. A.; Watson, K. M.; Ragatz, R. A. 1954. *Chemical process principles: Part I, Material and energy balances.* New York: John Wiley.

8. Ingalls, W. R. 1946. *Units of weights and measures.* New York: American Institute of Weights and Measures.

9. Ingalls, W. R. 1937. *Modern weights and measures.* New York: American Institute of Weights and Measures.

10. Peters, M. S. 1954. *Elementary chemical engineering.* New York: McGraw-Hill.

11. Research Department, Pillsbury Mills, Inc. 1945. *Conversion factors and technical data of the industry.* Minneapolis.

12. Schmidt, A. X., and List, H. L. 1962. *Material and energy balances.* Englewood Cliffs, N.J.: Prentice-Hall.

13. Simon and Schuster. 1967. *The way things work, an illustrated encyclopedia of technology.* New York.

14. Thatcher, C. M. 1962. *Fundamentals of chemical engineering.* Columbus: Charles E. Merrill.

15. Tyner, M. 1960. *Process engineering calculations: Material and energy balances.* New York: Ronald Press.

16. U.S. National Bureau of Standards. 1913. *Tables of equivalents of the U.S. customary and metric weights and measures.* Washington, D.C.

17. United Nations Department of Economics and Social Affairs. *World weights and measures, a handbook for statisticians.* New York.

18. Zimmerman, O. T., and Lavine, I. 1955. *Conversion factors and tables.* Dover, N.H.: Industrial Research Service.

PROBLEMS

2.1 Gravitational Acceleration

Determine the value of the standard gravitational acceleration (32.2 ft/sec^2) when the time unit is hours.

2.2   Viscosity in the American Engineering System

The viscosity of water at room temperature is approximately 1 centipoise. What is the value in American engineering units of lb_m/ft-sec?

2.3   Conversion of Velocity Units

Convert 60 mi/hr to:

1. km/hr   2. ft/sec

2.4   Viscosity Conversions

A liquid has a viscosity of 2000 centipoises. Find the viscosity in:

1. lb_f-sec/ft^2 2. g/cm-sec   3. lb_m/ft-sec

2.5   Conversion

1. What are the magnitude and units of g_c in the mks and fps systems?

2. List in order of increasing magnitude the following force units: newton, dyne, pound-force, poundal, pound-weight.

2.6   Radio and Radar Waves

Radio and radar waves travel at the speed of light, 186,000 mi/sec.

1. When astronauts land on the moon, how long does it take for their radio communication to reach the earth? The moon is 240,000 mi from earth.

2. Compare this time with that involved if the astronauts were on Pluto, whose orbital radius is 3.68×10^9 mi compared to the earth's mean orbital radius of 93×10^6 mi.

2.7   Use of g_c

An automobile with a mass of 4000 lb_m is moving at 50 mi/hr. Find the kinetic energy of this automobile.

2.8 Confidence in Using g_c

1. Atop a mountain, gravitational acceleration is 975 cm/sec^2. What force (lb_f) will be exerted on a body whose mass is 5000 lb_m?

2. Determine the kinetic energy of a body whose mass is 10 lb_m moving at 3 ft/sec.

2.9 More Confidence in Using g_c

A Martian of mass 10 flugs weighs 100 frigs on Mars. Acceleration due to gravity on Mars is 11 ft/sec^2 and on earth 32.2 ft/sec^2.

1. What is the mass of the Martian on earth?

2. What is g_c in flug-ft/frig-sec^2?

3. What is the weight of the Martian on earth?

2.10 Relationship between Mass and Weight

What is the weight in lb_f of a 150 lb_m object at the surface of:

1. Mars   2. Jupiter   3. Saturn

Given: Gravitational acceleration relative to earth.

Earth, 1.00   Mars, 0.37   Jupiter, 2.64   Saturn, 1.17

2.11 Mass of the Sun and the Einstein Equation

The energy falling on one cm^2 at normal incidence outside the earth's atmosphere at the mean distance (93×10^6 mi) from the sun is 1.94 calories per minute. Consider that the sun is getting its energy from the reaction

$$2 H_2 \rightarrow He + \Delta E$$

$$4(1.0080) \rightarrow 4.0039$$

and that the change in energy is given by the Einstein equation

$$\Delta E = \Delta m C^2$$

where

$$\Delta E = \text{change in energy, dyne-cm}$$

$$\Delta m = \text{change in mass, g}$$

$$C = \text{velocity of light, } 3.00 \times 10^{10} \text{ cm/sec}$$

1. Determine the percent decrease of the sun's mass (1.987×10^{33} g) per year.
2. Determine the time for the end of the word.

2.12 Dimensional Consistency of the Hagen-Poiseuille Equation

Laminar flow of Newtonian fluids in circular horizontal tubes is described by the Hagen-Poiseuille law:

$$Q = \frac{\pi \, \Delta P \, R^4}{8 \, \mu \, L}$$

where

$$Q = \text{volumetric flow rate, cm}^3/\text{sec}$$

$$\Delta p = \text{absolute pressure drop across tube, dynes/cm}^2$$

$$R = \text{tube radius, cm}$$

$$\mu = \text{fluid viscosity, g/cm-sec}$$

$$L = \text{tube length, cm}$$

Determine whether this equation is dimensionally consistent.

2.13 Leakage from a Tank

A slow leak in the bottom of a water tank discharges according to the equation

$$Q = 0.61 \, A_O \sqrt{\frac{2g_c \Delta P}{\rho}}$$

where

$$A_O = \text{cross-sectional area of leak}$$

$$\Delta P = \text{driving pressure across leak}$$

$$\rho = \text{density of fluid}$$

Assuming that the water level in the tank is kept at 30 ft above the bottom and the cross-sectional area of the leak is 10^{-6} ft^2, find the loss from the tank in gal/day.

2.14 Volumetric Flow Rate and the Hagen-Poiseuille Law

Using the Hagen-Poiseuille law, determine the volumetric flow rate of air (cm^3/sec) that will pass through a capillary 20 in. long with a 0.003 in. radius. The pressure difference is 25 mm Hg. Viscosity of air at 25°C is

$$\mu = 1.23 \times 10^{-5} \text{ lb}_m/\text{ft-sec}$$

2.15 Capillary Rheometer and the Hagen-Poiseuille Law

Olive oil flows through a capillary rheometer. This rheometer is a horizontal tube 2 ft long with 0.05 in. inside diameter. The experimental temperature is 10°C and the flow rate is 0.006 ft^3/min. Determine the pressure drop (psia) through the tube. At 10°C,

$$\mu_{\text{olive oil}} = 138 \text{ cp} \qquad \rho_{\text{olive oil}} = 0.92 \text{ g/cm}^3$$

2.16 Characteristics of a Wire Mesh Packing

A mesh packing is composed of aluminum wire of 0.010 in. diameter ($\rho = 2.70$ g/cm^3). This packing is formed by knitting a single strand of wire into a loose mesh stocking that is then compressed into a solid of 20 lb/ft^3. For 1 ft^3 of packing, determine:

1. Percent void space
2. Length of the wire/ft^3
3. Lateral area of the wire/ft^3

2.17 Magnitude of the Reynolds Number

Reynolds number is a dimensionless number usually encountered in the study of fluid flow. It is defined by

$$\text{Re} = \frac{DV\rho}{\mu}$$

where

$$\text{Re} = \text{Reynolds number, dimensionless}$$

$$D = \text{tube diameter}$$

$$V = \text{fluid velocity}$$

$$\mu = \text{fluid viscosity}$$

$$\rho = \text{fluid density}$$

What is Re for a fluid flowing at 150 ft/min through 2-in. I.D. pipe?

$$\rho_{\text{fluid}} = 2.4 \text{ g/cm}^3 \quad \text{and} \quad \mu_{\text{fluid}} = 2.1 \times 10^{-5} \text{ lb}_f\text{-sec/ft}^2$$

2.18 Dimensions and the Drag Coefficient

The friction factor or drag coefficient for flow of fluids around submerged spheres is given by

$$C_D = \frac{4}{3} \frac{gD}{V_\infty^2} \left(\frac{\rho_s - \rho}{\rho} \right)$$

where

$$C_D = \text{Friction factor}$$

$$g = \text{Gravitational acceleration}$$

$$D = \text{Sphere diameter}$$

$$V_\infty = \text{Approach velocity of the fluid upstream from sphere}$$

$$\rho_s = \text{Density of sphere}$$

$$\rho = \text{Density of fluid}$$

1. What are the dimensions of C_D?

2. Would you modify the equation in any way?

2.19 Dimensions and the Grashof Number

In natural convection heat transfer, one encounters the Grashof number:

$$Gr = \frac{D^3 g \rho^2 \beta \Delta T}{\mu^2}$$

For the given system,

$$D = 0.5 \text{ ft}$$
$$g = 32.2 \text{ ft/sec}^2$$
$$\rho = 0.003 \text{ lb}_m/\text{ft}^3$$
$$\beta = 1/°F$$
$$T = 75°C$$
$$\mu = 0.02 \text{ cp}$$

Find:

1. Gr in American engineering system units.

2. Gr in cgs units.

2.20 Rate of Gasoline Consumption in the United States

Estimate the gallons of gasoline burned per day in U.S. automobiles. The following figures may be used.

$$\text{Population} = 200 \times 10^6$$
One car per family
Average family $= 3\ 3/4$ people
Average car mileage $= 10,000$ mi/year
Average car gas mileage $= 15$ mi/gal

2.21   Dimensional Consistency

Find the value and units of Nu/(Re Pr) in the cgs system, where

$$\text{Nu} = hD/k$$
$$\text{Re} = DV\rho/\mu$$
$$\text{Pr} = C_p\mu/k$$

and

$$h \;=\; 150 \text{ Btu/hr-ft}^2\text{-}^\circ\text{F}$$
$$C_p \;=\; 6.95 \text{ cal/(g-mole)-}^\circ\text{C}$$
$$\rho \;=\; 4.43 \times 10^{-5} \text{ lb}_m/\text{in.}^3$$
$$V \;=\; 250 \text{ cm/sec}$$
$$\text{Nu} \;=\; \text{Nusselt number}$$
$$\text{Re} \;=\; \text{Reynolds number}$$
$$\text{Pr} \;=\; \text{Prandtl number}$$

2.22   Dimensional Consistency: Black Body Radiation

When a black body is surrounded by another black body, the net exchange of heat by radiation is given by

$$Q = \sigma A_1 \, (T_1^4 - T_2^4)$$

where

$$Q \;=\; \text{net heat exchange, Btu/hr}$$
$$\sigma = \text{Stefan-Botzmann constant}$$
$$= 0.17 \times 10^{-8} \text{ Btu/hr-ft}^2\text{-}^\circ\text{R}^4$$
$$A_1 \;=\; \text{area of the surrounded body, ft}^2$$
$$T_1 \;=\; \text{absolute temperature of first body, }^\circ\text{R}$$
$$T_2 \;=\; \text{absolute temperature of second body, }^\circ\text{R}$$

Find the value of σ in the cgs system.

2.23 Heat Transfer Coefficient from the Dittus-Boelter Equation

For highly turbulent flow in tubes, the individual heat transfer coefficient is given by

$$\frac{hD}{k} = 0.026 \left(\frac{DV\rho}{\mu}\right)^{0.8} \left(\frac{C_p \mu}{k}\right)^{1/3} \left(\frac{\mu}{\mu_w}\right)^{0.4}$$

where

h = individual heat transfer coefficient

D = tube diameter

k = thermal conductivity of fluid

V = average velocity of fluid

ρ = density of fluid

μ = bulk viscosity of fluid

C_p = heat capacity of fluid

μ_w = viscosity of fluid at the wall

Find the dimensions of h in the American engineering system.

2.24 Diffusivity in CGS System

In mass transfer operations, the Schmidt number

$$Sc = \frac{\mu}{\rho D_{AB}}$$

is often encountered. In this expression,

Sc = Schmidt number, dimensionless

μ = viscosity, g/cm-sec

ρ = density, g/cm^3

D_{AB} = diffusivity for the gaseous system A and B

Find the units of diffusivity.

2.25 Prandtl Number for Air

What is the value of the Prandtl number for air at $100°F$? Given:

$$Pr = \frac{C_p \mu}{k}$$

where

Pr = Prandtl number

C_p = heat capacity = 0.24 Btu/lb$_m$-°F

μ = viscosity = 0.046 lb$_m$/ft-hr

k = thermal conductivity = 0.016 Btu/hr-ft-°F

2.26 Heat Transfer Coefficient in the CGS System

Perry's *Chemical Engineer's Handbook* gives the following expression for the heat transfer coefficient to or from a stream of gas in turbulent flow in a tube:

$$h = 16.6 \frac{C_p (G')^{0.8}}{(D')^{0.2}}$$

where

h = heat transfer coefficient, Btu/hr-ft^2-°F

C_p = heat capacity, Btu/lb$_m$-°F

G' = (velocity) (density) = mass velocity, lb$_m$/ft^2-sec

D' = tube diameter, in.

Change the formula to give h in the cgs system as a function of C_p, cal/g-°C; G', g/cm^2-sec; and D', cm.

2.27 Ostwald-deWaele Equation and Newton's Law of Viscosity

In non-Newtonian fluid flow, we often use the power law or Ostwald-deWaele model:

$$\tau = K(du/dy)^n$$

where

$\tau =$ shear stress, $\mathrm{lb}_f/\mathrm{in}^2$

$K =$ a measure of the consistency of the fluid; the higher K is, the more viscous is the fluid

$du/dy =$ velocity gradient, or change of velocity with respect to the dimension y, shear rate

$n =$ flow index, a measure of the deviation from Newtonian behavior

For a Newtonian fluid one gets Newton's law of viscosity:

$$T = \mu \left(\frac{du}{dy}\right) \qquad K = \mu, n = 1$$

How should you modify this formula to get the proper units for μ (fluid viscosity)?

2.28 Local Velocity from a Pitot Tube

The local velocity of fluid is measured by a Pitot tube and calculated by the equation

$$v = \sqrt{2g_c H_v}$$

where H_v is the head due to the difference between impact and static pressure. What are the units of H_v?

2.29 Units of Shear Rate in the Mooney-Rabinowitsch Equation

In non-Newtonian technology for flow in tubes, one gets acquainted with the Mooney-Rabinowitsch equation:

$$\left(-\frac{du}{dr}\right)_{\text{wall}} = 8\ V/D \left[\frac{3}{4} + \frac{1}{4}\frac{d\ln(8\ V/D)}{d\ln\tau_w}\right]$$

where

$$\left(-\frac{du}{dr}\right)_{\text{wall}} = \text{shear rate}$$

$$V = \text{average velocity of fluid in tube}$$

$$D = \text{tube diameter}$$

$$\tau_w = \text{shear stress at the wall of the tube, } lb_f/in.^2$$

$$\frac{d \ln (8 \, V/D)}{d \ln \tau_w} = \text{change of the quantity } \ln (8 \, V/D) \text{ with respect}$$
$$\text{to the change in } \ln \tau_w.$$

Find the units of du/dr.

2.30 Naming of Chemical Compounds

Name the following.

$$Zn(ClO_3)_2 \qquad Cd_3(PO_4)_2$$

$$Ca(ClO)_2 \qquad CaH(PO_4)$$

$$Cu(NO_3)_2 \qquad Ag(ClO_4)$$

$$CaCl_2O \qquad HClO$$

2.31 Mole Fractions

A solution contains

Component	Wt %
H_2O	40
C_2H_5OH	30
CH_3OH	10
CH_3COOH	20
	——
	100

What is the mole fraction of each component in this solution?

2.32 Finding Molecular Weights

Find the molecular weight of

1. Potassium bromate
2. Cupric nitrate
3. Potassium permanganate
4. Copper sulfate-hepta hydrate
5. Dolomite

2.33 Molarity and Molality

A 10% by weight NaCl solution has a density of 1.07 g/cm^3. Find the molarity and molality of NaCl in this solution.

2.34 Faraday's Law and Electroplating

According to Faraday's law, 96,500 ampere-seconds are required to electrodeposit 1 gram-equivalent weight of metal. If a current of 3 amps is used, how long would it take to deposit 1/50,000 in. of gold on a 1 $in.^2$ electrode?

2.35 Relative Abundance of Isotopes

The molecular weight of chlorine is usually given as 70.91. Determine the relative abundance (expressed in fractions) of the chlorine isotopes with mass numbers 35 and 37.

2.36 Requirements for Preparation of H_2SO_4 Solution

Sulfuric acid (96 wt %) is to be used in making up a 0.10 molar solution at STP. Determine the following for the final solution, using the density value of 1.858 g/cm^3 at STP for 96 wt % H_2SO_4.

1. Mass of 96% acid used per liter
2. Volume of 96% acid used per liter
3. Density
4. Mass per liter
5. Molality

2.37 Mole and Weight Percent in an Alcohol Solution

Industrial alcohol, C_2H_5OH, is normally sold as 95% by volume, which is the highest practical concentration obtained by fractional distillation at atmospheric pressure. Suppose that 95 cm^3 of pure alcohol (with specific gravity 0.794) is added to 6.18 cm^3 of water to make 100 cm^3 of solution. This anomaly is due to contraction of solution on mixing. Determine

1. Mole percent of alcohol
2. Weight percent of alcohol

2.38   Weight Percent, Mole Percent, and Average Molecular Weight in a Toluene Feed

Toluene is processed into benzene in the presence of hydrogen by the following reaction.

$$\bighexagon\ CH_3 + H_2 \xrightarrow{\text{catalyst}} \bighexagon + CH_4$$

One hundred moles of pure toluene feed is used and the hydrogen is specified to be present in the feed as a 6/1 mol ratio of hydrogen to toluene. Determine for this feed:

1. Weight percent composition

2. Mole percent composition

3. Average molecular weight

2.39   Specific Gravity-Composition of Alcohol-Water Solution

Absolute ethyl alcohol is called 200 proof. A proof gallon is a 100 proof mixture made up by mixing 0.500 gal of 200 proof alcohol at 60°F (where its specific gravity 60/60 is 0.7939) with 0.5373 gal of water at 60°F. Determine in the proof gallon:

1. Volume percent alcohol

2. Weight percent alcohol

3. Mole percent

4. Specific gravity 60°/60°

5. Volume fractions of alcohol and water in the final proof gallon. Account for the sum being greater than unity.

2.40   Amount of Gold in the Ocean

1. Determine the total value of gold in the oceans of the world. The ocean contains 6×10^{-6} ppm of gold. It can be assumed that the oceans cover 3/4 of the earth's surface to an average depth of 2 mi. Let the arbitrary price of gold be $42.30 per troy ounce. The earth has a mean diameter of 8,000 mi. Density of sea water is 1.07 g/cm^3, and 1 troy ounce = 31.1 g.

2. Determine the value of gold in 1 ton of sea water.

3. Compare the value of gold with that of Mg in one ton of sea water which contains 1300 ppm of Mg. Assume that this metal in bulk is being quoted at $0.36/lb.

2.41   Amount of Sedimentary Deposit

An outfall (sewer outlet), with a flow of 25,000 gpm which contains 200 ppm of solids, flows into a river 200 ft wide, and all the solids deposit over a 500 ft length. The density of the wet deposit is 90 lb_m/ft^3, and the actual density of solids is 380 lb_m/ft^3. The Army Corps of Engineers maintains the river depth below 27 ft by dredging 2-ft increments when needed. How often must this section be dredged?

2.42   Neutralization Reaction

If 15 ml of 0.5 N ammonium hydroxide neutralizes 30 ml of a sulfuric acid solution, what is the concentration of this solution?

2.43   Density and Composition of Salt Solution

If one dissolves 480 g of sodium chloride in 4000 g of water, find

1. Molarity   2. Molality

The density of the solution is 1.084 g/cm^3.

2.44   Concentration Change by Evaporation

You have originally two liters of 2.0 N sodium sulfate solution. You evaporate water until the final solution reaches 2.5 N. What is the volume of water evaporated?

2.45   Weight of a Monolayer of Water

A monolayer of water is 3.68×10^{-4} microns thick. What is the weight of water in this layer covering an area 1 ft × 1 ft?

2.46   True Density, Apparent Density, and Specific Gravity, True and Apparent

A 96% sulfuric acid solution has a density of 1.8305 g/cm^3 at 25°C. The density of air at 25°C is 1.19×10^{-3} g/cm^3. Determine

true wt
— bouyant force
= apparent wt.

its mass

1. True density at temperature t (weights in vacuum)

$$= \frac{\text{weight of a given volume of solution at temperature } t}{\text{weight of same volume of water at } 4°C}$$

2. Apparent density at temperature t (weights in air)

$$= \frac{\text{weight of a given volume of solution at temperature } t}{\text{weight of same volume of water at } 4°C}$$

3. True specific gravity at temperature t (weights in vacuum)

$$= \frac{\text{weight of a given volume of solution at temperature } t}{\text{weight of same volume of water at temperature } t}$$

4. Apparent specific gravity at temperature t (weights in air)

$$= \frac{\text{weight of a given volume of solution at temperature } t}{\text{weight of same volume of water at temperature } t}$$

find weight of air displaced = bouyant force

2.47   Density of a Fiber-Glass Filter

Fiber-glass mats are compressed into thin layers and used as liquid filters. An original mat of glass 1/2 in. thick and 12 × 12 in. square weighs 114 g. If 16 mats are compressed into a filter layer 1/2 in. thick, what is the apparent density of the filter and the percentage of void space? The true density of glass is 2.3 g/cm^3.

2.48   Surface Area of Aluminum Dust

The finest powder produced is aluminum dust, with an average diameter of 0.03 micron. Determine surface area in cm^2/g, assuming that the particles are spheres. The density of aluminum is 2.70 g/cm^3.

2.49   Error in a Mercury Barometer Reading

The density of mercury is 13.596 g/cm^3 at 0°C and its coefficient of cubical expansion is 0.000182 per °C. Neglecting the expansion of glass and knowing that the barometer reading at 0°C is 750 mm Hg, find the percentage of error in reading the mercury barometer at:

1. 10°C   2. 25°C

2.50   Density of a Solution from Component Densities

Sea water typically contains 18,980 ppm of chlorine, 10,561 ppm of sodium, and 1,272 ppm of magnesium. Assuming these components are present as NaCl and $MgCl_2$ and taking only limiting concentrations, determine the density of sea water. The densities of NaCl and $MgCl_2$ are 2.17 and 2.32 g/cm^3, respectively.

2.51   Specific Volumes of Gases

What is the specific volume at STP of

1. Helium
2. Freon-12 $(CCl_2 F_2)$
3. Carbon dioxide
4. Nitrogen

2.52   Specific Gravity of Gases

Considering air as the reference substance, find the specific gravity of

1. Oxygen
2. Ammonia
3. Hydrogen chloride
4. Sulfur dioxide

2.53   Pressure Exerted by the Point of a Pin

What is the pressure in psi exerted by the point of a pin being pushed by hand with a force of 10 N considering the effective diameter of the point to be 0.2 mm?

2.54   Conversion of Pressure Units

Convert 100 psia to:

1. Centimeters of Hg
2. Inches of H_2O
3. Feet of oil (specific gravity $= 0.9$)
4. Feet of air ($\rho = 1.293$ g/liter)

2.55   Fluid Pressure in a Tank

Find the pressure (psia) exerted at the bottom of the pressurized tank shown in Figure P2.55.

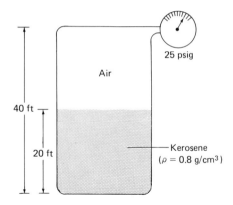

Figure P2.55.

2.56 Gas Pressure Supporting a Fluid Column

The gas in a tank supports 5 in. of mercury ($\rho_{Hg} = 13.6$ g/cm^3). Find the pressure (psia) of the gas, assuming the atmospheric pressure to be 750 mm Hg. See Figure P2.56.

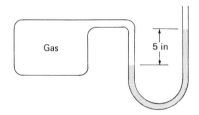

Figure P2.56.

2.57 Pressure in a Tank

A U-tube manometer is attached with one leg to a tank containing compressed gas; the other leg is open to the atmosphere. Considering that the manometer reads 10 in. of mercury, find the pressure in the tank in:

1. psia   2. psig

2.58 Pressure at the Base of a Tank

A tank contains a light petroleum distillate of specific gravity 0.82. The vapor space above the distillate is at a pressure of 60 psig. What is the pressure in psig at the base of the tank if the liquid depth is 90 ft?

2.59 Pressure in a Gas Tank

A manometer connected to a gas tank under pressure reads 5 in. of a liquid having a specific gravity of 3.85 at $25°C/4°C$. The barometric pressure is 750 mm Hg. Find the tank pressure (psia).

2.60 Conversion of Units

A relationship expressed as $M = 3\sqrt{AP}$ is valid when A is expressed as ft^2 and P as atm. If this is to be rewritten with A expressed as cm^2 and P as mm Hg, what is the number that replaces 3?

2.61 Conversion of Specific Heat Units

The specific heat of copper is:

Temperature, °C	C_p of copper, cal/g-°C
0	0.0919
200	0.0965
1000	0.1149

Find the heat capacity (C_p) of copper at $700°C$ in Btu/lb$_m$-°F.

2.62 Temperature Change in Heating Olive Oil

If the average specific heat of olive oil is 0.4 cal/g-°C, what is the amount of heat in Btu gained by heating 100 lb$_m$ of this oil from $32°F$ to $75°F$?

2.63 Power Station Output

A central power station in a large city burns 100 tons of coal per hour. The heating value of the coal used is 14,000 Btu/lb$_m$, and the overall plant efficiency is 30%. What is the rated power output of this plant?

2.64 Readings of an Iron Constantan Thermocouple

An iron constantan thermocouple is calibrated against the ice point (0°C) and the boiling point of water at 760 mm Hg (100°C), at which temperature difference it reads 4.28 millivolts. Assuming that the reading 4.28 mv/100°C is the same for any temperature range, determine

1. The reading in mv if the ice water junction is allowed to warm up to a room temperature of 25°C (a temperature difference of 75°C).

2. The reading if the hot junction is at a room temperature of 25°C and the cold junction is immersed in liquid nitrogen at its boiling point, −196°C.

2.65 Hot Air Gun

A hot air gun is used to shrink plastic tubing on electronic wiring. Estimate the temperature of the hot air, given the following conditions.

> Rating = 1.5 kW
>
> Air volume = 25 SCFM (at 70°F)
>
> Specific volume of entering air = 385 ft^3/lb-mole
>
> Room temperature = 70°F
>
> Heat capacity of air = 0.24 Btu/lb$_m$-°F

2.66 Conversion of Electrical Energy to Heat

An electric motor running an air circulator in a closed room draws 7 amperes at 125 volts (power factor = 0.80). How much heat in Btu/hr is the motor adding to the room, assuming that all the electrical energy is going to heat?

2.67 Reading of a Chromel-Alumel Thermocouple

A chromel-alumel thermocouple has been calibrated accurately by using the ice point 0°C as the cold junction, with the results shown in the following table.

Determine mv reading for a room temperature of 28°C and hot junction of 47°C by

1. Using the average value of 4.10 mv/100°C for the range 0-100°C;

2. Using the temperature difference referred to 0°C (from table);

3. Taking the difference in mv reading for each junction referred to 0°C. (The correct method is #3.)

°C	mv	°C	mv	°C	mv
0	0	25	1.00	49	2.00
3	0.10	28	1.10	52	2.10
5	0.20	30	1.20	54	2.20
8	0.30	32	1.30		
10	0.40	35	1.40	100	4.10
13	0.50	37	1.50		
15	0.60	40	1.60		
18	0.70	42	1.70		
20	0.80	45	1.80		
23	0.90	47	1.90		
25	1.00	49	2.00		

2.68 Air Contaminants from Automobiles

The following are the federal emission standards for cars and light trucks.

Exhaust	Typical emissions	Allowable emission 1968	Allowable emission 1970
Hydrocarbons	900 ppm	275 ppm 3.29 g/v.mile	180 ppm (Ex. Comp) 2.2 g/v.mile
Carbon monoxide	3.5%	1.5% 33 g/v.mile	1.0% 23 g/v.mile
Crankcase blowby 20-25% of total hydrocarbons emitted		0	0
Evaporation from tank 15% of total hydrocarbons emitted		—	—

Assuming that each vehicle gets 15 mi per gal, estimate for the items in the table the total amount of contaminants in millions of tons/year-mi^2 for

1. Entire country (U.S.A.)
2. Illinois
3. Chicago

There were 8.3×10^6 cars sold in 1969. It will be necessary to estimate the total number of cars in a given area or to look up the car population in an almanac.

2.69 Available Water on the Earth's Surface

The rivers of the world deliver annually 4×10^9 tons of dissolved solids to the seas, and this water contains on the average 120 ppm of solids. The ocean now contains 35,000 ppm of dissolved solids. The earth has an average radius of 3,900 miles and is 70% covered with water. The world's population is 3.6×10^9 people. The United States has a population (50 states) of 200×10^6 people. Determine

g/person

1. Available water gpd/person (world population)
2. Available water gpd/person (U.S. population)
3. Rate of change in sea water concentration, ppm/yr
4. Estimated age of the earth from Part 3 of this problem

Assume that the average depth of ocean is 1 mi.

2.70 Water Usage per Person

The Metropolitan Sanitary District of Chicago serves 5.5×10^6 people. Three plants treat a total of 1.5×10^9 gal/day and produce 900 tons/day dry solids at a total operating cost of $\$32 \times 10^6$/yr. Determine

1. Water usage per person per day
2. lb solids/lb water
3. Processing cost in $/gal

2.71 Available Fresh Water in the Chicago Environment

The average water use in the city of Chicago, based on sewage treatment figures, is 160 gal/day-person. The following data are given.

Lake Michigan watershed:

People 5.5×10^6

Cattle 2.4×10^6 (One cow consumes as much water as 20 people)

Area 6.7×10^3 mi^2

Average rainfall 26-34 in./yr

Compare the amount of water used to the amount of water that is available per day.

2.72 Composition of Dry Air

Determine the average molecular weight of air. The composition of dry air up to about 25 Km is given in the following table.

Component	Mole %
N_2	78.09
O_2	20.95
Ar	0.93
CO_2	0.03
Ne	1.8×10^{-3}
He	5.24×10^{-4}
Kr	1.0×10^{-4}
H_2	5.0×10^{-5}
Xe	8.0×10^{-6}
O_3	1.0×10^{-6}
Rn	6.0×10^{-18}

2.73 Expressing the Concentration of Pollutants

The atmosphere of an industrial city contains 124 $\mu g/m^3$ of particulate matter, and 221 $\mu g/m^3$ of sulfur dioxide. Change these concentrations to

1. Parts per million (ppm), parts per hundred million (pphm), parts per billion (ppb), lb/ft^3, and grains/ft^3, for both particulates and SO_2

2. Moles/liter and moles/ft^3 for SO_2

3. Grams/m^3 of sulfur

3.

Gases, Liquids, and Humidity

The state of matter in nature is defined by proper attributes or properties. Since pressure, volume, and temperature are easy to measure and control, they are the most often used properties in describing a state. Thus, one speaks of P-V-T relationships. These will be discussed in the course of this chapter, along with basic fundamentals for gases, liquids, and humidity.

3.1 P-V-T DATA FOR PURE SUBSTANCES

A typical laboratory experiment for obtaining pressure-volume-temperature data is shown in Figure 3.1.

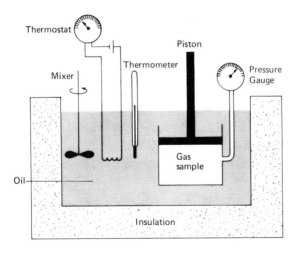

Figure 3.1. Constant-temperature bath for obtaining P-V-T data

79

The oil bath is heated to a desired temperature that is controlled with a thermostat. A mixer keeps the temperature uniform, and a thermometer gives the temperature reading. A known quantity of gas sample is placed in a cylinder fitted with a piston that allows the experimenter to apply the desired pressure, which is read from the pressure gauge.

Let us now consider several experiments that will illustrate P-V-T relations. Assume that the first temperature used is a high one indicated by T_1. For a given pressure there is a corresponding volume indicated by the position of the piston. If we increase the pressure at the given temperature T_1, a series of volumes corresponds to the series of pressures. If we change the temperature T_1 to lower temperatures T_2 and T_c, another series of pressures and volumes may be obtained. These results are shown in Figure 3.2.

The temperature T_c is called the *critical temperature*, and the corresponding pressure and volume are the critical pressure and critical volume, respectively; at this point, liquid and vapor become indistinguishable. If we cool the bath to a temperature, say T_3, that is lower than the critical temperature T_c and then repeat the experiment, we find that upon compression the gas will follow the path T_3a, and from a to b we obtain a horizontal line where the pressure and temperature remain constant, although volume is decreasing. The straight line indicates a change in phase, and point a, where the first droplet of liquid is formed, is called the *dew point*, indicating that the vapor is saturated; from $a \rightarrow b$ we have vapor-liquid mixture at equilibrium. At point b all the gas has condensed and we have only liquid. Since liquids are highly incompressible, the line bc is almost vertical.

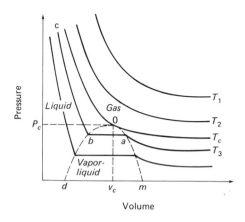

Figure 3.2. Typical *P-V-T* diagram for a pure substance

If the direction of the experiment is reversed, and we start with a liquid at point c and lower the pressure through expansion, the point b is reached where the first bubble of vapor is formed. This point b is called the *bubble point,* and at b the liquid is said to be saturated. The horizontal line ba is obtained again, indicating a change of phase and a vapor-liquid equilibrium.

When the experiment is continued to cover other ranges of temperature a *dome* (d-o-m) is obtained. This dome is the locus of all the dew points and bubble points. The portion of the curve to the right of the dew points $o \rightarrow m$ is termed *superheated vapor*; the portion of the curve to the left of the bubble points $o \rightarrow d$ is termed *subcooled liquid.*

The *Gibbs phase rule*, presented by the American mathematician and physicist J. Willard Gibbs in 1876, gives a relationship for determining the number of degrees of freedom for a general system involving varying numbers of components and phases. By *degrees of freedom* is meant the smallest number of independent variables (for example, pressure and temperature) that must be specified before the other variables of the system may be found. The Gibbs Phase rule is

$$F = C - \mathcal{P} + 2 \tag{3.1}$$

where

$$F \;=\; \text{degrees of freedom}$$

$$C \;=\; \text{number of components in the system}$$

$$\mathcal{P} \;=\; \text{number of phases in the system}$$

As an example, the portion encompassed by the dome in Figure 3.2 indicates two phases and one pure component. From the phase rule:

$$F = 1 - 2 + 2 = 1$$

Thus, for this state of vapor-liquid equilibrium, by defining only one variable — pressure, for example — other variables may be obtained.

3.2 IDEAL GASES

The Basic Laws

A gas is considered to be ideal if the actual volume of the molecules is negligible and the intermolecular attractions are very small under all conditions. The basic laws for these gases are as follows.

1. Boyle or Mariotte law

$$\frac{P_1}{P_2} = \frac{V_2}{V_1}$$

$$P_1 V_1 = P_2 V_2 = \text{constant (at constant temperature)} \qquad (3.2)$$

where

$$P = \text{pressure}$$

$$V = \text{volume}$$

(Subscripts 1 and 2 refer to states 1 and 2.)

This law states that the volume of a gas at a given temperature is inversely proportional to the applied pressure. This law is accredited to Boyle in English-speaking countries and to Mariotte in French-speaking countries.

2. Charles or Gay-Lussac law

$$\frac{V_1}{V_2} = \frac{T_1}{T_2}$$

or

$$\frac{V_1}{T_1} = \frac{V_2}{T_2} = \frac{V}{T} = k$$

$$V = kT \text{ (at constant } P) \qquad (3.3)$$

where

$$k = \text{constant}$$

$$T = \text{absolute temperature}$$

That is, at constant pressure, the volume of a given quantity of a gas is directly proportional to its absolute temperature.

Ideal Gas Law

The ideal or perfect gas law is a combination of the laws of Boyle and Charles; it is derived as follows.

Consider a gas going from the initial state P_1-V_1-T_1 to the final state P_2-V_2-T_2; however, let this gas go through the intermediate state P_2-V'-T_1 as depicted in Figure 3.3.

For the first path (constant temperature) we can apply Boyle's law:

$$P_1 V_1 = P_2 V'$$

or

$$V' = \frac{P_1 V_1}{P_2} \tag{3.4}$$

and for the second path (constant pressure) we can apply Charles's law:

$$\frac{V'}{T_1} = \frac{V_2}{T_2}$$

or

$$V' = \frac{V_2 T_1}{T_2}$$

Replacing V' from Equation 3.4 we obtain

$$\frac{P_1 V_1}{P_2} = \frac{V_2 T_1}{T_2} \tag{3.5}$$

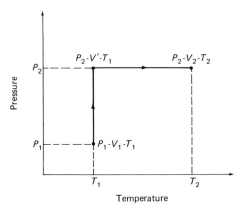

Figure 3.3.   Convenient path for a given gas

multiply both sides of this equation by P_2/T_1:

$$\left(\frac{P_1 V_1}{P_2}\right)\frac{P_2}{T_1} = \left(\frac{V_2 T_1}{T_2}\right)\frac{P_2}{T_1}$$

or

$$\frac{P_1 V_1}{T_1} = \frac{P_2 V_2}{T_2} = \text{constant} = k_1 \tag{3.6}$$

In general,

$$PV = k_1 T \tag{3.7}$$

For convenience this constant is taken to be

$$k_1 = nR$$

where (see Appendix for other units)

$$n = \text{number of moles of gas}$$

$$R = \text{universal gas constant} = 1.99 \text{ Btu/lb-mole-}^\circ\text{K}$$

Thus the ideal gas law is

$$PV = nRT \tag{3.8}$$

or

$$PV \text{ MW} = (n \text{ MW})(RT)$$

$$P \text{ MW} = (n \text{ MW}/V)RT = \rho RT$$

and

$$P = \rho RT/\text{MW} \tag{3.9}$$

where

$$\text{MW} = \text{molecular weight}$$

$$\rho = \text{density}$$

From the kinetic theory of gases we obtain*

*This derivation may be found in most physics and physical chemistry books.

$$PV = nRT = \text{constant} = 1/3\ n(Nm)u^2 = 1/3\ n\ MW\ u^2 \qquad (3.10)$$

where

N = Avogadro's number = 6.023×10^{23} molecules/g-mole

m = mass of one molecule (Nm = molecular weight)

u = average translational velocity of the molecules

In perfect gas computations, the ideal gas law is widely used. In this connection it is helpful to know that the molar volume of an ideal gas is 359 ft³/lb-mole or 22.4 liters/g-mole at standard conditions, or STP (standard temperature and pressure of 32°F and 14.7 psia, or correspondingly, 0°C and one atmosphere). These conditions are most widely used, but they are not necessarily universal. For example, in the natural gas industry standard conditions are 60°F and one atmosphere, and one lb-mole of an ideal gas occupies a volume of 379 ft³ under these conditions. The standard conditions for air pollution laws are 70°F and one atmosphere; the corresponding molar volume is 386 ft³.

The *"common sense" law* is also used to a large extent. This law states that for a given mass, a new volume may be found by multiplying the old volume by a ratio of pressures and temperatures, namely:

$$\text{New volume} = \text{old volume (absolute pressure}$$
$$\text{ratio) (absolute temperature ratio)} \qquad (3.11)$$

The ratios are selected, based on prior knowledge, as more or less than one. As an example, consider a pressure increase which we know will cause the volume to decrease; then the pressure ratio should be less than one. If a temperature increase takes place, it will cause the volume to increase, and the temperature ratio should be larger than one.

Example 3.1 Density and specific gravity of air

For an air stream at 615 psi and −73°F, determine

1. Density of the air stream in g/cm³ and lb/ft³

2. Specific gravity of this stream relative to air at STP (14.7 psia and 32°F)

Solution

1. The molar volume of 359 ft^3/lb-mole should decrease by the pressure ratio, since the pressure is more than atmospheric. The pressure of 615 psi is taken to be 615 psig in the absence of a specific definition.

    Similarly, the molar volume should decrease by the absolute temperature ratio since $-73°$F is below ambient.

    The molar volume at 615 psig and $-73°$F is

$$MV = 22,400 \ \frac{cm^3}{\text{g-mole}} \times \frac{14.7 \text{ psia}}{(615 + 14.7) \text{ psia}} \times \frac{(460 - 73)°R}{(460 + 32)°R}$$

and the density at this pressure and temperature is

$$\rho = \frac{MW}{MV} = \frac{\text{molecular weight}}{\text{molar volume}}$$

$$= \frac{29 \text{ g/g-mole}}{22,400 \ \frac{cm^3}{\text{g-mole}} \times \frac{14.7}{615 + 14.7} \times \frac{460 - 73}{460 + 32}}$$

$$= 0.705 \text{ g/cm}^3$$

or

$$\rho = \frac{29 \text{ lb/lb-mole}}{359 \text{ ft}^3/\text{lb-mole} \times \frac{14.7 \text{ psia}}{(615 + 14.7) \text{ psia}} \times \frac{(460 - 73)°R}{(460 + 32)°R}}$$

$$= 4.4 \text{ lb/ft}^3 \ \lhd$$

2.
$$\text{Specific gravity} = \frac{4.4 \text{ lb/ft}^3}{\frac{29 \text{ lb/lb-mole}}{359 \text{ ft}^3/\text{lb-mole}}} = 50 \ \lhd$$

Example 3.2   Simple calculation of R

Find R, using any system you choose.

Solution

An easy choice would be to use 1 lb-mole occupying a volume of 359 ft^3 at STP (1 atmosphere, $273°$K):

$$PV = nRT$$

$$R = \frac{PV}{nT} = \frac{1 \text{ atm } (359 \text{ ft}^3)}{1 \text{ lb-mole } (273°\text{K})} = \frac{359}{273} \frac{\text{atm-ft}^3}{\text{lb-mole-}°\text{K}}$$

$$= 1.31 \frac{\text{atm-ft}^3}{\text{lb-mole-}°\text{K}}$$ ◁

Example 3.3   Value of R

Determine the value of R expressed in

1. Fundamental cgs units of cm, g, sec, g-mole, and $°$K
2. cal/g-mole-$°$K

Solution

1. Using the molar volume of 359 ft^3/lb-mole at 14.7 psia and 492$°$R:

$$R = PV/nT$$

$$= 14.7 \frac{\text{lb}_f}{\text{in.}^2} \times 359 \frac{\text{ft}^3}{\text{lb}_m\text{-mole}} \times \frac{1}{492°\text{R}} \times 32.2 \frac{\text{lb}_m\text{-ft}}{\text{lb}_f\text{-sec}^2}$$

$$\times 144 \frac{\text{in.}^2}{\text{ft}^2} \times 454 \frac{\text{g}}{\text{lb}_m} \times \frac{1 \text{ ft}}{30.48 \text{ cm}} \times (30.48)^3 \frac{\text{cm}^3}{\text{ft}^3}$$

$$\times \frac{1 \text{ lb}_m\text{-mole}}{454 \text{ g-mole}} \times 1.8 \frac{°\text{R}}{°\text{K}}$$

$$R = 8.31 \times 10^7 \frac{\text{g-cm}^2}{\text{sec}^2}/\text{g-mole-}°\text{K}$$

or

$$R = 8.31 \times 10^7 \text{ ergs/g-mole-}°\text{K}$$ ◁

2. Using STP (14.7 psia, 0$°$C):

$$R = \frac{PV}{nT} = 14.7 \frac{\text{lb}_f}{\text{in.}^2} \times 144 \frac{\text{in.}^2}{\text{ft}^2} \times 359 \frac{\text{ft}^3}{\text{lb-mole}} \times \frac{1 \text{ Btu}}{778 \text{ ft-lb}_f}$$

$$\times 252 \frac{\text{cal}}{\text{Btu}} \times \frac{1}{298°\text{K}} \times \frac{\text{lb-mole}}{454 \text{ g-mole}}$$

$$= 1.99 \text{ cal/g-mole-}°\text{K} \quad \triangleleft$$

Example 3.4   Molecular velocity of air

Determine the molecular velocity of air at 68°F and one atmosphere.

Solution

For $n = 1$ lb-mole, $PV = RT = 1/3$ MW u^2 or

$$u^2 = \frac{3\,RT}{\text{MW}}$$

$$= \frac{3\,(1.98\,\frac{\text{cal}}{\text{g-mole-}°\text{K}})(\frac{460 + 68}{1.8})°\text{K}}{29 \text{ g/g-mole}}$$

$$= \frac{(3)(1.98)(528)}{(29)(1.8)} \frac{\text{cal}}{\text{g}} \times 4.18 \times 10^7 \frac{\text{g-cm}^2}{\text{sec}^2} / \text{cal}$$

$$= 0.25 \times 10^{10} \text{ cm}^2/\text{sec}^2$$

$$u = 0.50 \times 10^5 \text{ cm/sec} = 1650 \text{ ft/sec} \quad \triangleleft$$

Example 3.5   Air pressure in a heated tire

A car tire holds air at 30 psig and 75°F. What is the gauge pressure when the temperature of the air inside the tire becomes 140°F?

Solution

Assume that (1) the change in the volume of the tire is negligible, and (2) the ideal gas law is operative in this case. For the initial condition,

$$P_1 V_1 = n_1 R T_1$$

For the final condition,

$$P_2 V_1 = n_1 R T_2$$

or

$$\frac{P_1 V_1}{P_2 V_1} = \frac{n_1 R T_1}{n_1 R T_2}$$

and

$$\frac{P_1}{P_2} = \frac{T_1}{T_2}$$

$$P_2 = P_1 \frac{T_2}{T_1} = (30 + 14.7) \text{ psia } \frac{(140 + 460)^\circ \text{R}}{(75 + 460)^\circ \text{R}}$$

$$P_2 = \text{final pressure} = 44.7 \, (600/535) = 50.2 \text{ psia} = 35.5 \text{ psig}$$

3.3 MIXTURES OF IDEAL GASES

In gaseous mixtures, each molecule contributes its share toward the pressure and volume of the mixture. Before discussing any quantitative relationships, we must define two basic terms:

1. The *partial pressure* of a component is the pressure exerted when this component alone occupies the total volume of the system at the same temperature.

2. The *partial volume* of a pure component is the volume occupied when this component is under the total pressure of the system at the same temperature.

The laws governing ideal gas mixtures are described below.

Dalton's Law of Partial Pressures

This law states that the total pressure exerted by a gaseous mixture is equal to the sum of the partial pressures, namely,

$$P = \sum_{0}^{i} P_i \qquad (3.12)$$

where

$$P = \text{total pressure}$$

$$P_i = \text{partial pressure of the } i\text{th component}$$

Amagat's Law of Partial Volumes

This law states that the total volume of a gaseous mixture is equal to the sum of the partial volumes, namely,

$$V = \sum_{0}^{i} v_i \qquad (3.13)$$

where

$$V = \text{total volume}$$

$$v_i = \text{partial volume of the } i\text{th component}$$

Graham's Law of Diffusion

This law states that the rate of diffusion of a gas is inversely proportional to the square root of its molecular weight. This follows directly from the kinetic theory of gases:

$$PV = nRT = \text{constant} = 1/3\ n\ \text{MW}_1 u_1{}^2 = 1/3\ n\ \text{MW}_2 u_2{}^2 \qquad (3.10)$$

For one lb-mole of each gas, Equation 3.10 reduces to

$$\text{MW}_1 u_1{}^2 = \text{MW}_2 u_2{}^2$$

or

$$u_2/u_1 = \sqrt{\text{MW}_1/\text{MW}_2} \qquad (3.14)$$

This is Graham's law, where

u_1, u_2 = average translational velocities of the molecules of components 1 and 2, respectively

MW_1, MW_2 = molecular weights of components 1 and 2, respectively

Probably the most important application of this law has been in the separation of uranium isotopes by diffusion. The fluorides, $^{238}U F_6$ (MW=352) and $^{235}U F_6$ (MW = 349), according to Graham's law will diffuse through a porous barrier according to the square roots of the molecular weights:

$$u_2/u_1 = \sqrt{MW_1/MW_2} = \sqrt{352/349} = 1.0116$$

Compositions of ideal gas mixtures are often expressed in mole fractions, and in this regard relationships between partial pressure and total volume are desirable. For a given component, we have

$$P_A V = n_A RT \tag{3.15}$$

where

P_A = partial pressure of component A

n_A = moles of component A in the gaseous mixture

For a three-component system,

$$PV = (n_A + n_B + n_C)RT \tag{3.16}$$

Eliminating V from Equations 3.15 and 3.16, we have

$$V = \frac{n_A RT}{P_A} = \frac{(n_A + n_B + n_C)RT}{P} \tag{3.17}$$

or, after simplification,

$$P_A = P\frac{n_A}{n_A + n_B + n_C} = P\frac{\text{moles of } A}{\text{total number of moles}} \tag{3.18}$$

Thus

$$P_A = PY_A \tag{3.19}$$

where Y_A is the mole fraction of component A.

Equation 3.19 states that the partial pressure of component A is equal to the total pressure of the mixture multiplied by the mole fraction of A. Similarly, one finds that the partial volume of a component is equal to the total volume multiplied by the mole fraction of that component, or

$$V_A = VY_A \tag{3.20}$$

Note that for ideal gases, pressure fraction, volume fraction, and mole fraction are equal. Thus

$$P_A/P = V_A/V = n_A/n \tag{3.21}$$

Before we proceed to some examples, remember that *Orsat analysis* means gas analysis on a dry basis; this is sometimes called *flue gas analysis*. *Stack gas analysis* includes water vapor. In most analyses the percent composition of a gas is taken as mole % or volume %, and that of a liquid or solid is taken as weight %. One final definition must be made, and that is of percent excess air:

$$\% \text{ excess air} = \frac{\text{air input} - \text{air required}}{\text{air required}} \times 100 \tag{3.22}$$

The amount of air required is based on *complete combustion* whether the reaction is complete or not.

Example 3.6   Partial pressures of oxygen and nitrogen in the air

Show that the sum of the partial pressures of oxygen and nitrogen in the air equals the barometric pressure. The volumetric composition of air is 21% oxygen and 79% nitrogen.

Solution

Basis: 100 ft^3 of air at 14.7 psia.

Component	Volume (ft^3)
O_2	21
N_2	79
Total	100

Let P = total pressure = barometric pressure. The partial pressures are

$$P_{O_2} = \frac{21}{100}P = Y_{O_2}P$$

$$P_{N_2} = \frac{79}{100}P = Y_{N_2}P$$

and

$$P_{O_2} + P_{N_2} = \left(\frac{21}{100} + \frac{79}{100}\right) P = P \;\lhd$$

Example 3.7 Equivalence of mole, volume, and pressure percent

Show that the composition of air is identical, whether expressed in moles, volume, or pressure percentages.

Solution

Basis: 100 ft^3 of air at total pressure P and temperature T.

Component	Volume (ft^3)	Moles*	Mole %	Partial pressure†	Pressure %
N_2	79	4.10 P/T	79	79/100 P	79
O_2	21	1.09 P/T	21	21/100 P	21
Total	100	5.19 P/T	100	1 P	100

$$*\text{Moles of } N_2 = n_A = \frac{PV_A}{RT} = \frac{P(79 \text{ ft}^3)}{\dfrac{(14.7 \text{ psia})(359 \text{ ft}^3)}{(1 \text{ lb-mole}) 273°\text{K}} T} = 4.10\frac{P}{T}$$

†Partial pressure of $N_2 = P_{N_2} = Y_{N_2}(P) = 79/100 \; P$

Example 3.8 Combustion of natural gas

Natural gas, 96% methane and 4% ethane, is burned with 10% excess air to fire space heaters in a plant. The gases leave the heaters at 500°F. Determine

1. Average molecular weight of vent gas.
2. Volume of vent gas in SCF (70°F) and CF.

Solution

1. Basis: 100 lb-moles of inlet gas containing 96 lb-moles CH_4 and 4 lb-moles C_2H_6.

$$CH_4 + 2O_2 \rightarrow CO_2 + 2H_2O$$

$$C_2H_6 + 7/2\,O_2 \rightarrow 2CO_2 + 3H_2O$$

O_2 required $= 2(96) + (7/2)(4) = 192 + 14 = 206$ lb-mole

Total O_2 input $= (206)\,1.1 = 226.6$ lb-mole

Total N_2 input $= 226.6 \times (79/21) = 854$ lb-mole

O_2 out with vent gas $= 226.6 - 206 = 20.6$ lb-mole

Let us tabulate, since tabulation is very convenient with this type of problem.

Vent gas components	lb-moles	MW	Mass (lb_m)
CO_2	$96 + 2(4) = 104.0$	44	4,580
H_2O	$2(96) + 3(4) = 204.0$	18	3,670
O_2	20.6	32	660
N_2	854.0	28	23,900
Total	1182.6		32,810

$$\text{Average molecular weight} = \frac{32{,}810\ lb_m}{1182.6\ \text{lb-mole}} = 27.73\ \frac{lb_m}{\text{lb-mole}} \quad \text{}$$

2. The SCF of vent gas at $70°F$ and one atmosphere is

$$SCF = \frac{nRT}{P} = \frac{(1182.6\ \text{lb-moles})\,R\,(70 + 460)°R}{14.7\ \text{psia}}$$

It is easier to determine R than to memorize its proper value. From STP we have

$$R = \frac{PV}{nT} = \frac{14.7\ \text{psia}\,(359\ ft^3)}{\text{lb-mole}\,(460 + 32)°R}$$

Thus

$$SCF = 1182.6 \text{ lb-moles} \times \frac{14.7 \text{ psia } (359 \text{ ft}^3)}{\text{lb-mole } (460 + 32)°R} \times \frac{(70 + 460)°R}{14.7 \text{ psia}}$$

$$= \frac{1182.6 \times 14.7 \times 359 \times 530}{492 \times 14.7} \text{ ft}^3$$

$$SCF = 4.58 \times 10^6 \text{ ft}^3 \text{ at } 70°F \text{ and } 1 \text{ atm} \quad \triangleleft$$

$$CF = 4.58 \times 10^6 \text{ ft}^3 \times \frac{14.7 \text{ psia}}{14.7 \text{ psia}} \times \frac{(460 + 500)°R}{(460 + 70)°R}$$

$$CF = \frac{4.58 \times 10^6 \times 960}{530} \text{ ft}^3 = 8.30 \times 10^6 \text{ ft}^3 \text{ at } 500°F \text{ and } 1 \text{ atm} \quad \triangleleft$$

Example 3.9 Graham's law of diffusion

Estimate by means of Graham's law the percentage of oxygen and nitrogen in a stream of air after it has passed through a porous diffusion barrier. Assume that there is no interaction between the molecules inside the pores of the barrier and that there is no back diffusion.

Solution

Basis: 100 lb-moles of air input.

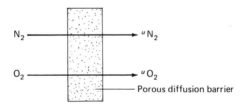

$$u_{N_2} = \sqrt{(32/28)}\ u_{O_2} = 1.065\ u_{O_2}$$

Therefore relative amounts beyond barrier are

$$N_2 = 79 \times 1.065 = 84.5$$

$$O_2 = 21$$

$$\text{Total} = 84.5 + 21 = 105.5 \text{ lb-moles}$$

Component	Amount beyond barrier	Mole %
N_2	84.5	81.1
O_2	21.0	18.9
Total	105.5	100.0

3.4 REAL GASES

Many processes in industry are conducted at high pressures and some at low temperatures, and the ideal gas laws are not applicable. *P-V-T* data are essential to the chemical process industries; since these data are limited in availability, and in many cases expensive to obtain, certain methods must be devised to predict what may be needed in design. These methods for predicting real gas behavior encompass algebraic representation of data, general charts accounting for non-ideality, and pseudoproperties for mixtures of real gases.

Equations of State

Algebraic equations relating pressure, temperature, and volume are called *equations of state*. They are numerous and often contain a good number of constants. Many of these equations are empirical, fitting data for only a given range of pressure and temperature; outside this range, their applicability may lead to serious errors.

The simplest and most well known among these relationships is the *van der Waals equation of state*:

$$(P + \frac{n^2 a}{V^2})(V - nb) = nRT \tag{3.23}$$

where

a = constant characteristic of each gas (see Appendix)
   = correction for intermolecular attractive forces

b = correction for actual volume of molecules (see Appendix)

Here, the deviation of real gases from ideal behavior is accounted for; the quantity $(n^2 a/V^2)$ expresses the magnitude of the correction for intermolecular attractions, and the quantity nb gives the magnitude of correction for the actual volume of the molecules. The use of this relationship is straightforward except for finding volumes. They can be solved for readily by using the perfect gas law as a first approximation, and any degree of accuracy may be obtained by continuing this approach of trial and error.

The *Beattie-Bridgeman* equation of state with five constants is

$$PV = RT + \frac{\beta}{V} + \frac{\gamma}{V^2} + \frac{\delta}{V^3} \qquad (3.24)$$

where

$$V = \text{volume per mole}$$

$$\beta = RTB_o - A_o - Rc'/T^2$$

$$\gamma = -RTB_ob' + A_oa' - Rc'B_o/T^2$$

$$\delta = RB_ob'c'/T^2$$

A_o, B_o, a', b', and c' are constants characteristic of each gas.

This equation is accurate within 0.3% for pressures as high as 100 atmospheres and temperatures as low as $-150°C$. Fluid properties at high densities are more accurately represented by a modification of the Beattie-Bridgeman equation. This modification gives the *Benedict-Webb-Rubin* equation with eight constants, making it a good candidate for computer usage.

A popular approach is to present *P-V-T* data in a power series form. Leading in this regard is the *Kamerlingh-Onnes* equation of state:

$$PV = A + BP + CP^2 + DP^3 + \cdots \qquad (3.25)$$

The constants *A, B, C,* and *D* are known as the first, second, third, and fourth *virial coefficients.* *

For estimating purposes and overall utility, none of the equations of state can compare with the correlation which follows.

Law of Corresponding States

This law states that at any given reduced temperature and any given reduced pressure, all materials have the same reduced volume. These reduced properties are based on absolute pressure and absolute temperature, and they are defined by

*See S. H. Maron and C. F. Prutton, *Principles of Physical Chemistry*, 3d ed. (New York: Macmillan, 1958), p. 35.

$$P_r = P/P_c$$

$$T_r = T/T_c$$

$$V_r = V/V_c \tag{3.26}$$

where P_r, T_r, V_r = reduced pressure, temperature, and volume, respectively.

P_c, T_c, V_c = critical pressure, temperature, and volume, respectively.

The point at which no distinction between liquid and vapor can be made is called the critical point; and no gas may be liquefied under any applied pressure unless it is cooled below its critical point.

Stated differently, the law of corresponding states means that gases at the same reduced pressure and same reduced temperature have the *same deviation from ideality*. A convenient way of expressing this is to introduce the correction factor Z to the ideal gas law:

$$PV = ZnRT \tag{3.27}$$

where Z is the compressibility factor accounting for nonideal behavior.

The deviation of Z from unity is an index of the degree of nonideality, since $Z = 1$ for ideal behavior. This factor may be obtained from general compressibility charts; these are obtained through the use of the law of corresponding states, which permits the plot of Z versus P_r, with T_r as a parameter. These plots have been prepared by Nelson and Ober (11), and Hougen and Watson (6);* they are widespread in the literature. A typical general chart is presented in Figure 3.4 a and b. Their accuracy was found to vary from 2 to 5%; but for

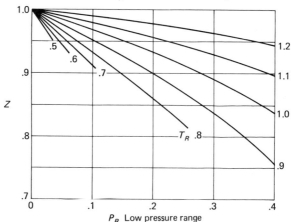

Figure 3.4a.   **Compressibility factors of gases and vapors (6).**

*Numbers in parentheses are keyed to the references at the end of the chapter.

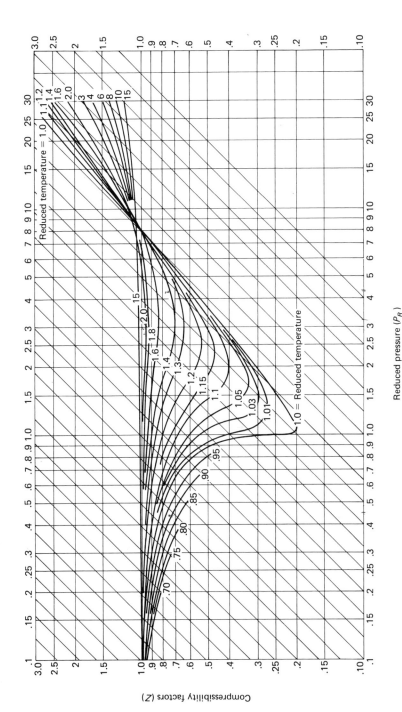

Figure 3.4b. Compressibility factors of gases and vapors (6).

hydrogen, helium, and *argon,* the critical values for pressure and temperature, expressed in atmospheres and $^\circ$K, must be increased by 8 for better correlation.

Compressibilities for Mixtures of Real Gases

The correct Z value for mixtures of gases is difficult to determine. *Amagat's* relationship gives the simplest solution, and it is generally valid at high pressures:

$$Z_m = \sum_0^i Z_i Y_i \tag{3.28}$$

where

Z_m = mean compressibility of the mixture

Z_i = compressibility of the ith component evaluated at T_r and total pressure of the mixture

Y_i = mole fraction of the ith component

Kay* proposed a reasonably simple treatment that works well, especially with hydrocarbon mixtures. *Kay's method* gives pseudocritical pressure and temperature as follows:

$$(P_c)_m = \sum_0^i P_{c_i} Y_i \tag{3.29}$$

$$(T_c)_m = \sum_0^i T_{c_i} Y_i \tag{3.30}$$

where

$(P_c)_m$ = effective critical pressure of mixture

P_{c_i} = critical pressure of ith component

$(T_c)_m$ = effective critical temperature of mixture

T_{c_i} = critical temperature of ith component

*W.B. Kay. 1936. Density of hydrocarbon gases and vapors at high temperature and pressure. *Industrial and Engineering Chemistry* 28:1014-1019.

These relationships are weighted averages, and the contribution of each component toward the effective pseudocritical value of $(T_c)_m$ or $(P_c)_m$ is directly proportional to its mole fraction. Once pseudocritical pressure and temperature are determined, Z is obtained from general compressibility charts as shown in Figure 3.4.

Several other methods are available in the literature, but Kay's method is quite accurate and is the most widely used.

Example 3.10   Van der Waals equation of state

Nitrogen gas occupies a volume of 240 ft³ at 68°F and one atmosphere. Determine the volume of this gas under isothermal conditions and a pressure of 2300 psi, using

1. Ideal gas behavior
2. Van der Waals equation (trial and error)

Solution

1. Using the "common-sense" law:

$$V_2 = 240 \text{ ft}^3 \times \frac{(68 + 460)°\text{R}}{(68 + 460)°\text{R}} \times \frac{14.7 \text{ psia}}{(2300* + 14.7) \text{ psia}}$$

$$V_2 = 1.53 \text{ ft}^3 \text{ at } 68°\text{F and } 2300 \text{ psig} \quad \triangleleft$$

2. The moles of nitrogen are

$$n = 240 \text{ ft}^3 \frac{(460 + 32)°\text{R†}}{(460 + 68)°\text{R}} \times \frac{\text{lb-mole}}{359 \text{ ft}^3}$$

$$= 0.625 \text{ lb-mole}$$

Use the van der Waals equation for $n = 1$ lb-mole:

---

*Since there is no mention whether the pressure is absolute or gauge, it is most likely a gauge pressure; this is the usual assumption.

†This is the volume at STP.

$$(P + \frac{a}{V^2})(V - b) = RT$$

As a first assumption take the ideal volume,

$$\frac{1.53 \text{ ft}^3}{0.625 \text{ lb-mole}} = 2.45 \text{ ft}^3/\text{lb-mole}$$

From the Appendix, we have

$$a = 346 \text{ atm} \left(\frac{\text{ft}^3}{\text{lb-mole}} \right)^2$$

$$b = 0.62 \text{ ft}^3/\text{lb-mole}$$

$$\frac{a}{V^2} = \frac{346 \frac{\text{atm-ft}^6}{(\text{lb-mole})^2}}{(2.45)^2 \text{ ft}^6/(\text{lb-mole})^2} = 57.6 \text{ atm}$$

$$\left(\frac{RT}{P + \frac{a}{V^2}} \right) = \frac{\frac{1 \text{ atm} \times 359 \text{ ft}^3}{\text{lb-mole} (460 + 32)^\circ R} \times (68 + 460)^\circ R}{(2314.7/14.7) \text{ atm} + 57.6 \text{ atm}} = \frac{359 \times 528}{215 \times 492}$$

$$= 1.79 \text{ ft}^3/\text{lb-mole} \triangleleft$$

$$\text{Calculated volume} = V = \frac{RT}{P + a/V^2} + b$$

$$= 1.79 + 0.62 = 2.41 \text{ ft}^3/\text{lb-mole}$$

The procedure is to continue assuming volumes until the assumed volume is approximately equal to the calculated one. Let us make more assumptions and tabulate.

V assumed (ft^3/lb-mole)	a/V^2 (atm)	$\frac{RT}{P + a/V^2}$ (ft^3/lb-mole)	V calculated (ft^3/lb-mole)	Difference
2.45	57.6	1.79	2.41	0.04
2.40	60.5	1.76	2.38	0.02
2.38	61.0	1.76	2.38	0.00

Since the gas has 0.625 lb-mole, the volume of this compressed gas is

$$V = 2.38 \frac{ft^3}{lb\text{-mole}} \times 0.625 \text{ lb-mole}$$

$$V = 1.49 \text{ ft}^3 \text{ at } 68°F \text{ and } 2300 \text{ psig} \quad \triangleleft$$

Example 3.11 Compressibility factor

Determine by means of compressibility charts the moles of oxygen and nitrogen that separately fill a gas cylinder. The gas is compressed to 2315 psig. Volume of the cylinder is 240 ft^3, and the temperature of this system is maintained at 68°F.

Solution

	P_c(atm)	T_c(°K)	P/P_c	T/T_c	Z
Oxygen	49.7	154	3.16	1.90	0.93
Nitrogen	33.5	126	4.7	2.32	1.05

From the equation

$$PV = ZnRT, \quad n = \frac{PV}{ZRT}$$

$$n_{O_2} = 2315 \frac{lb_f}{in.^2} \times \frac{1 \text{ atm}}{14.7 \text{ lb}_f/in.^2} \times 240 \text{ ft}^3 \times \frac{1}{0.93}$$

$$\times \frac{1}{0.73 \frac{ft^3\text{-atm}}{lb\text{-mole-}°R}} \times \frac{1}{528°R}$$

$$= 105 \text{ lb-moles} \quad \triangleleft$$

$$n_{N_2} = \frac{(2315)(240)}{(14.7)(1.05)(528)(0.73)}$$

$$= 95 \text{ lb-moles} \quad \triangleleft$$

Example 3.12   Pseudocritical values for mixtures

Determine the volume (ft^3) occupied by one pound of a 50-50 vol % mixture* of CH_4 and C_3H_8, at 50 atm (absolute) and 90°C, using

1. Amagat's relationship for mixtures
2. Kay's pseudocritical method
3. Compare results with measured values of Sage et al., 1934, *Industrial and Engineering Chemistry* 26:2149.

Solution

Basis: 1 lb-mole of gaseous mixture.

1.

Component	T_c(°K)	P_c(atm)	P_r	T_r	Z
CH_4	191	45.6	1.1	1.90	0.97
C_3H_8	370	42.0	1.19	0.98	0.20 (liquid region)

$$Z_m = (0.97)(0.50) + 0.20(0.50) = 0.585$$

$$PV = ZRT$$

$$V = \frac{ZRT}{P} = \frac{0.585 \quad \dfrac{1 \times 359}{273} \quad (273 + 90)}{50}$$

$$V = 5.58 \ ft^3/\text{lb-mole}$$

Average MW = 0.50 (16 + 44) = 30 lb/lb-mole

The required volume per pound mixture is

$$5.58 \frac{ft^3}{\text{lb-mole}} \times \frac{\text{lb-mole}}{30 \ \text{lb}} = 0.186 \frac{ft^3}{\text{lb of mixture}} \quad \triangleleft$$

*Made up at atmospheric pressure and room temperature, so that vol % = mole %.

2. $(P_c)_m = 0.5\,(45.6) + 0.5\,(42.0) = 43.9$ atm

$(T_c)_m = 0.5\,(191) + 0.5\,(370) = 280.5°R$

$(P_r)_m = 50/43.9 = 1.14$

$(T_r)_m = 363/280.5 = 1.29$

Form generalized charts, we have

$$Z_m = 0.83$$

Using the ratio of Z factors from parts 1 and 2 of this solution, the required volume is

$$0.186\,(0.83/0.585) = 0.263 \text{ ft}^3/\text{lb-mixture} \triangleleft$$

3. From Sage et al., 1 g-mole of this 50-50 mole % mixture has a volume of 0.477 liter. From part 1, volume per g-mole is

$$5.58\,\frac{\text{ft}^3}{\text{lb-mole}} \left(\frac{28.31}{\text{ft}^3}\right) \left(\frac{1 \text{ lb-mole}}{454 \text{ g-mole}}\right) = 0.348 \text{ liter/g-mole}$$

$$\begin{array}{l}\text{\% error in using} \\ \text{Amagat's approach}\end{array} = \left(\frac{0.477 - 0.348}{0.477}\right) 100 = 27\%* \triangleleft$$

From part 2, volume per g-mole using Z ratios is

$$(0.348)\,\frac{0.83}{0.585} = 0.488 \text{ liter/g-mole}$$

$$\begin{array}{l}\text{\% error in} \\ \text{using Kay's method}\end{array} = \left(\frac{0.477 - 0.488}{0.477}\right)100 = 2.3\% \triangleleft$$

3.5 LIQUIDS

Vapor Pressure of Pure Liquids

The pressure exerted by the vapor in equilibrium with a liquid at a given temperature is called the *saturated vapor pressure* or *vapor pressure*. The vapor pressure

---

*This large error is due to the propane being in the liquid region; that is, T_r is less than 1, and P_r is more than 1.

as a function of temperature must be measured experimentally, although, as shown in Table 3.1, changes can be calculated thermodynamically. One will find vapor pressures of all common liquids tabulated in the handbooks of chemistry and chemical engineering.

To get a better understanding of vapor pressure, consider the following process (Figure 3.5). We have an evacuated chamber maintained at 25°C. If a small amount of water is admitted into the chamber, it will vaporize and the system pressure will rise. As more water is admitted, the vaporization process will continue until the vapor pressure reaches 23.8 mm Hg, which is the saturated vapor pressure of water at 25°C. The admission of additional water will not change the pressure reading, since if a drop of water evaporates from one section, the same amount will condense at another.

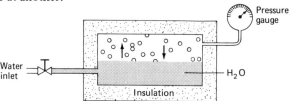

Figure 3.5. Saturated vapor pressure

When we change the temperature to 100°C, the vapor pressure becomes 760 mm Hg. For every temperature there is a definite vapor pressure. Note that 100°C is the normal boiling point of water at one atmosphere, and that a liquid will boil whenever its vapor pressure is equal to the pressure of the vessel in which the liquid is contained. Typical vapor pressures are shown in Table 3.1.

Table 3.1   VAPOR PRESSURES FOR CERTAIN LIQUIDS

Temperature (°C)	Vapor pressure (mm Hg)		
	H_2O	C_2H_5OH	C_6H_6
20	17.5	44.5	75.6
50	92.5	219.9	271.4
80	355.1	812.9	753.6
100	760.0	1693.0	1344.3

Useful data for various fluids are widespread in the literature. In addition, the value of vapor pressures may also be obtained from the following relationships and charts.

Clausius-Clapeyron equation. This equation permits the estimation of vapor pressure as a function of temperature. The initial relation is

$$\frac{dP}{dT} = \frac{\Delta H}{T \Delta V} \tag{3.31}$$

where

P = saturated vapor pressure of the liquid at temperature T

T = absolute temperature of the liquid

ΔH = molar heat of vaporization

ΔV = volume difference between gas and liquid phases

To integrate this expression, ΔH and ΔV must be expressed in terms of T and P. This is done with these assumptions: (a) ΔH is a constant. (b) ΔV equals the volume of gas, neglecting the liquid volume, and it is taken as RT/P.

The final relationships are

$$\ln P = -(\Delta H/R)\,(1/T) + c \tag{3.32}$$

or

$$2.303 \log_{10}\left(\frac{P_1}{P_2}\right) = \frac{\Delta H}{R}\left(\frac{T_1 - T_2}{T_1 T_2}\right) \tag{3.33}$$

where

P_1, P_2 = vapor pressure at temperatures T_1 and T_2, respectively

c = constant of integration

Equation 3.33 is the *Clausius-Clapeyron* equation, which is valid for a small range of temperatures. It is derived and discussed in more detail in Chapter 5, which is on energy. The Clausius-Clapeyron equation could be used to determine the effect of pressure on the melting point of solids; in this case the ΔH is the heat of fusion. This relationship can also be used to determine the vapor pressure of solids by making ΔH represent the heat of sublimation.

Empirical equations. A typical relationship between vapor pressure and temperature over a reasonable range of temperature is

$$\log_{10} P = A + B/T \tag{3.34}$$

where

P = absolute vapor pressure

A, B = constants for a given substance

T = absolute temperature

When two known values of vapor pressure and temperature are replaced in Equation 3.34, two equations are obtained that can be solved simultaneously to give A and B; at this stage, one can determine the vapor pressure at other temperatures.

Graphical presentation of the Clausius-Clapeyron equation. From Equation 3.32, we have

$$\ln P = -(\Delta H/R)(1/T) + c \tag{3.35}$$

A plot of $\ln P$ versus $1/T$ should yield a straight line for most substances when the temperature range is small. Equation 3.35 is similar to the equation of a straight line:

$$y = mx + b \tag{3.36}$$

where

y, x = variables

m = slope

b = intercept

The slope of such a plot will be $m = -(\Delta H/R)$, and the intercept will be $b = c$. These relationships are illustrated in Figure 3.6. Note that for convenience the abscissa has been changed to temperature in °C rather than $1/T$.

Cox chart.* Cox takes advantage of the fact that, for most substances, plots of vapor pressure versus temperature are similar in shape. If a method can be devised to give a straight-line relationship for one substance, the other substances will give approximately straight lines too.

The convenient substance used here is water. An arbitrary sloping line is drawn on paper (see Figure 3.7). The abscissa is a logarithmic pressure scale and the ordinate is an odd temperature scale. This temperature scale is obtained from the

*E. R. Cox, 1923, *Industrial and Engineering Chemistry* 15:592.

vapor pressure data for water. For example, at 90°F the vapor pressure of water is 0.7 psia; from a point on the water line corresponding to 0.7 psia, an ordinate is made to indicate 90°F. The procedure is repeated for a wide range of vapor pressures until the entire temperature scale is built. If this scale looks odd and out of proportion, the water line may be drawn again at a new arbitrary position and the whole procedure repeated until a suitable position is obtained that will give a reasonably proportionate scale.

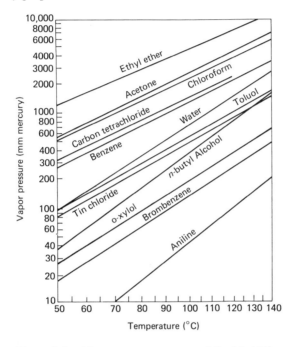

Figure 3.6. Vapor pressure curves of liquids (11)

Most paraffins and hydrocarbons drawn on a Cox chart have a common intersection at the right corner of the curve; for these substances, a knowledge of one point on the vapor pressure curve, for example the normal boiling point, will permit one to draw the entire curve. This is done simply by drawing a straight line between the one point and the common intersection.

Dühring lines. In this method, temperatures of the unknown and of the *reference substance,* usually water, are chosen such that their vapor pressures are the same. When these temperatures are plotted, a straight line results. For example, at 78.4°C the vapor pressure of ethanol is one atmosphere, and at 100°C water has

110

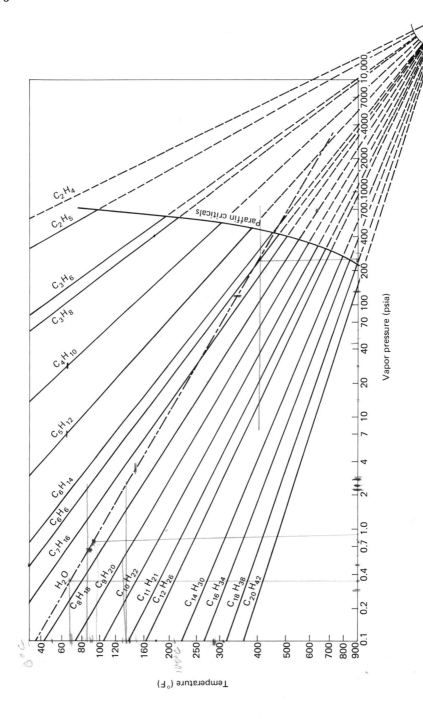

Figure 3.7. Cox chart for hydrocarbons (14)

the same vapor pressure; the alcohol temperature 78.4°C is plotted versus the water temperature 100°C, and whenever another datum point is obtained, a straight line is drawn between the two points for possible extrapolation of the available data. Figure 3.8 shows Dühring lines for some common liquids. Note that water is used as a reference substance because of the availability of its data. However, better correlations are obtained if the reference liquid is structurally related to the compounds in question.

The error involved in these methods for obtaining vapor pressure can approach 25%, depending on the degree of extrapolation and the type of assumptions involved. However, these methods are widely used for preliminary estimations whenever other data are not available.

Liquid Mixtures

When liquids are mixed, they are completely miscible, partially miscible, or totally immiscible. The closer the chemical structure of two liquids, the more miscible they are. We are interested in the simplified case, namely, ideal solutions. An *ideal solution* exhibits no change in the properties of its constituents beyond that of dilution.

Raoult's law is a basic law governing ideal solutions. It states that the partial vapor pressure of one component of the solution is equal to the vapor pressure

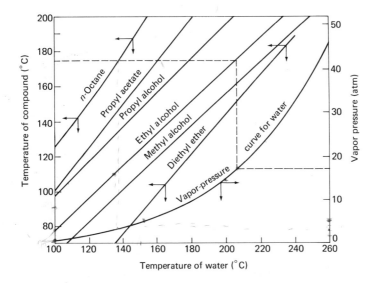

Figure 3.8. Dühring lines for various liquids (14)

of the pure component if it was alone at the same temperature, multiplied by the mole fraction of that component in the solution. Thus, for a two-component solution,

$$P_A = P_A{}^0 X_A \tag{3.37a}$$

$$P_B = P_B{}^0 X_B \tag{3.37b}$$

where

P_A, P_B = partial vapor pressure of components A and B, respectively, at the temperature of the solution

$P_A{}^0, P_B{}^0$ = vapor pressure of pure components A and B, respectively

X_A, X_B = mole fraction of A and B, respectively

The total vapor pressure above the solution is

$$\begin{aligned} P &= P_A + P_B \\ &= P_A{}^0 X_A + P_B{}^0 X_B \end{aligned} \tag{3.38}$$

Since

$$X_B = 1 - X_A$$

Equation 3.38 becomes

$$\begin{aligned} P &= P_A{}^0 X_A + P_B{}^0 (1 - X_A) \\ &= P_A{}^0 X_A + P_B{}^0 - P_B{}^0 X_A \end{aligned}$$

and

$$P = (P_A{}^0 - P_B{}^0) X_A + P_B{}^0 \tag{3.39}$$

This equation gives the total pressure above the solution as a function of the vapor pressure of the components and the mole fraction of one component in the solution. Equations 3.37a and 3.39 give straight lines, as shown in Figure 3.9.

The composition of the vapor above the solution is also important. It may be determined by combining Dalton's law and Raoult's law. We have

$$Y_A = P_A / P \tag{3.40}$$

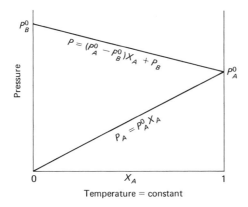

Figure 3.9. Raoult's law for ideal solutions

where Y_A is the mole fraction of component A in the vapor mixture above that solution. Taking P_A from Equation 3.37a and P from Equation 3.39, we find

$$Y_A = \frac{P_A{}^0 X_A}{(P_A{}^0 - P_B{}^0) X_A + P_B{}^0}$$
(3.41)

Raoult's law in general and this relationship in particular are very useful, especially in distillation operations.

At this point, another relationship is worth mentioning. This is *Henry's law*, which is applicable for dilute solutions. It states that the concentration of a gas dissolved in a solution or solvent is directly proportional to the partial pressure of the gas above the solution. Here, the vapor pressure in Raoult's law is replaced by a proportionality constant, as shown in this form of Henry's law:

$$P_g = k X_g$$
(3.42)

where

P_g = partial pressure of the gas above the solution

k = Henry's law coefficient; it depends on temperature and nature of the gas and solvent; when using literature data, note the units of k

X_g = mole fraction of the gas in the solution

This law is limited to low pressures and to solutions in which the dissolved gas does not ionize and does not react with the solvent.

Example 3.13   Vapor pressure in the evaporation of benzene

Nitrogen is bubbled through benzene at atmospheric pressure. Given that the temperature is 26.1°C and the vapor pressure of benzene is 100 mm Hg, determine the moles of nitrogen needed to vaporize 10 lb-moles of C_6H_6.

Solution

Assume ideal behavior. Thus the partial pressure ratio is equal to the mole ratio, or

$$\frac{(760 - 100) \text{ mm Hg}}{100 \text{ mm Hg}} = \frac{\text{lb-mole nitrogen}}{\text{lb-mole benzene}}$$

$$= \frac{6.60 \text{ lb-moles N}_2}{\text{lb-mole C}_6\text{H}_6}$$

To evaporate 10 lb-moles of C_6H_6 we need

$$6.60 \frac{\text{lb-mole N}_2}{\text{lb-mole C}_6\text{H}_6} \times 10 \text{ lb-mole C}_6\text{H}_6 = 66 \text{ lb-moles N}_2 \quad \triangleleft$$

Example 3.14   Vapor pressure of water at 25°C

Estimate the vapor pressure of water at 25°C, and compare with the tabulated value of 23.8 mm Hg, using the normal boiling point values of 760 mm Hg and 100°C, and the ΔH values of 970 Btu/lb at 100°C and 1049 Btu/lb at 25°C.

Solution

$$\Delta H_{avg} = \frac{970 + 1049}{2} = 1004 \text{ Btu/lb}$$

Use the Clausius-Clapeyron equation:

$$2.303 \log_{10} \left(\frac{P_2}{P_1}\right) = -\frac{\Delta H}{R} \left(\frac{T_1 - T_2}{T_1 T_2}\right)$$

or

$$2.303 \log_{10}\left(\frac{P_2}{P_1}\right) = -\frac{1004 \text{ Btu/lb}}{1.98 \frac{\text{cal}}{\text{g-mole-}^\circ\text{K}}} \times 252 \frac{\text{cal}}{\text{Btu}} \times 18 \frac{\text{lb}}{\text{lb-mole}}$$

$$\times \frac{1 \text{ lb}}{454 \text{ g}}\left[\frac{(373 - 298)}{(273 + 100)(273 + 25)}\right]$$

$$\log_{10}\left(\frac{P_2}{P_1}\right) = 1.48$$

$$\frac{P_2}{P_1} = 30.2$$

and

$$P_1 = \frac{760}{30.2} = 25.2 \text{ mm Hg at } 25^\circ\text{C} \quad \triangleleft$$

$$\% \text{ error} = \frac{25.2 - 23.8}{23.8} \times 100 = 5.9\% \text{ high} \quad \triangleleft$$

Example 3.15   Raoult's law applied to a mixture of n-heptane and n-octane

Normal (n) heptane (C_7H_{16}) has a vapor pressure of 795.2 mm Hg at 100°C, and n-octane (C_8H_{18}) has a vapor pressure of 353.6 mm Hg at 100°C.

1. What composition does a solution of the above have if it boils at 100°C under 740 mm Hg pressure?

2. What is the composition of the vapor that first boils from this solution?

3. What is the total pressure exerted by a vapor in equilibrium with a solution of n-heptane and n-octane at 100°C in which the mole fraction of n-heptane is 0.37?

Solution

1. From Raoult's law the total vapor pressure above the solution is

$$P = P_A{}^0 X_A + P_B{}^0 X_B$$

Let X = mole fraction of n-C_7H_{16} in solution

$$740 = (795.2)X + (353.6)(1 - X)$$

and

$$X = \frac{740.0 - 353.6}{795.2 - 353.6} = 0.876$$

Composition of solution:

$$\text{mole fraction of } n\text{-}C_7H_{16} = 0.876$$

$$\text{mole fraction of } n\text{-}C_8H_{18} = 0.124$$

2. For the vapor phase, use Equation 3.40

$$Y_A = \frac{P_A}{P} = \frac{P_A{}^0 X_A}{P}$$

or

$$Y_{n\text{-}C_7H_{16}} = \frac{(795.2)\,(0.876)}{740.0} = 0.941$$

$$Y_{n\text{-}C_8H_{18}} = 1 - 0.941 = 0.059$$

3.
$$X_{n\text{-}C_7H_{16}} = 0.37$$

$$X_{n\text{-}C_8H_{18}} = 0.63$$

Using Equation 3.38:

$$P = P_A{}^0 X_A + P_B{}^0 X_B$$

$$= (795.2)\,(0.37) + 353.6\,(0.63)$$

$$P = 516.1 \text{ mm Hg}$$

3.6 HUMIDITY

Air-water contact is widely practiced in air conditioning, whether for cooling, humidifying, or dehumidifying. Some definitions are essential before proceeding to the description of an important chart called the humidity chart.

Definitions

1. **Absolute humidity.** This is the pounds of water vapor carried per pound of dry air:

$$H = \left(\frac{P_w}{P - P_w}\right)\frac{18}{29} = \left(\frac{P_w}{P_{air}}\right)\frac{18}{29} \tag{3.43}$$

For operations at one atmosphere:

$$H = \left(\frac{P_w}{1 - P_w}\right)\frac{18}{29} \tag{3.44}$$

where

H = absolute humidity, nominally just humidity, which is lb water/lb dry air; in other formulas it may be given as grains of water/lb dry air (7000 grains = 1 lb)

P = barometric pressure, nominally 14.7 psia

P_w = partial pressure of water vapor in air

2. Humidity at saturation. When air is saturated with water vapor at air temperature, the partial pressure of water vapor is equal to the saturated vapor pressure of water at that temperature. The humidity at saturation is defined by

$$H_S = \left(\frac{P_w^{\,0}}{P - P_w^{\,0}}\right)\frac{18}{29} \tag{3.45}$$

where

H_S = humidity at saturation

$P_w^{\,0}$ = saturated vapor pressure of water at ambient temperature

3. Percentage or percent humidity. This is the ratio of absolute humidity to the humidity at saturation:

$$H_P = \frac{H}{H_S} \times 100 \tag{3.46}$$

4. Relative humidity. This is a relative expression telling us how far we are from saturation. Relative humidity is the ratio of the partial pressure of water vapor in the air to the saturated vapor pressure of water at the same temperature:

$$H_R = \frac{P_w}{P_w^{\,0}} \times 100 \qquad (3.47)$$

where H_R = relative humidity, sometimes represented by RH; when the radio or TV announcer says humidity is 75%, he means relative humidity H_R = 75%.

The above relationships also apply for a mixture of a permanent gas and a vapor; for such a case the term "humidity" is replaced by "saturation."

5. Humid heat. This is the amount of heat necessary to raise by 1°F the temperature of one pound of dry air plus whatever water vapor it contains. Humid heat, which is close kin to heat capacity, is defined by

$$C_S = 0.24 + 0.46\,H \qquad (3.48)$$

where

$$C_S = \text{humid heat expressed in Btu/lb-°F}$$

6. Humid volume. The volume of one pound of dry air plus whatever water it contains at one atmosphere and air temperature is called humid volume. It may be determined by use of the ideal gas laws.

7. Dew point. The temperature at which the first droplet of water forms from an air-water vapor mixture is called dew point. This is the point at which percentage humidity H_P = 100 and $H = H_S$.

The classical measurement involves cooling a cup filled with ether by blowing air through it. The polished external surface clouds over with dew when the saturation temperature is reached. Presently, electronic readout devices based on moisture absorption are available to give a direct measurement.

8. Dry and wet bulb temperatures. A useful measurement of humidity is based on wet and dry bulb thermometry. The temperature indicated by a dry thermometer, well shielded to avoid the effect of radiation, is called *dry bulb temperature.* When a thermometer whose bulb is surrounded by a well-moistened wick is swung around and around until the air velocity is about 15 ft/sec (to minimize the effect of radiation), it registers a temperature called *wet bulb temperature.* The rotation must be continued until reproducible results are obtained. Both the dry and wet bulb temperatures may be read by an instrument called a sling psychrometer.

9. **Adiabatic saturation temperature.** Consider the air-water system shown in Figure 3.10. Air enters at temperature t and with a humidity H. The chamber is insulated so that there is no heat exchange with the surroundings (adiabatic operation). Water is pumped and sprayed for the purpose of good contact with the air. Since the air is relatively dry, some water will evaporate and the air will pick up moisture, until at steady state it becomes saturated at t_S and with a humidity H_S. The steady state *water* temperature t_S, called the *adiabatic saturation temperature*, is always lower than the air temperature unless the entering air is saturated.

The heat needed for evaporating the water comes from the heat lost by the air:

$$(H_S - H)\lambda = C_S(t - t_S) \tag{3.49}$$

or

$$H_S - H = \frac{C_S}{\lambda}(t - t_S) \tag{3.50}$$

where λ is the latent heat of vaporization for water at temperature t_S, nominally 1000 Btu/lb.

This equation shows that a plot of H versus t will give a straight line for every value of H_S and t_S. A series of these adiabatic cooling lines is presented on the humidity chart in Figure 3.11. Note that for air-water systems the wet bulb temperature and the adiabatic saturation temperature are essentially equal for all practical purposes. For systems other than air-water this equality does not hold, due to the difference in mass transfer mechanisms for the various systems; in such cases other relationships must be derived.

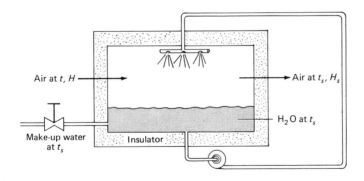

Figure 3.10.   Adiabatic saturation chamber

Use of the Humidity Chart

Humidity or psychrometric charts represent a collection of useful data arranged graphically in a convenient form. We are concerned here with the humidity chart for air-water systems at one atmosphere, shown in Figure 3.11. The slanted parallel lines are the adiabatic cooling lines, and the temperature indicated at the upper left of each of these lines is the adiabatic saturation temperature. The exponential curves indicate percentage humidity H_p, sometimes called percent humidity.

To illustrate the use of this chart, assume that moist air has a dry bulb temperature of $110°F$ and a wet bulb temperature of $80°F$. We need to find on the chart the point that identifies this mixture; from the dry bulb temperature, or $110°F$, draw the vertical line tA; now locate the wet bulb temperature or adiabatic saturation temperature of $80°F$ and draw an *adiabatic cooling line WA* through it (you may have to interpolate in other cases). These two lines intersect at point A, which characterizes this mixture. The absolute humidity is obtained by drawing the horizontal line AH. The intersection with the humidity ordinate gives

$$H = 0.015 \text{ lb } H_2O/\text{lb dry air}$$

Humidity at saturation is at the intersection of the horizontal line through W with the ordinate:

$$H_S = 0.022 \text{ lb } H_2O/\text{lb dry air}$$

The percentage humidity, or percent humidity, is obtained by drawing the curve AP through A, matching in shape the exponential curves on the chart. Thus

$$H_p = 26\%$$

The dew point is found by cooling this mixture until the first droplet of water is formed. Thus from point A draw a horizontal line AD to the left; a vertical line drawn from D intercepts the abscissa at point d, and the dew point is

$$d = 69°F$$

If we add water vapor to this air at the same temperature $110°F$, *saturation* will be reached, and the humidity in this case is obtained by drawing a vertical line AV to the 100% saturation curve and from V a horizontal line to the right. Point h gives a humidity of 0.059 lb H_2O/lb dry air. To find *humid heat* draw a horizontal line through A; this line intersects the humid heat line at C. From point C draw a vertical line CR to get

$$\text{Humid heat} = C_S = 0.247 \text{ Btu/lb dry air-}°F$$

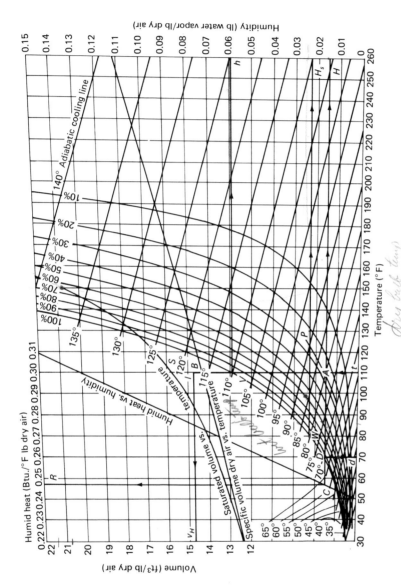

Figure 3.11. Humidity chart. Air-water system at one atmosphere. (The adiabatic cooling lines on this chart are straight and parallel.) (10)

The humid volume is obtained by drawing a vertical line through A and by interpolating between the curves the volume of dry air and saturated volume. The vertical line intersects these two curves at B and S. Since the air is relatively unsaturated ($H_P = 25\%$), the point that will describe this mixture should be closer to the dry air line. This point l should be at $BS \times (25/100)$. From point l draw a horizontal line to the left, and at point v_H read

$$\text{Humid volume} = v_H = 14.7 \text{ ft}^3/\text{lb dry air at } 110°\text{F and 1 atm}$$

Example 3.16   Humidity in air conditioning

Standard air conditioning generally requires room conditions of 50% humidity at 70°F. Determine

1. Absolute humidity H
2. Humidity at saturation H_S
3. Percent relative humidity RH

Solution

1. $$P_w^0 \text{ at } 70°\text{F} = 18.7 \text{ mm Hg}$$

   Using 50% humidity as percentage humidity, we obtain from the chart

   $$H = 0.0078 \text{ lb } H_2O/\text{lb dry air}$$

2. From the humidity chart, we have

   $$H_S = 0.016 \text{ lb } H_2O/\text{lb dry air}$$

   or

   $$H_S = \left(\frac{P_w^0}{760 - P_w^0}\right)\frac{18}{29} = \left(\frac{18.7}{760 - 18.7}\right)\frac{18}{29}$$

   $$H_S = 0.0156 \text{ lb } H_2O/\text{lb dry air}$$

3. Percent relative humidity is

   $$RH = \frac{P_w}{P_w^0} 100$$

$$P_w = \text{(total pressure) (mole fraction of water vapor)}$$

The mole fraction is

$$X_w = \frac{\text{moles of water vapor}}{\text{(moles of water vapor)} + \text{(moles of dry air)}}$$

$$= \frac{0.0078 \text{ lb}/(18 \text{ lb/lb-mole})}{\left(\dfrac{0.0078 \text{ lb}}{18 \text{ lb/lb-mole}}\right) + \dfrac{1 \text{ lb}}{29 \text{ lb/lb-mole}}} = \frac{4.33 \times 10^{-4}}{4.33 \times 10^{-4} + 344.8 \times 10^{-4}}$$

$$X_w = \frac{4.33 \times 10^{-4}}{349.13 \times 10^{-4}} = 0.0124$$

$$P_w = (760 \text{ mm Hg}) \, 0.0124 = 9.44 \text{ mm Hg}$$
$$RH = (9.44/18.7) \, 100 = 50.5\%$$

Note that the difference between relative humidity and percentage humidity is very small.

Example 3.17 Humidity from dew point value

A process stream of pure methane is dried to a dew point of $14°F$ $(P_w{}^0 = 2 \text{ mm Hg})$ prior to entering a reactor. The methane stream enters the drying tower at $70°F$. Use basic definitions to determine

$$1.\, H \qquad 2.\, H_p \qquad 3.\, RH$$

Solution

The partial pressure of water vapor in the methane at $70°F$ is 2 mm Hg, which is also the saturated vapor pressure at the dew point.

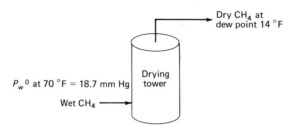

1. $$H = \frac{2}{760-2}\frac{18}{16} = 0.0029 \text{ lb } H_2O/\text{lb } CH_4$$

2. $$H_P = \frac{H}{H_S} = \frac{2/(760-2)}{\frac{18.7}{760-18.7}} \times 100 = 10.5\%$$

3. $$RH = \frac{2}{18.7} \times 100 = 10.7\%$$

Example 3.18   Humidity values for compressed gases

Gases like nitrogen can be compressed into cylinders at 2300 psig by oil- or water-:
lubricated compressors. If you use a water-lubricated compressor, and you open·
the cylinder valve to obtain some nitrogen, determine for this gas:

1. Absolute humidity H
2. Percentage humidity H_P
3. Relative humidity RH
4. Dew point of the delivered gas

Solution

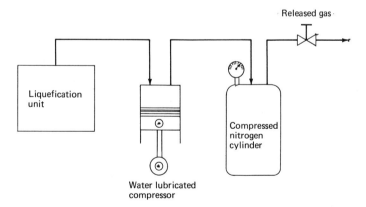

Let us focus our attention on the nitrogen cylinder and the released gas. Assume
that the temperature of the cylinder is 70°F and that the nitrogen in the cylinder
is saturated with water vapor. Let us solve for P_w in the released gas:

$$P_w = \frac{\text{moles } H_2O}{\text{moles } (N_2 + H_2O)} \text{ (total pressure of released gas)}$$

$$= X_w \text{ (total pressure of released gas)}$$

$$X_w = \frac{\text{moles } H_2O}{\text{moles } (N_2 + H_2O)} = \frac{18.7}{(2300 + 14.7)(760/14.7)} = 1.56 \times 10^{-4}$$

$$P_w = 1.56 \times 10^{-4} \times 760 \text{ mm Hg} = 0.12 \text{ mm Hg}$$

For the released gas we have

1.
$$H = \frac{0.12}{760 - 0.12} \frac{18}{28*} = 0.0001 \text{ lb } H_2O/\text{lb } N_2$$

2.
$$H_S = \frac{18.7}{760 - 18.7} \frac{18}{28} = 0.0163 \text{ lb } H_2O/\text{lb } N_2$$

$$H_P = \frac{H}{H_S} 100 = \frac{0.0001}{0.0163} 100 = 0.61\%$$

3.
$$RH = \frac{P_w}{P_w^{\ 0}} 100 = \frac{0.12}{18.7} 100 = 0.64\%$$

4.
$$P_w = 0.12 \text{ mm Hg} \frac{14.7 \text{ psia}}{760 \text{ mm Hg}} = 0.0023 \text{ psia}$$

To find the dew point we should search for the temperature that will give a saturated vapor pressure of 0.0023 psia. From Perry's handbook, we have

$$P_w^{\ 0} \text{ at } -35°F = 0.00254 \text{ psia}$$
$$P_w^{\ 0} \text{ at } -40°F = \underline{0.00186 \text{ psia}}$$
$$\text{Difference} = 0.00068 \text{ psia}$$

By interpolation we obtain

$$P_w^{\ 0} = 0.0023 \text{ psia at } -36.8°F$$

Thus

$$\text{Dew point} = -36.8°F$$

*Molecular weight of $N_2 = 28$.

Example 3.19   Use of humidity chart

An air mixture has a dry bulb temperature of 79°F and a wet bulb temperature of 64°F. Using the humidity chart, determine H, H_p, and the dew point.

Solution

Following the procedure described in the text for the use of the humidity chart, we find

$$H = 0.0092 \text{ lb } H_2O/\text{lb dry air}$$

$$H_p = 43\% \approx RH$$

$$\text{Dew point} = 55°F$$

NOMENCLATURE

Symbol	Meaning
A	Constant for a given substance
A_o	Constant characteristics of each gas, used in Equation 3.24
a	Constant, correction for intermolecular attractive forces, Equation 3.23
a'	Constant in Equation 3.24
B	Constant for a given substance
B_o	Constant in Equation 3.24
b	Constant, correction for actual volume of molecules in Equation 3.23
b'	Constant in Equation 3.24
C	Number of components in the phase rule
C_S	Humid heat, Btu/lb-°F
c'	Constant in Equation 3.24
F	Degrees of freedom in the phase rule
H	Absolute humidity, nominally just humidity, lb water/lb dry air
H_R, RH	Relative humidity

Symbol	*Meaning*
H_S	Humidity at saturation
ΔH	Molar heat of vaporization
k	Henry's law coefficient
MW	Molecular weight
MW_1, MW_2	Molecular weight of components 1 and 2, respectively
m	Mass of one molecule
N	Avogadro's number $= 6.023 \times 10^{23}$ molecules/g-mole
n	Number of moles of gas
$\mathcal{P}$	Number of phases in the phase rule
p	Pressure
P	Saturated vapor pressure, or vapor pressure of a liquid at temperature T in Equation 3.31
P_A	Partial pressure of component A
P_B	Partial pressure of component B
P_c	Critical pressure
P_g	Partial pressure of the gas above a solution
P_i	Partial pressure of the ith component
P_w	Partial pressure of water vapor in air
P_r	Reduced pressure
P_{c_i}	Critical pressure of the ith component
$(P_c)_m$	Effective critical pressure of mixture
P_1, P_2	Vapor pressure at temperatures T_1 and T_2, respectively
$P_A{}^0, P_B{}^0$	Vapor pressure for pure components A and B, respectively
$P_w{}^0$	Saturated vapor pressure of water at ambient temperature
R	Universal gas constant $= 1.99$ Btu/lb-mole-°K
T	Absolute temperature
T_c	Critical temperature
T_r	Reduced temperature
T_{c_i}	Critical temperature of ith component

Symbol	Meaning
$(T_c)_m$	Effective critical temperature of mixture
t_S	Adiabatic saturation temperature
u	Average translational velocity of the molecules
u_1, u_2	Average translational velocities of the molecules of components 1 and 2, respectively
V	Volume, volume difference between gas and liquid phases
V	Volume per mole
V_c	Critical volume
V_r	Reduced volume
V_i	Partial volume of the ith component
X_A, X_B	Mole fraction of A and B, respectively, in the liquid
X_g	Mole fraction of the gas in the solution
Y_A	Mole fraction of component A in the vapor
Y_i	Mole fraction of the ith component in a gaseous mixture
Z	Compressibility factor accounting for nonideal behavior
Z_i	Compressibility of the ith component evaluated at T_r and total P_r of the mixture
Z_m	Mean compressibility of the mixture

Greek letters	Meaning
ρ	Density
λ	Latent heat of vaporization for water at temperature t_S, nominally 1000 Btu/lb

REFERENCES

1. American Petroleum Institute, Division of Refining. 1966. *Technical data book – Petroleum refining.* New York.

2. Badger, W. L., and McCabe, W. L. 1936. *Elements of chemical engineering.* 2d ed. New York: McGraw-Hill.

3. Daniels, F., and Alberty, R. A. 1955. *Physical chemistry.* New York: John Wiley.

4. Glasstone, S. 1946. *Textbook of physical chemistry,* Chapter 7. New York: Van Nostrand.

5. Henley, E. J., and Bieber, H. 1959. *Chemical engineering calculations.* New York: McGraw-Hill.

6. Hougen, O. A., and Watson, K. M. 1936. *Industrial chemical calculations.* 2d ed. New York: John Wiley.

7. Larian, M. G. 1958. *Fundamentals of chemical engineering operations,* Chapter 7. Englewood Cliffs, N. J.: Prentice-Hall.

8. Littlejohn, C. E., and Meenaghan, G. F. 1959. *An introduction to chemical engineering.* New York: Reinhold.

9. Maron, S. H., and Prutton, C. F. 1958. *Principles of physical chemistry,* 3d ed, Chapter 3. New York: Macmillan.

10. McCabe, W. L., and Smith, J. C. 1967. *Unit operations of chemical engineering,* Chapter 22. New York: McGraw-Hill.

11. Perry, J. H. 1950. *Chemical engineers' handbook,* 3d ed. New York: McGraw-Hill.

12. Thatcher, C. M. 1962. *Fundamentals of chemical engineering.* Columbus: Charles E. Merrill.

13. Walker, W. H.; Lewis, W. K.; McAdams, W. H.; and Gulliland, E. R. 1937. *Principles of chemical engineering,* 3d ed. New York: McGraw-Hill.

14. Weber, H. G., and Meissner, H. P. 1957. *Thermodynamics for chemical engineers,* 2d ed. New York: John Wiley.

PROBLEMS

3.1 Ideal Gas Law

By using the ideal gas law, find the molar volume (ft^3/lb-mole) at typical room conditions (1 atm and 75°F).

3.2 Chimney Gas

A chimney gas has the following composition:

Component	Mole %
CO_2	9.5
CO	0.2
O_2	9.6
N_2	80.7
Total	100.0

Assuming ideal behavior, calculate

1. Its composition by weight
2. Average molecular weight
3. Density of the gas at 75°F and 27 psia

3.3 Volume of Air

What is the volume of 58 lb of air at 1000°F and 30 psig?

3.4 The Ideal Gas Law and the Kinetic Theory of Gases

Derive the ideal gas law, taking into account the ideas involved in the kinetic theory of gases. For simplicity it can be assumed that the gas molecules move at the root-mean-square velocity.

3.5 Gas Law Constant in Different Units

Determine the ideal gas law constant for the cases shown in the accompanying table. List both items 5 and 6.

1	P	Psig	Psig	mm Hg	mm Hg	dynes/cm^2	atm
2	V	ft^3	ft^3	liters	ft^3	ml	ml
3	n	lb-mole	lb	g-mole	lb-mole	g-mole	g
4	T	°R	°F	°K	°K	°K	°C
5	R	$\dfrac{(14.7)(359)}{(1)(492)}$					
6	R	10.7					

3.6 Combustion

A dry gaseous mixture containing 90 mol % CH_4 and 10% C_2H_6 is burned with air. Orsat analysis of the combustion gas shows 5.3% CO_2 and no CO. The air enters at 35°F and normal barometer, and the partial pressure of water vapor in the air is 3 mm Hg. Calculate

1. Percent excess air

2. Cubic feet of flue gas, at 600°F and normal barometer, per cubic foot of gas measured at standard conditions

3.7 Steel-Annealing Furnace

A steel-annealing furnace burns a fuel oil, the composition of which can be represented as $(CH_2)n$. It is planned to burn this fuel with 15% excess air. Calculate the Orsat analysis of the flue gas

1. Assuming complete combustion

2. Assuming that 6% of the carbon in the fuel is burnt to CO

3.8 Effect of Temperature on Reservoir Volume

A natural gas reservoir consists of a large floating bell, shown schematically in Figure P3.8. The indicator on a cold day of −20°F shows a height of 10 ft, corresponding to 50% full.

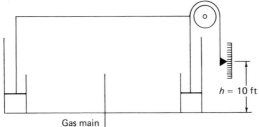

Figure P3.8.

With no demand on the system, determine

1. Percent full if the temperature goes up to 32°F. Assume the gas temperature is the same as ambient temperature.

2. Height

3.9 Cryogenic Pumping

Cryogenic pumping is employed to evacuate large environmental chambers. It involves condensing the inert gases by employing a condenser at liquid helium temperature ($4°K$). The noncondensible helium is pumped from the system by a high vacuum pump. See Figure P3.9.

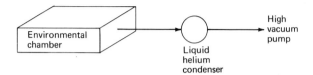

Figure P3.9

If the pumping speed for N_2 is 100,000 ft³/sec, what is the speed for H_2 assuming that the duct to the helium condenser is large enough to eliminate conductance effects?

3.10 Gaseous Mixture

A gas mixture has the following composition.

Component	Vol %
O_2	5
N_2	65
CO_2	20
H_2O	10
Total	100

This mixture occupies 1100 ft³ at 125°F and 750 mm Hg. Determine

1. Partial pressure of water
2. Volume of oxygen
3. Average molecular weight of the mixture
4. Density of the mixture

3.11 Property of a Gas Mixture

A gas cylinder 100 ml in volume is immersed in liquid helium and then evacuated. After evacuation the liquid helium bath is removed and the cylinder is warmed to a room temperature of 68°F. Then it is filled with certain gases from a series of one-liter round-bottom flasks. The amount of gases added is determined by measuring respective pressures in the flasks. See Figure P3.11.

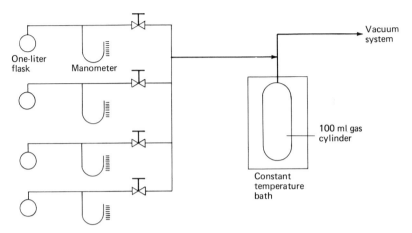

Figure P3.11

Given:

Gas	Temperature in flask ($^\circ$F)	Initial pressure in flask (mm Hg)	Final pressure in flask (mm Hg)
N_2	68	760	542
O_2	68	432	138
CH_4	68	584	267
C_2H_6	68	146	105

Assuming ideal gas behavior, determine for the gas cylinder:

1. Pressure

2. Average density of the gaseous mixture

3. Volume percent composition of this mixture

3.12 Van der Waals Equation of State

Give the Van der Waals equation of state for gases and describe the nature of the terms that correct for nonideality.

3.13 Temperature from the Van der Waals Equation and the Law of Corresponding States

An oxygen cylinder is filled at 68°F and 2300 psig.

1. Using the Van der Waals equation of state, determine the temperature of the cylinder when the pressure is increased to 3000 psia.
2. Find this temperature by using the law of corresponding states.

3.14 Pressure in Oxygen Tank Exposed to Sun

A cylinder of oxygen is filled at 68°F to a pressure of 2300 psi. The safety relief valve is set for 3000 psi and the ideal gas law applies.

1. What temperature must the contents reach to activate the safety valve?
2. Is this temperature possible by exposure to the sun?

3.15 Deviation from Ideal Behavior

List the following cases for gaseous systems in order of increasing deviation from ideal behavior.

	P_r	T_r
1.	1.20	1.01
2.	0.30	0.80
3.	0.03	1.20
4.	15.00	15.00

3.16 Generalized Method versus Ideal Behavior

Forty pounds of oxygen are stored in a 1 ft³ cylinder at a temperature of −182°F.

1. Estimate the resulting pressure using generalized Z methods.
2. What percentage error (based on the result of part 1) results from assuming that the oxygen behaves as an ideal gas?

3.17   Volume of Gas Mixture at High Pressure

Given the mixture of gases at 350°C and 2000 psi described below, compare the volume per lb-mole calculated by

1. Perfect gas law
2. Amagat's relationship
3. Kay's pseudocritical method
4. Determine vol % by pseudocritical method

Component	Mole %
Methane	60
Ethane	30
Propane	10

3.18   Measurement of the Compressibility Coefficient

The compressibility coefficient $Z = PV/nRT$ is to be determined for N_2 in the apparatus shown in Figure P3.18.

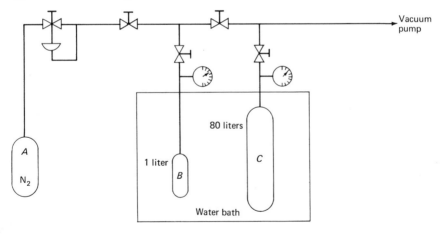

Figure P3.18

Tank B is filled to a pressure of 2000 psi. Tank C is evacuated to a pressure of less than 10^{-3} torr (1 torr = 1 mm Hg absolute) by means of a high vacuum pump. The gas is then expanded from B to C.

1. Determine the compressibility coefficient for N_2 at 2000 psi and at room temperature 68°F when the pressure after expansion is 16.8 psig.

2. Compare the compressibility coefficient you obtain against the value obtained from compressibility charts.

3.19 Compressibility Coefficient by the Barnett Apparatus

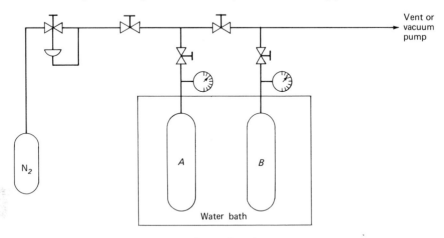

Figure P3.19

A and B are the two small gas bombs with identical volumes (see Figure P3.19). Compressibility factors are determined by filling bomb A with nitrogen to some

Pressure, psig		Pressure, psig	
Initial	Expanded	Initial	Expanded
950	647	44	30
647	442	30	21
442	305	21	14
305	207	14	9
207	142	9	6
142	96	6	4
96	65	4	2
65	44	3	2
		2	1

high pressure and then expanding the gas into the evacuated bomb B. The data in the preceding table were obtained by expanding A into B, which was only released to the atmosphere due to malfunctioning of the vacuum pump.

Determine Z as a function of pressure and compare with the value obtained from the theorem of corresponding states.

3.20   Vapor Pressure

What is meant by the vapor pressure of a liquid?

3.21   Measurement of Vapor Pressure

Describe an appropriate method for measuring the vapor pressure of a moderately volatile liquid.

3.22   Vapor Pressure of Isopropanol

The normal boiling point of isopropanol is $82.3°C$ and the heat of vaporization is 160 cal/g. What is the vapor pressure of isopropanol at $25°C$?

3.23   Freezing Temperature of Compressed Air Lines

Air is compressed to 250 psi and cooled to $35°F$ by direct contact with a spray of water. The air is then regulated down to 75 psi and sent through the plant. What outside weather temperature will cause ice to freeze out in the air lines in the 75 psi process?

3.24   Vapor Pressure and the Law of Corresponding States

One simple form for the relationship between vapor pressure and temperature is

$$\log_{10} P = - \frac{0.05223\,a}{T} + b$$

where P is in mm of Hg and T is in $°K$. For methanol, $a = 38.324$ and $b = 8.8017$ in the above expression (a and b are not Van der Waals constants). Using the law of corresponding states, compute the values of a and b for *ethanol*, making use of the following critical data if necessary.

Substance	Critical pressure (atm)	Critical temperature (°C)	Critical density (g/cm^3)
Methanol	98.7	240.1	0.272
Ethanol	63.1	243.1	0.275

3.25 Boiling Point for Vapor Pressure Relationship

Vapor pressure may be found by using Antoine's equation:

$$\log_{10} P = A - \frac{B}{C+t}$$

where

$$P = \text{vapor pressure, mm Hg}$$

$$A,B,C = \text{constants for a particular substance}$$

$$t = \text{temperature, °C}$$

The following data are given:

Component	A	B	C
Benzene	7.42912	1628.32	279.56
Toluene	6.95334	1343.943	219.38

From these data determine the normal boiling points for benzene and toluene. Compare your values with those obtained from Perry's *Handbook*.

3.26 Vapor Pressure as a Function of Temperature

Assume that the vapor pressure of a substance can be approximated by the equation $\log P = A - B/T$, where T is the absolute temperature (°K or °R). If the normal boiling point is 77°C and the bp at 60 mm Hg is 16.6°C, what is the vapor pressure at 50°C?

3.27 Dissolved Gases and System Pressure

A Nash vacuum pump is rated at 15 cubic feet per minute (cfm). A vacuum evaporator is being fed with 500 gallons per minute (gpm) of liquor which contains 0.05 ft^3 of dissolved air (SCF) per ft^3 of liquor. Calculate the vacuum at which the system will operate. See Figure P3.27.

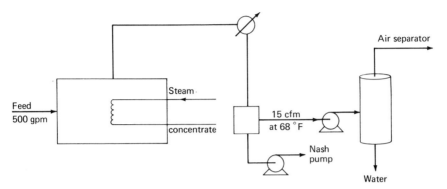

Figure P3.27

3.28 Cox Chart

1. Draw a Cox chart for benzene and toluene using the data shown in the table.

Vapor pressure		Temperature ($^\circ$C) benzene	Temperature ($^\circ$C) toluene
mm Hg	1	− 36.7	− 26.7
	5	− 19.6	− 4.4
	10	− 11.5	6.4
	20	− 2.6	18.4
	40	7.6	31.8
	100	26.1	51.9
	200	42.2	69.5
	400	60.6	89.5
	760	80.1	110.6
atm	2	103.8	136.5
	5	142.5	178.0
	10	178.8	215.8
	20	221.5	262.5
	40	272.3	319.0

2. Compare the slope at $100°C$ with the value calculated by the Clausius-Clapeyron equation.

3.29 Dühring Plot

Draw a Dühring plot for benzene and toluene using the data given in Problem 3.28 and using water as the reference substance.

3.30 Raoult's Law, Immiscible and Miscible Liquids

A and B compose a system of immiscible liquid phases. At a given temperature T, the vapor pressures of A and B are

$$P_A{}^0 = 300 \text{ mm Hg} \qquad P_B{}^0 = 1000 \text{ mm Hg}$$

1. What is the total vapor pressure of the A and B mixtures?

2. The equilibrium vapor in contact with *both* liquid phases contains what mole fraction of B?

3. Had A and B formed miscible liquid phases, what would be the total vapor pressure of a mixture of 30 mole % A and 70 mole % B? Assume that Raoult's law is applicable.

4. What is the composition of the vapor phase in equilibrium of a solution with 30 mole % A, and 70 mole % B, if A and B form miscible liquid solutions?

3.31 Raoult's Law and Miscible Liquids

Describe the variation of vapor pressure with composition for a mixture of two miscible liquids that follow Raoult's law. Derive an equation for the vapor composition as a function of the liquid composition at constant temperature.

3.32 Raoult's Law and the Molecular Weight of an Unknown

Water and an unknown immiscible liquid are distilled together at a total pressure of 734.4 mm Hg. The boiling temperature is constant at $90°C$, and at this temperature the vapor pressure of water is 526.0 mm Hg. A sample of distillate is collected and separated and found to contain 28.8% water by weight. Estimate the molecular weight of the unknown compound.

3.33   Benzene-Toluene Mixture and Raoult's Law

Mixtures of benzene (C_6H_6) and toluene (C_7H_8) follow Raoult's law; at $30°C$, the vapor pressure of pure benzene is 118.2 mm Hg and that of pure toluene is 36.7 mm Hg. Determine the total vapor pressure and weight composition of the vapor in equilibrium with a liquid mixture consisting of equal weights of benzene and toluene.

3.34   Molecular Weight of a Solute

The vapor pressure of a solution containing 13 g of solute in 100 g of water at $28°C$ is 27.372 mm Hg. Calculate the molecular weight of the solute. The vapor pressure of water at this temperature is 28.065 mm Hg.

3.35   Vapor Composition of an Ethanol-Methanol Mixture

C_2H_5OH has a vapor pressure of 353 mm Hg at $60°C$. CH_3OH has a vapor pressure of 625 mm Hg at $60°C$. If one has at this temperature a mixture containing 50 wt % of each constituent, what is the vapor composition above the solution?

3.36   Humidity

Air at $95°F$ and 743 mm Hg that contains 0.0225 lb H_2O/lb dry air is sent to a cooler at the rate of 900 ft^3/min. The air leaves the cooler at $55°F$ and 743 mm Hg, saturated with water vapor. Calculate

1. Final air humidity, lb H_2O/lb dry air
2. Water condensed in the cooler, lb/hr

3.37   Air-Water System

Three thousand cubic feet of air are saturated with water vapor at 14.7 psia and $150°F$. The gas is confined over water at this temperature. Vapor pressure of water at $150°F$ is 3.72 psia. How many pounds of water are in the gas?

3.38   Molal Humidity at Saturation

What is the saturation molal humidity of air at $105°F$ and 1 atm? The vapor pressure of water at this temperature and pressure is 1.1 psia.

$$\text{Molal humidity at saturation} = n_{vapor}/n_{air}$$

3.39　Humidity of a Volatile Solvent

A volatile solvent has a boiling temperature of $250°F$, a vapor pressure of 15.2 mm Hg at $68°F$, and a molecular weight of 100. What will be its saturation humidity in air at $68°F$ and 1 atm?

3.40　Humidity

A quantity of air at $120°F$ and 40% humidity is available at 1 atm total pressure. At $120°F$,

$$P^0_{H_2O} = 1.6924 \text{ psia}$$
$$P^0_{H_2O} = \text{saturated vapor pressure of water}$$

1. What is the absolute humidity in lb H_2O/lb dry air, as calculated and as read from the humidity chart?

2. What is the maximum quantity of water vapor that can be contained in this air at $120°F$, as calculated and as read from the chart?

3. From the chart, look up the dew point temperature of the air.

4. If the air is humidified adiabatically and in this way cooled to $100°F$, what is the resulting humidity as read from the chart?

3.41　Humidity and Wet Bulb Temperature

Air at $100°F$ is found by experiment to have a wet bulb temperature of $70°F$.

1. What is the humidity of the air in lb H_2O/lb dry air?

2. What is the percent absolute humidity?

3.42　Analysis and Humidity of a Wet Gas

A gas at 700 mm Hg and $140°F$ is analyzed to contain 66.67% nitrogen and 33.33% carbon dioxide on a dry basis, and it contains 0.111 moles of water vapor per mole of dry gas. Calculate

1. Wet analysis in weight percent

2. Average molecular weight of wet gas

3. Density of wet gas

4. Dew point of the mixture

5. Percent relative humidity and percent humidity of the mixture

3.43 Humidity on a Mountain

The dew point of air on a mountain top, with the barometer reading 660 mm Hg, is measured as $13°F$. Determine H, H_p, and RH.

3.44 Humidity from Wet and Dry Bulb

An airstream has a $65°F$ wet bulb temperature and $90°F$ dry bulb. Determine absolute humidity from the humidity chart and check the value using any other method.

3.45 Drying Air with Silica Gel

A tower 5 ft in diameter is packed with 10 ft of silica gel. Air (average conditions $68°F$ and 50% RH) is passed through at a superficial velocity (i.e., a flow calculated as though the tower contained no gel) of 1 ft/sec. The air is dried to a dew point below $-30°F$, and at breakthrough (when the dew point of the exiting air reaches $-30°F$) the silica gel has absorbed on the average 0.25 lb water/lb silica. Determine

1. Volume of air that has been dried

2. Length of the drying cycle

3.46 Drying Food

Water, at the rate of 100 lb/hr, is evaporated from a food material being dried in a dryer. Available air has a humidity of 0.02 lb H_2O/lb dry air and a temperature of $90°F$, which is raised to $155°F$, before entering the dryer. Air leaving the dryer has a dry bulb temperature of $110°F$ and a wet bulb temperature of $100°F$. Calculate air consumption in pounds without regard to material being dried or type of dryer.

3.47 Stack Gas Properties

A stack gas at 400°F has the vol % composition shown below.

Component	Vol %
N_2	72.3
CO_2	11.4
CO	0.3
O_2	1.0
H_2O	15.0
Total	100.0

Determine

1. Density at 400°F

2. Weight %

3. Volume % water if gases are cooled to 68°F, where P_w is 23.8 mm Hg (consequently some water will condense out)

4. Density at 68°F

3.48 *P-T* Diagram

Consider the equilibrium *P-T* diagram (Figure P3.48) for a pure substance,

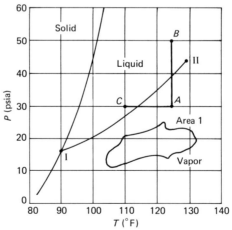

Figure P3.48

and perform these steps:

1. How many degrees of superheat does point A represent?

2. What is the dew point temperature of the vapor at point A?

3. How many degrees of subcooling does point C represent?

4. What is the bubble point temperature of the liquid at point C?

5. Represent processes B-A and C-A on the corresponding P-V diagram for this substance.

6. What is the vapor pressure of this substance at $100°$F?

7. How would you plot the P-T data from point I to point II to get an approximate linear relationship?

3.49 Humidity of Air at Home

The air in your home has a dry bulb temperature of $85°$F and a wet bulb temperature of $62°$F. Determine

1. Absolute humidity of the air

2. Dew point

3. Absolute humidity when this air is saturated at $85°$F

3.50 Correction of Humidity Values for Barometer Other than 29.92 Inches Hg

Humidity computations usually include corrections for barometric pressure differing from 29.92 in. Hg. (See Perry's *Chemical Engineers' Handbook*, 3d ed. p. 768.) What is the humidity of an air sample when the barometric pressure is 29.0 in. Hg, the dry bulb temperature is $90°$F, and the wet bulb temperature is $65°$F?

Stoichiometry and Material Balances

The law of conservation of mass states that matter is neither created nor destroyed. This is universally true for processes where nuclear reactions are not involved. In 1789, Antoine L. Lavoisier was the first scientist to prove this law by conducting a rigorous chemical experiment. Thus he is the first one to make a material balance on a process with a chemical reaction. His key word is stoichiometry. What is it?

4.1 STOICHIOMETRY AND CHEMICAL EQUATIONS

Stoichiometry is the application of the following:

1. Conservation of mass
2. Conservation of energy
3. Combining weights in chemical reactions

It is a combination of two Greek words, *stoicheion,* meaning "element" and *metrein,* meaning "to measure." Material balances are a direct application of the law of conservation of mass, and they are basically important to the practicing chemical engineer. Because of emphasis on material balances in the profession, this topic will be treated after a brief review of stoichiometry and the chemical equation.

The chemical equation is a kind of symbolism that indicates

1. The identity of reactants and products
2. The mass relationships between reactants and products, based on complete reaction or, equivalently, 100% conversion

If reactants are made available in quantities proportional to those indicated in the chemical equation, these reactants are said to be available in *stoichiometric quantities,* or stoichiometric proportion. Thus the amount of a reactant theoretically required for the complete conversion of other reactants is called the stoichiometric quantity. When a reaction is incomplete because of the limited availability of one of the reactants, the *limiting reactant* is that existing in the smallest stoichiometric quantity. Other reactants are called *excess* reactants simply because they are supplied in excess of the stoichiometric amount.

One speaks of percent excess, defined as

$$\text{Mole \% excess} = \frac{(\text{input}) - (\text{required})}{(\text{required})} \times 100 \tag{4.1}$$

where

$$\text{input} = \text{total input (moles) of excess reactant}$$

$$\text{required} = \text{moles of excess reactant required to react}$$
$$\textit{completely} \text{ with limiting reactant}$$

Note that the percent excess is based on 100% conversion of the limiting reactant, regardless of whether the actual reaction is complete or incomplete. Incomplete reactions are usually encountered in industry due to many limitations; among these we list mass transfer, reaction rates, heat transfer rates, and so on.

In this regard, the following definitions are useful.

$$\frac{\text{Degree of completeness}}{\text{of a reaction}} = \frac{\text{quantity of limiting substance reacted}}{\text{total quantity of limiting substance available for reaction}} \tag{4.2}$$

$$\text{Percent conversion} = \frac{\text{quantity of substance reacted}}{\text{total quantity available for reaction}} \times 100 \tag{4.3}$$

The latter expression is usually the same as the expression for the degree of completeness, except that the percent conversion is usually applied to any reactant. The basis for computing the degree of completeness and percent conversion must be clearly specified. Another useful definition is

$$\text{Percent yield} = \frac{\text{quantity of a specified final product}}{\text{quantity of a specified reactant that has reacted}} \times 100 \tag{4.4}$$

It is also important to define *selectivity*, which is associated with the amount of limiting reactant that forms the desired product. It is expressed as a percentage of the total quantity of the limiting reactant that has been converted. For example, consider the reactions

$$A \rightarrow B + C \quad \text{main reaction}$$

$$A \rightarrow D \quad \text{side reaction}$$

and assume the desired product is B.

Total amount of A converted $=$ (amount of A)   (% conversion)

Amount of A going into $B =$ (total amount of A converted)   (selectivity)

In solving problems dealing with chemical equations, these steps are recommended.

1. Draw a diagram whenever possible.

2. Choose a basis.

3. Write a balanced equation representing the chemical reaction that is taking place.

4. Set up a proportion, as dictated by the law of combining weights.

5. From this proportion solve for the unknown.

6. When you don't know what to do, do something.

Let us illustrate how one can apply these rules of stoichiometry to actual problems. We should also adopt the following convention: unless otherwise specified, the percent composition of liquids is based on weight percent, and that of gases is based on mole percent.

Example 4.1   Use of the chemical equation

Determine the mass of oxygen that can be produced by the complete decomposition of 490 lb of potassium chlorate.

Solution

1.

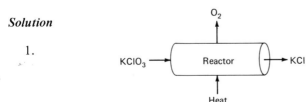

2. Basis: 490 lb $KClO_3$

3. $\qquad 2KClO_3 \xrightarrow{\Delta} 2KCl + 3O_2$

$\qquad$ MW of $KClO_3 = (39 + 35.5 + 48) = 122.5$ lb/lb-mole

$\qquad 2KClO_3 = 2 \times 122.5 = 245$

$\qquad$ MW of $O_2 = (16)(2) = 32$ lb/lb-mole

$\qquad 3O_2 = 3(32) = 96$

Let X be the mass of O_2 liberated.

4. The proportion dictated by the law of combining weights is expressed by this scheme:

$$2KClO_3 \xrightarrow{\Delta} 2KCl + 3O_2$$

$\qquad$ 2(122.5) lb $\qquad\qquad\qquad$ 3(32) lb

$\qquad\qquad$ 490 lb $\qquad\qquad\qquad\qquad$ X lb

Set a proportion

$$\frac{2(122.5)}{490} = \frac{3(32)}{X}$$

or

$$X = 192 \text{ lb } O_2/490 \text{ lb } KClO_3 \quad \triangleleft$$

or stated in another form: The chemical equation tells us that every 245 lb of $KClO_3$ produces 96 lb of O_2. How much O_2 can we produce if we have 490 lb $KClO_3$?

$$245 \text{ lb } KClO_3 \rightarrow 96 \text{ lb } O_2$$

$$490 \text{ lb } KClO_3 \rightarrow X$$

and

$$X = \frac{96 \text{ lb } O_2 \times 490}{245}$$

$$= 192 \text{ lb } O_2 \quad \triangleleft$$

Example 4.2 Stoichiometry in the synthesis of urea

Urea (widely used as solid fertilizer) is made according to the following reactions:

$$2NH_3 + CO_2 \rightleftharpoons NII_2COONH_4 \text{ (exothermic)}$$
$$\text{(ammonium carbamate)}$$

$$NH_2COONH_4 \rightleftharpoons NH_2CONH_2 + H_2O \text{ (endothermic)}$$
$$\text{(urea)}$$

The first reaction is 100% complete and the second has a conversion of 50%. Determine

1. The weight of ammonia required to make two tons of urea per day

2. Percent nitrogen in urea

Solution

Basis: Two tons of urea per day

1.
$$2NH_3 + CO_2 \overset{100\%}{\rightleftharpoons} NH_2COONH_4 \overset{50\%}{\rightleftharpoons} NH_2CONH_2 + H_2O$$

$$2(17) \qquad\qquad\qquad (60)\,(0.50)$$
$$X \qquad\qquad\qquad\qquad 2 \text{ tons}$$

$$\frac{2(17)}{X} = \frac{60(0.50)}{2}$$

$$X = 2.27 \text{ tons } NH_3$$

2.

Component	Moles	MW	Mass (lb_m)
N	2	14	28
H	4	1	4
C	1	12	12
O	1	16	16
			60

$$\text{Nitrogen in urea} = \frac{28}{60} \times 100 = 46.7\% \text{ by weight} \quad \triangleleft$$

Example 4.3   Molecular weight and formula of an unknown

The combustion of 0.624 g of an unknown organic substance gave 2.112 g CO_2 and 0.432 g H_2O. The specific gravity of the vapor of this substance is 2.7 at $25°C$ and 760 mm Hg. Determine

1. Molecular weight of unknown

2. Its formula

Solution

1. Assuming that the vapor of the substance behaves as an ideal gas, we have

$$P = \frac{n}{V}RT = \frac{m}{V}RT \cdot \frac{1}{MW}$$

$$MW = \frac{m}{V} \cdot \frac{RT}{P} = (2.7 \times 1.185 \frac{g}{\text{liter}}) \frac{(0.082 \text{ liter-atm}/°\text{K-g-mole}) (298°\text{K})}{1 \text{ atm}}$$

$$= 78 \text{ g/g-mole} \quad \triangleleft$$

Alternatively, by definition the substance is 2.7 times as dense as air:

$$MW = 2.7 \text{ (MW air)}$$

$$= 2.7 \text{ (28.9)}$$

$$= 78 \frac{g}{\text{g-mole}} \quad \triangleleft$$

2. $$2.112 \text{ g } CO_2 \times \frac{1\text{-g-mole}}{44 \text{ g } CO_2} = 0.048 \text{ g-mole } CO_2$$

$$0.432 \text{ g } H_2O \times \frac{1 \text{ g-mole}}{18 \text{ g } H_2O} = 0.024 \text{ g-mole } H_2O$$

$$0.624 \text{ g unknown} \times \frac{1 \text{ g-mole}}{78 \text{ g unknown}} = 0.008 \text{ g-mole unknown}$$

$$\frac{0.048 \text{ g-mole } CO_2}{0.008 \text{ g-mole unknown}} \times \frac{1 \text{ g-mole C}}{1 \text{ g-mole } CO_2} = 6 \frac{\text{g-mole C}}{\text{g-mole unknown}}$$

$$\frac{0.024 \text{ g-mole } H_2O}{0.008 \text{ g-mole unknown}} \times \frac{2 \text{ g-mole H}}{1 \text{ g-mole } H_2O} = 6 \frac{\text{g-mole H}}{\text{g-mole unknown}}$$

The formula is

$$C_6H_6 \quad (MW = 78)$$

Example 4.4   Stoichiometry

A mixture of $CaCO_3$ and $BaCO_3$ weighing 1.1 g reacts completely with 20 ml of 1 N HCl. Determine

1. The weight composition of the mixture
2. The volume (ft^3 at 25°C and 760 mm Hg) of CO_2 produced by reacting 150 lb_m of this mixture
3. The weight percent composition of a mixture of Na_2CO_3 and K_2CO_3 which, on an equal weight basis, would give the same volume of CO_2 as the $BaCO_3$, $CaCO_3$ mixture

Solution

Pertinent reactions:

$$CaCO_3 + 2HCl \rightarrow CaCl_2 + CO_2 + H_2O$$

$$BaCO_3 + 2HCl \rightarrow BaCl_2 + CO_2 + H_2O$$

$$Na_2CO_3 + 2HCl \rightarrow 2NaCl + CO_2 + H_2O$$

$$K_2CO_3 + 2HCl \rightarrow 2KCl + CO_2 + H_2O$$

1. $\text{Amount HCl} = \dfrac{1 \text{ g-equiv HCl}}{\text{liter solution}} \times \dfrac{36.5 \text{ g HCl}}{1 \text{ g-equiv HCl}}$

$\times \dfrac{1 \text{ g-mole HCl}}{36.5 \text{ g HCl}} \times 0.020 \text{ liter solution}$

$= 0.02 \text{ g-mole}$

Let X = mole fraction of $CaCO_3$. From stoichiometry, the mixture contains 0.01 g-mole total of $BaCO_3$ and $CaCO_3$, since the total amount of HCl is 0.02 g-moles, and every two moles of HCl requires one mole of $CaCO_3$ or one mole of $BaCO_3$.

$$1.1 \text{ g} = \frac{100 \text{ g CaCO}_3}{\text{g-mole CaCO}_3} (0.01X \text{ g-mole})$$

$$+ \frac{179.3 \text{ g BaCO}_3}{\text{g-mole BaCO}_3} \times 0.01 (1 - X) \text{ g-mole BaCO}_3$$

$$X = 0.885$$

$$\frac{0.885 \text{ g-mole CaCO}_3}{(1 - 0.885) \text{ g-mole BaCO}_3} \times \frac{100 \text{ g CaCO}_3/\text{g-mole CaCO}_3}{179.3 \text{ g BaCO}_3/\text{g-mole BaCO}_3} = \frac{4.55 \text{g CaCO}_3}{\text{g BaCO}_3}$$

$$\text{Weight \% CaCO}_3 = \frac{4.55 \text{ g CaCO}_3}{5.55 \text{ g total}} \times 100 = 82\% \text{ CaCO}_3 \; ; 18\% \text{ BaCO}_3 \quad \triangleleft$$

2. By the stoichiometry, 0.01 g-mole CO_2 is produced per 0.02 g-mole HCl.

$$\frac{0.01 \text{ g-mole CO}_2}{1.1 \text{ g mixture}} \times \frac{454 \text{ g}}{\text{lb}_m} \times 150 \text{ lb}_m = 620 \text{ g-mole CO}_2$$

Assuming CO_2 to behave as an ideal gas at 25°C and 760 mm Hg, we have

$$V = \frac{nRT}{P} = \frac{(62,000 \text{ g-mole}) (0.082 \text{ liter-atm/g-mole-°K}) (298°\text{K})}{(760 \text{ mm Hg}) (\text{liter-atm}/760 \text{ mm Hg})} \times \frac{1 \text{ ft}^3}{28.32 \text{ liter}}$$

$$V = 535 \text{ ft}^3 \text{ CO}_2 \quad \triangleleft$$

3. Let Y = mole fraction of K_2CO_3. We know that a 1.1 g mixture must produce 0.01 g-mole CO_2. Therefore, by the stoichiometry, the mixture contains a total of 0.01 g-mole of K_2CO_3 and Na_2CO_3.

$$1.1 \text{ g} = \frac{138.4 \text{ g K}_2\text{CO}_3}{\text{g-mole}} \times (0.01Y) \text{ g-mole} + \frac{106 \text{ g Na}_2\text{CO}_3}{\text{g-mole}} \times (0.01)(1 - Y)\text{g-mole}$$

$$Y = 0.123$$

$$\frac{0.123 \text{ g-mole K}_2\text{CO}_3}{(1-0.123) \text{ g-mole Na}_2\text{CO}_3} \times \frac{138.4 \text{ g K}_2\text{CO}_3/\text{g-mole}}{106 \text{ g Na}_2\text{CO}_3/\text{g-mole}} = 0.184 \frac{\text{g K}_2\text{CO}_3}{\text{g Na}_2\text{CO}_3}$$

$$\text{Amount of K}_2\text{CO}_3 = \frac{0.184 \text{ g K}_2\text{CO}_3}{1.184 \text{ g total}} \times 100 = 15.5\%$$

Component	Weight %
K_2CO_3	15.5
Na_2CO_3	84.5
	100.0

Example 4.5 Combustion of methane, ethylene, and hydrogen

A gaseous mixture whose volume is 40 cm³, containing methane, ethylene, and hydrogen, is placed in a container with 130 cm³ of oxygen. After igniting the mixture and cooling it back to room temperature, the volume of products is 94 cm³; 56 cm³ of this is absorbed with KOH and the rest with phosphorus.

1. Write the chemical equations of combustion and absorption.

2. Compute the mole percent of each component in the initial gaseous mixture.

Solution

1.
$$CH_4 + 2O_2 \rightarrow CO_2 + 2H_2O$$
$$C_2H_4 + 3O_2 \rightarrow 2CO_2 + 2H_2O$$
$$2H_2 + O_2 \rightarrow 2H_2O$$

Let
$$V_1 = \text{initial volume of CH}_4$$
$$V_2 = \text{initial volume of C}_2H_4.$$
$$V_3 = \text{initial volume of H}_2$$

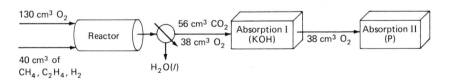

Absorption reactions are

$$2KOH + CO_2 \rightarrow K_2CO_3 + H_2O$$

$$4P + 5/2\,O_2 \rightarrow 2P_2O_5$$

2. CO_2 volume balance:

$$V_1 + 2V_2 = 56 \qquad (1)$$

O_2 volume balance:

$$2V_1 + 3V_2 + 0.5V_3 = 130 - [94 - 56] = 92 \qquad (2)$$

Gas volume balance:

$$V_1 + V_2 + V_3 = 40 \qquad (3)$$

Multiply Equation (2) by 2:

$$4V_1 + 6V_2 + V_3 = 184 \qquad (4)$$

Subtract (3) from (4):

$$3V_1 + 5V_2 = 144 \qquad (5)$$

Multiply (1) by 3:

$$3V_1 + 6V_2 = 168 \qquad (6)$$

Subtract (5) from (6):

$$V_2 = 24 \text{ cm}^3$$
$$V_1 = 56 - 48 = 8 \text{ cm}^3$$
$$V_3 = 40 - 8 - 24 = 8 \text{ cm}^3$$

Component	Volume (cm^3)	Volume % = mole %
CH_4	8	20
C_2H_4	24	60
H_2	8	20
Total	40	100

Example 4.6   Limiting reactant in the production of a disinfectant

Consider the formation of sodium hypochlorite according to the chemical reaction

$$2NaOH + Cl_2 \rightarrow NaOCl + NaCl + H_2O$$

You are given 120 lb of sodium hydroxide and 71 lb of chlorine. What is the amount of NaOCl produced in the chlorinator?

Solution

1. Reaction: $\qquad$ $2NaOH + Cl_2 \rightarrow NaOCl + NaCl + H_2O$
2. Moles: $\qquad$ 2 $\quad$ 1 $\qquad$ 1 $\quad$ 1 $\quad$ 1
3. Stoichiometric weights: $\qquad$ 2×40 $\quad$ 71 $\qquad$ 74.5 $\quad$ 58.5 $\quad$ 18
4. Weight of available
   reactants: $\qquad$ 120 $\quad$ 71
5. The limiting reactant is chlorine, since it is not available in excess of the stoichiometric quantity.

6. $\qquad$ Mass of NaOCl $= \dfrac{74.5 \ lb_m \ NaOCl}{71 \ lb_m \ Cl_2}$

   $\times 71 \ lb_m \ Cl_2$ reacted $= 74.5 \ lb_m \ NaOCl$ ◁

**Example 4.7 Degree of completion, percent conversion,
                  and yield (generalized case)**

Given: The reactants *A* (limiting) and *B* (excess) that constitute a main reaction

$$A + B \rightarrow C + D$$

and a side reaction

$$A + B \rightarrow E + F$$

The desired product is *C*.
  The data in the accompanying table are given.

Substance	Initial (moles)	Final (moles)
A	1.0	0.10
B	10.0	0.30
C	0.2	0.65
D	—	—
E	—	—
F	—	—

Find (on a mole basis)

1. Degree of completion
2. Percent conversion
3. Percent yield

Solution

1.
$$\text{Degree of completion} = \frac{1.0 - 0.1}{1} = 0.9 \triangleleft$$

2. Since percent conversion is not completely specified, it should be determined for both A and B.

$$\text{Percent conversion of } A = \frac{1.0 - 0.1}{1} \times 100 = 90\%$$

$$\text{Percent conversion of } B = \frac{10.0 - 9.3}{10} \times 100 = 7\% \triangleleft$$

3. Since percent yield is not specified, it should be determined, using A and then B as a basis.

$$\text{Mole \% yield based on } A = \frac{0.65 - 0.20}{1.0 - 0.1} \times 100$$

$$= \frac{0.45}{0.90} \times 100 = 50\% \triangleleft$$

$$\text{Mole \% yield based on } B = \frac{0.65 - 0.20}{10.0 - 9.3} \times 100$$

$$= \frac{0.45}{0.70} \times 100 = 64.3\% \triangleleft$$

Example 4.8 Degree of completion, percent conversion, yield

Nitrous oxide N_2O (called laughing gas, because of the mild hysteria produced from breathing the gas for a short time), is produced from ammonium nitrate under conditions such that 200 lb of NH_4NO_3 give 70 lb of N_2O. Determine:

1. Degree of completion

2. Percent conversion

3. Percent yield

Solution

1. Degree of completion. The chemical reaction is

$$NH_4NO_3 \rightarrow N_2O + 2H_2O$$

$$NH_4NO_3 = 80 \text{ lb/lb-mole}$$

$$N_2O = 44 \text{ lb/lb-mole}$$

The amount of NH_4NO_3 decomposed is

$$80 \text{ lb } NH_4NO_3 \rightarrow 44 \text{ lb } N_2O$$

$$X \rightarrow 70 \text{ lb } N_2O$$

$$X = \frac{70 \text{ lb } N_2O \times 80 \text{ lb } NH_4NO_3}{44 \text{ lb } N_2O}$$

$$= 127 \text{ lb } NH_4NO_3 \text{ reacted}$$

Unreacted $NH_4NO_3 = 200 - 127 = 73$ lb

$$\text{Degree of completion} = \frac{127 \text{ lb } NH_4NO_3 \text{ reacted}}{200 \text{ lb } NH_4NO_3 \text{ available for reaction}} = 0.635 \triangleleft$$

2. $\text{Percent conversion} = \frac{127 \text{ lb } NH_4NO_3 \text{ reacted}}{200 \text{ lb } NH_4NO_3 \text{ available for reaction}} \times 100 = 63.5\% \triangleleft$

If a chemcial reaction has more than one reactant, the basis for finding the percent conversion must be clearly stated; that is, which reactant was chosen for finding the percent conversion.

3. $$\text{Weight } \% \text{ yield} = \frac{70 \text{ lb } N_2O \text{ produced}}{127 \text{ lb } NH_4NO_3 \text{ reacted}} \times 100 = 55\% \triangleleft$$

$$\text{Mole } \% \text{ yield} = \frac{70/44}{127/80} \times 100 = \frac{1.59}{1.59} \times 100 = 100\% \triangleleft$$

4.2 STEADY STATE MATERIAL BALANCES

What Are They?

Material balances are based on the law of conservation of mass. For a given system,

$$\text{(Rate of accumulation)} = \text{(rate of mass input)} - \text{(rate of mass output)} \quad \textbf{(4.5)}$$

For a steady state, there can be no accumulation in the system, and the mass balance reduces to

$$\text{input} = \text{output} \quad \textbf{(4.6)}$$

Most of the problems encountered in introductory chemical engineering are of the steady state type. Material balances are usually made in order to

1. Check the consistency of measurements on mass flow rates and concentrations
2. Calculate unmetered streams or unknown concentrations
3. Determine the efficiency and feasibility of a given process
4. Comprehend the problem thoroughly

Guidelines and Methods for Calculations

One can present various guidelines that may be helpful, but they will not guarantee that you will be able to solve the problems you will encounter. Ability in solving these problems is gained through practice and reliance on *good judgment* and *basic principles*.

You should attack mass balance problems as follows:

1. Draw a block flow diagram of the given process. Figure 4.1 is presented to aid in drawing such a diagram.
2. Include on this diagram all available *information*, even what may appear to be obvious, such as the composition of air (79% N_2 and 21% O_2 on a volume basis).
3. Write any pertinent chemical reactions or physical *equations*.
4. Choose a basis for calculations. Make sure that all streams entering in your balance are compatible with the chosen basis.

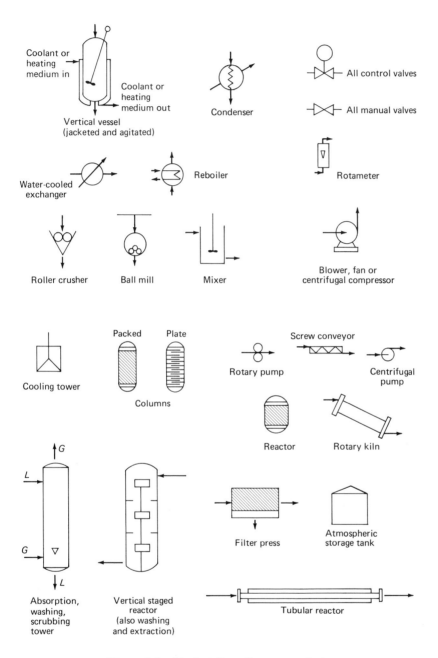

Figure 4.1. Typical flow-diagram symbols

5. Define your system *boundaries* by circling the section of interest, and make an overall mass balance. Note that only mass balances are universally valid.

6. When there is no chemical reaction, make *component* mass *balances* for each component in the system, keeping in mind that the number of independent equations you can have is equal only to the number of components in the system.

7. When there is a chemical reaction, one may choose to make mass and/or mole balances on *elements* or radicals.

8. Solve for the unknowns and always *tabulate* your results.

The method most suitable for these calculations is called the *algebraic method.* Basically, it is used to obtain the needed equations to solve for the unknowns, as in ordinary algebra. Another method may be used when a tie substance exists. A *tie substance* is defined as a substance that enters the process in one stream and leaves unchanged in only one outgoing stream. As an example, consider two streams, one of air and one of methane, entering a combustion chamber as shown in the diagram.

It should be obvious that nitrogen is a *tie substance,* since it enters in one stream and leaves unchanged in one outgoing stream.

Glossary for Combustion Problems

When solving combustion problems one is usually dealing with air as the source of oxygen. We define

$$\text{Percent excess air} = \frac{(\text{air input}) - (\text{air required for complete combustion})}{(\text{air required for complete combustion})} (100) \quad (4.7)$$

The percent excess is based on complete reaction, whether the reaction is complete or not. Can you prove the following?

$$\text{Percent excess air} = \text{percent excess oxygen}$$

When dealing with combustion, more often than not, you will be asked to give an analysis of the gas. You can give

1. Flue gas analysis: which includes all product gases except water vapor. This analysis is sometimes called *Orsat analysis,* or gas analysis on a *dry basis.*

2. Stack gas analysis: which includes all product gases of the combustion. This is sometimes called analysis on a *wet basis* because it includes water vapor.

3. Analysis on a particular *substance-free basis*: this means that the substance mentioned is not included in the analysis. When one says, "Give me the exit gas analysis on an SO_2-free basis," he means that SO_2 is not included, and that the other substances add to 100%.

Let us now illustrate with the following problems on material balances.

Example 4.9 Simple material balance for a coal slurry

Coal is mixed with water to form a slurry for transportation by pipelines. If 2 tons/hr of coal are mixed with water to give a slurry containing 50% coal by weight, find the mass of water added.

Solution

Algebraic method:

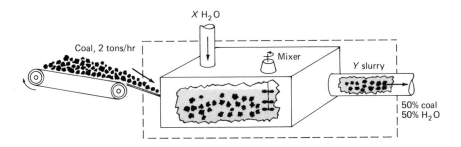

Basis: one hour of operation. By inspection (the leaving water is equivalent to the leaving coal; coal is a tie substance),

$$\text{Water input} = 2 \text{ tons/hr}$$

Alternatively the overall material balance around the encircled system is

$$2 + X = Y \tag{1}$$

The component balance on coal is

$$2 = 0.50\ Y \qquad (2)$$

$$Y = 2/0.50 = 4 \text{ tons}$$

From Equation (1) we get

$$X = Y - 2 = 2 \text{ tons/hr} \quad \triangleleft$$

Tie element method:

Since the coal enters in one stream and leaves unchanged in one outgoing stream, the coal is a tie element or tie substance. The exit stream must have 2 tons of coal, and the coal concentration is

$$0.50 = \frac{2}{X + 2}$$

where X is the mass of water added. From the above equation, we derive

$$X = 2 \text{ tons } H_2O/\text{hr} \quad \triangleleft$$

Example 4.10 Concentrating coal slurry for a furnace

You have a furnace designed to burn a coal slurry containing 70% coal and 30% water by weight. However, a supplier prepares a 45% concentrated slurry which you must render usable for your furnace. You are receiving 5000 lb/hr of this slurry and you wish to concentrate it from 45% to 70% by using an evaporator. Find the amount of water to be evaporated.

Solution

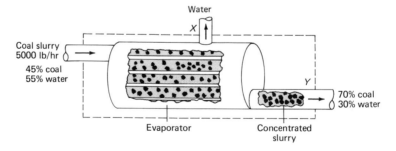

Basis: 5000 lb/hr coal slurry. The overall balance is

$$5000 \text{ lb/hr} = X + Y \qquad (1)$$

The component balances are

Coal: $$5000 \, (0.45) = Y \, (0.70) \qquad (2)$$

Water: $$5000 \, (0.55) = X + Y \, (0.30) \qquad (3)$$

First use Equations (1) and (2). For Equation (2),

$$Y = \frac{(5000) \, (0.45)}{0.70} = 3220 \text{ lb/hr of concentrated slurry}$$

From Equation (1),

$$X = 5000 - Y = 5000 - 3220$$

$$= 1780 \text{ lb/hr of water evaporated} \quad \triangleleft$$

Checking by Equation (3),

$$(5000) \, (0.55) = 1780 + 3220 \, (0.30)$$

$$2750 = 1780 + 966 = 2746 \text{ (close enough)}$$

Example 4.11 Measurement of flow rate by gas injection

Butane containing 5% oxygen by volume flows in a pipe at 100 psia and 100°F. The flow rate is measured by introducing 100 ft³/min of oxygen at 760 mm Hg and 40°F. The molar concentration of oxygen downstream is 10%. Find the volumetric flow rate for the initial stream.

Solution

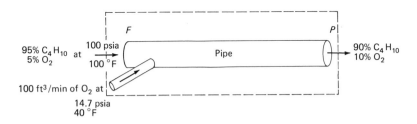

Basis: 1 minute.

$$n = \frac{PV}{RT} = \frac{(14.7 \text{ psia}) \, (100 \text{ ft}^3)}{(10.73 \text{ ft}^3\text{-psia/°R-lb-mole}) \, (500°\text{R})} = 0.275 \text{ lb-mole } O_2 \text{ initial stream}$$

Alternatively,

$$n = \frac{100\left(\dfrac{492}{460 + 40}\right)}{(359)} = 0.275 \text{ lb-moles } O_2$$

C_4H_{10} balance: $0.95\, F = 0.90\, P$

O_2 balance: $0.05\, F + 0.275 = 0.10\, P$

$$0.05\, F + 0.275 = 0.10\left(\frac{0.95}{0.90} F\right)$$

$$F = 4.95 \text{ lb-mole initial stream}$$

$$V_i = \frac{nRT}{\text{Pressure}}$$

$$= \frac{(4.95 \text{ lb-mole})(10.73 \text{ ft}^3\text{-psia/}^\circ\text{R-lb-mole})(560^\circ\text{R})}{100 \text{ psia}}$$

$$= 296 \text{ ft}^3/\text{min of initial stream}$$

Example 4.12 Batch material balance

A material containing two types of fibers, one being inert, is treated with alkali to hydrolyze it. Initially, 32 lb of dry fiber is added to the reactor. At the end of the run, the unreacted material, containing considerable moisture, is removed and found to weigh 93 lb. A small sample as received from the reactor weighed 16.4 g; and it was dried to a constant weight of 2.45 g. Determine the percentage of inert fiber in the initial material.

Solution

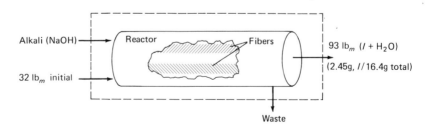

Basis: 32 lb_m initial material. I = inert fiber.

$$93 \; lb_m \; (I + H_2O) \times \frac{2.45 \; g \, I}{16.4 \; g \; (I + H_2O)} = 13.9 \; lb_m \; I$$

$$\text{Inert fiber} = \frac{13.9 \; lb_m}{32 \; lb_m} \times 100 = 43.2\% \text{ by weight}$$

Example 4.13   Use of algebra and determinants in problems with multiple streams

In a given plant operation, four streams are mixed to give a single stream with the desired composition. The four inlet streams to the mixer and the single exit stream (final product) have the composition shown in the table.

Stream number	Composition weight %			
	H_2SO_4	HNO_3	H_2O	Inerts
1	80	0	16	4
2	0	80	20	0
3	30	10	60	0
4	10	10	72	8
5 (exit stream)	40	27	31	2

Determine the mass flow rate of the individual streams for making 2000 lb/hr of final product.

Solution

Basis: 2000 lb/hr of final product. Refer to the figure on page 168.

A. Algebraic Method:

The overall mass balance is

$$w + x + y + z = 2000$$

The component mass balances follow on the next page.

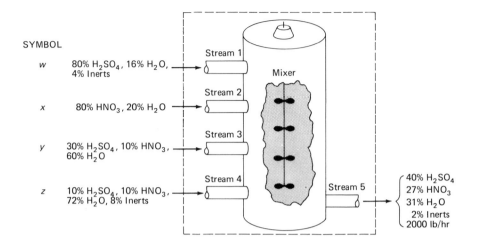

H_2SO_4: $\qquad$ $0.8w + 0x + 0.3y + 0.1z = 800$ $\qquad$ **(1)**

HNO_3: $\qquad$ $0w + 0.8x + 0.1y + 0.1z = 540$ $\qquad$ **(2)**

H_2O: $\qquad$ $0.16w + 0.2x + 0.6y + 0.72z = 620$ $\qquad$ **(3)**

Inerts: $\qquad$ $0.04w + 0x + 0y + 0.08z = 40$ $\qquad$ **(4)**

$-3(2)*$: $\qquad$ $-2.4x - 0.3y - 0.3z = -1620$ $\qquad$ **(5)**

Equation $(5) + (1)$: $\qquad$ $0.8w - 0.2z - 2.4x = -820$ $\qquad$ **(6)**

$(2) \times -6$: $\qquad$ $-4.8x - 0.6y - 0.6z = -3240$ $\qquad$ **(7)**

$(7) + (3)$: $\qquad$ $0.16w - 4.6x + 0.12z = -2620$ $\qquad$ **(8)**

$(6) \times 2.3$: $\qquad$ $1.84w - 0.46z - 5.52x = -1886$ $\qquad$ **(9)**

$(8) \times -1.2$: $\qquad$ $-0.192w + 5.52x - 0.144z = 3144$ $\qquad$ **(10)**

$(9) + (10)$: $\qquad$ $1.648w - 0.604z = 1258$ $\qquad$ **(11)**

$(4) \times 25$: $\qquad$ $w + 2z = 1000$ $\qquad$ **(12)**

$(12) \times -1.648$: $\qquad$ $-1.648w - 3.296z = -1648$ $\qquad$ **(13)**

$(11) + (13)$: $\qquad$ $-3.9z = -390$

*Parentheses signify an equation number; thus $-3(2)$ means -3 multiplied by Equation (2).

Stream 4 = z = 100 lb/hr ◁

By (12): $w = 1000 - 2z = 1000 - 200 = 800$

Stream 1 = w = 800 lb/hr ◁

By (1): $0.3y = 800 - 0.8w - 0.1z = 800 - 640 - 10 = 150$

Stream 3 = y = 150/0.3 = 500 lb/hr ◁

By (2): $0.8x = 540 - 0.1y - 0.1z = 540 - 50 - 10 = 480$

Stream 2 = x = 480/0.8 = 600 lb/hr ◁

B. Using the method of determinants, one gets for w (see Appendix for details):

$$w = \frac{\begin{vmatrix} 800 & 0 & 0.3 & 0.10 \\ 540 & 0.8 & 0.1 & 0.10 \\ 620 & 0.2 & 0.6 & 0.72 \\ 40 & 0 & 0 & 0.08 \end{vmatrix}}{D}$$

Solve for the determinant D as follows:

$$D = \begin{vmatrix} 0.80 & 0 & 0.3 & 0.10 \\ 0 & 0.8 & 0.1 & 0.10 \\ 0.16 & 0.2 & 0.6 & 0.72 \\ 0.04 & 0 & 0 & 0.08 \end{vmatrix}$$

$$= 0.8 \begin{vmatrix} 0.8 & 0.1 & 0.10 \\ 0.2 & 0.6 & 0.72 \\ 0 & 0 & 0.08 \end{vmatrix} + 0.3 \begin{vmatrix} 0 & 0.8 & 0.10 \\ 0.16 & 0.2 & 0.72 \\ 0.04 & 0 & 0.08 \end{vmatrix} - 0.1 \begin{vmatrix} 0 & 0.8 & 0.1 \\ 0.16 & 0.2 & 0.6 \\ 0.04 & 0 & 0 \end{vmatrix}$$

$D = 0.8 \, [0.08 \, (0.8 \times 0.6 - 0.2 \times 0.1)]$

$\quad + 0.3 \, [-0.8 \, (0.16 \times 0.08 - 0.04 \times 0.72)$

$\quad + 0.1 \, (0 - 0.04 \times 0.2)] - 0.1 \, [0.4 \, (0.8 \times 0.6 - 0.2 \times 0.1)]$

$D = 0.02944 + 0.0036 - 0.00184 = 0.0312$

and

$$w = \frac{24.96}{0.0312} = 800 \text{ lb/hr} \;\triangleleft$$

Similarly,

$$x = \frac{\begin{vmatrix} 0.80 & 800 & 0.3 & 0.10 \\ 0 & 540 & 0.1 & 0.10 \\ 0.16 & 620 & 0.6 & 0.72 \\ 0.04 & 40 & 0 & 0.08 \end{vmatrix}}{D} = \frac{18.72}{0.0312} = 600 \text{ lb/hr} \;\triangleleft$$

$$y = \frac{\begin{vmatrix} 0.8 & 0 & 800 & 0.10 \\ 0 & 0.8 & 540 & 0.10 \\ 0.16 & 0.2 & 620 & 0.72 \\ 0.04 & 0 & 40 & 0.08 \end{vmatrix}}{D} = \frac{15.60}{0.0312} = 500 \text{ lb/hr} \;\triangleleft$$

$$z = \frac{\begin{vmatrix} 0.80 & 0 & 0.3 & 800 \\ 0 & 0.8 & 0.1 & 540 \\ 0.16 & 0.2 & 0.6 & 620 \\ 0.04 & 0 & 0 & 40 \end{vmatrix}}{D} = \frac{3.12}{0.0312} = 100 \text{ lb/hr} \;\triangleleft$$

Check: $w + x + y + z = 800 + 600 + 500 + 100 = 2000 \text{ lb/hr}$

Tabulation:

Stream	Mass flow rate (lb/hr)
1	800
2	600
3	500
4	100
5	2000

Example 4.14   Composition of a gas mixture

If you go out camping in cold weather, you might appreciate having a small heater to use inside your tent. However, you have to know the composition of the tent atmosphere and how this may affect your health. Suppose that your heater uses white gas, and after operating it for some time, the atmosphere in your tent has the composition shown in the accompanying table for two different occasions, as determined by a mass spectrometer.

Component	First case (mole %)	Second case (mole %)
CO	0.02	0.020
CO_2	4.50	1.000
C_7H_{16}	7.00	0.007
C_8H_{18}	7.48	0.005
N_2	65.00	79.968
O_2	16.00	19.000
Total	100.00	100.000

1. Compute the heptane concentration in ppm.
2. If 100 ppm is allowable and 4000 ppm is lethal, what is the condition of the fellows in your tent?

Solution

First case:

1. Basis: 100 lb-moles of gas mixture.

Component	MW	Mass (lb_m)
CO	28	0.56
CO_2	44	198.00
C_7H_{16}	100	700.00
C_8H_{18}	114	852.00
N_2	28	1820.00
O_2	32	512.00
Total		4082.56

$$\text{Heptane concentration} = \frac{700.00 \text{ lb}_m \text{ } C_7H_{16}}{4082.56 \text{ lb}_m \text{ total}} \times 10^6 = 171{,}000 \text{ ppm} \triangleleft$$

2. Very dead $\triangleleft$

Second case:

1. Basis: 100 lb-mole of gas mixture.

Component	Mole %	lb-mole	MW	Mass (lb$_m$)
CO	0.020	0.020	28.0	0.560
CO_2	1.000	1.000	44.0	44.000
C_7H_{16}	0.007	0.007	100.0	0.700
C_8H_{18}	0.005	0.005	114.0	0.570
N_2	79.968	79.968	28.0	2239.104
O_2	19.000	19.000	32.0	608.000
Total	100	100		2892.934

$$\text{Heptane concentration} = \frac{0.70 \text{ lb } C_7H_{16}}{2892.934 \text{ lb total}} \times 10^6$$

$$= 242 \text{ ppm} \triangleleft$$

2. The fellows are not in a dangerous situation. $\triangleleft$

Example 4.15   Gaseous reaction

A gas having the following composition is burnt under a boiler with 50% excess air.

Component	Mole %
CH_4	70
C_3H_8	5
CO	15
O_2	5
N_2	5
	100

1. Compute the stack gas analysis.

2. Compute the volume of stack gas at $170°F$ and 1 atm pressure per ft^3 of gas mixture at $75°F$ and 1 atm.

Solution

1. Reactions:

$$CH_4 + 2O_2 \rightarrow CO_2 + 2H_2O$$

$$C_3H_8 + 5O_2 \rightarrow 3CO_2 + 4H_2O$$

$$2CO + O_2 \rightarrow 2CO_2$$

Since excess air is used, assume complete combustion.

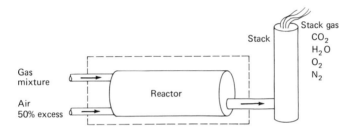

Basis: 1 lb-mole gas mixture.

$$CO_2 \text{ produced} = \frac{(0.7)\,(1)}{(1)} + \frac{(0.05)\,(3)}{(1)} + \frac{(0.15)\,(1)}{(1)}$$

$$= 1.0 \text{ lb-mole}$$

$$H_2O \text{ produced} = \frac{(0.7)\,(2)}{(1)} + \frac{(0.05)\,(4)}{(1)}$$

$$= 1.6 \text{ lb-moles}$$

$$O_2 \text{ required} = \frac{(0.7)\,(2)}{(1)} + \frac{(0.05)\,(5)}{(1)} + \frac{(0.15)\,(1)}{(2)}$$

$$= 1.725 \text{ lb-moles}$$

$$O_2 \text{ required from air} = 1.725 - 0.05$$

$$= 1.675 \text{ lb-moles}$$

$$O_2 \text{ in with air} = (1.675)(1.5)$$
$$= 2.515 \text{ lb-moles}$$

$$O_2 \text{ leaving reactor} = 2.515 - 1.675$$
$$- 0.840 \text{ lb-moles}$$

$$N_2 \text{ in with air} = \frac{(2.515)(79)}{(21)}$$
$$= 9.45 \text{ lb-moles}$$

$$\text{Total } N_2 \text{ leaving reactor} = 9.45 + 0.05$$
$$= 9.50 \text{ lb-moles}$$

Component	Moles	Mole %
CO_2	1.0	7.73
H_2O	1.6	12.35
O_2	0.84	6.48
N_2	9.50	73.44
Total	12.94	100.00

2. Assuming that all gas mixtures behave ideally, we have

$$P_1 V_1 = n_1 R T_1$$
$$P_2 V_2 = n_2 R T_2$$

or

$$\frac{V_2}{V_1} = \frac{n_2 T_2 P_1}{n_1 T_1 P_2}$$

$$V_2 = \frac{(12.94)(170 + 460)(1)}{(1)(75 + 460)(1)} \,(1)$$

$$= 15.25 \text{ ft}^3/\text{ft}^3 \text{ gas mixture} \quad$$

Example 4.16 Formation of formaldehyde from methanol (incomplete reaction)

Formaldehyde is made by the oxidation of methanol over a catalyst:

$$CH_3OH + \tfrac{1}{2} O_2 \rightleftharpoons HCHO + H_2O$$

Reactants and products are gaseous. If one uses 50% excess air and if the reaction is 75% complete, calculate the molar composition of the final gaseous mixture.

Solution

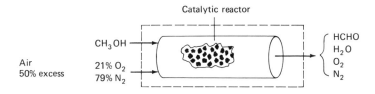

$$\overset{(1)}{CH_3OH} + \overset{(0.5)}{1/2\,O_2} \rightleftharpoons \overset{(1)}{HCHO} + \overset{(1)}{H_2O}$$

Basis: 1 mole CH_3OH.

$$O_2 \text{ (required)} = 0.5 \text{ mole}$$

$$O_2 \text{ (in)} = 1.50\,(0.5) = 0.75 \text{ mole}$$

$$N_2 \text{ (in)} = N_2 \text{ (out)} = 0.75\,(79/21) = 2.82 \text{ moles}$$

CH_3OH is the limiting reactant.

$$CH_3OH \text{ reacted} = 0.75\,(1) = 0.75 \text{ mole}$$

Therefore

$$HCHO \text{ (out)} = 0.75 \text{ mole}$$

$$CH_3OH \text{ (out)} = 1 - 0.75 = 0.25 \text{ mole}$$

$$O_2 \text{ (out)} = 0.75 - (0.75)\,(0.5) = 0.75 - 0.375 = 0.375 \text{ mole}$$

$$H_2O \text{ (out)} = 0.75\,(1) = 0.75 \text{ mole}$$

Component	Moles	Mole %
CH_3OH	0.250	5.0
HCHO	0.750	15.2
H_2O	0.750	15.2
O_2	0.375	7.6
N_2	2.820	57.0
Total	4.945	100.0

Example 4.17   Increasing salt concentration with an evaporator

A salt solution containing 25% dissolved salt is concentrated in an evaporator capable of removing 7000 lb/hr of water. The bottom product contains 75% precipitated salt, while the other 25% is a solid-free liquid solution. At the operating temperature, the solubility is

$$\frac{27 \text{ g of salt}}{100 \text{ g of solution}}$$

Assuming that one operates at maximum capacity, calculate

   1. Mass flow rate of feed

   2. Amount of solid salt produced per hour

Solution

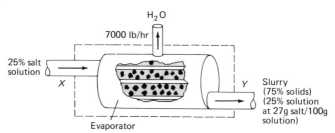

Evaporator

Basis: One hour. The overall balance is

$$X = 7000 + Y \tag{1a}$$

The salt balance is

$$0.25X = 0.75Y + \frac{27}{100}(0.25)Y = 0.8175Y \qquad (1)$$

The H_2O balance is

$$0.75X = \frac{73}{100}(0.25)Y + 7000 = 0.1825Y + 7000 \qquad (2)$$

Multiply Equation (1) by -3:

$$-0.75X = -2.4525Y \qquad (3)$$

Adding Equations (2) and (3), we find

$$0 = -2.27Y + 7000$$

$$Y = \frac{7000}{2.27} = 3080 \text{ lb/hr}$$

From Equation (1a) we have

1. $X = 7000 + 3080 = 10{,}080 \text{ lb}_m/\text{hr} = \text{mass flow rate (feed)}$

2. $0.75(3080) = 2310 \text{ lb}_m/\text{hr solid salt produced}$

4.3 RECYCLE OPERATIONS

It is a common occurrence in the chemical industry to recycle feed back to the processing unit for retreatment. When dealing with an incomplete reaction, the unreacted material is usually separated from the product and recycled to the reactor. In distillation, some of the overhead condensate is recycled to the top of the fractionating column to enhance separation. In drying, a portion of the exit air may be recycled to conserve heat. A typical recycle diagram is shown in Figure 4.2.

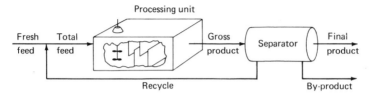

Figure 4.2. Recycle flow diagram

In solving recycle problems, follow these two basic guidelines.

1. Write an overall material balance for the fresh feed and outlet streams.

2. Write a once-through material balance on the processing unit relating inlet and outlet streams.

To illustrate a once-through balance, let us consider the process shown in Figure 4.3.

$$A \rightarrow B$$

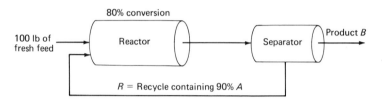

Figure 4.3.

Since we have 80% conversion per pass in the reactor, the once-through balance for A is

Amount of A unreacted = amount of A recycled

or

$$(100 + 0.90R)\ 0.20 = 0.90R$$

and

$$R = 27.8 \text{ lb}$$

In recycle operations, a build-up of impurities or inerts takes place gradually. To avoid this problem, a portion of the recycle is either purged (discarded) or passed through a device which removes impurities and inerts and feeds back the pure recycle to the system. Purging versus purification of recycle is generally governed by the costs involved. One speaks synonymously of a *purge, bleed,* or *blowdown.* A stream *bypassing* the processing unit is often used for the purpose of accurate controls in concentration or other properties. Also, in the case of gaseous purge, a gaseous *makeup* stream is added. Purge, makeup, bypass, and recycle are illustrated in Figure 4.4.

Recycle problems are notorious for disturbing beginning students in chemical engineering. This confusion can be eliminated by practice in solving recycle problems.

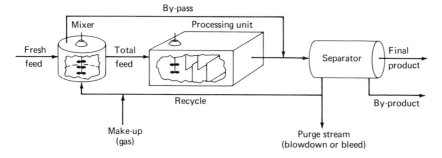

Figure 4.4.   Recycle, purge, makeup, and bypass streams

Example 4.18   Preparation of ether from ethyl alcohol:
                 Incomplete reaction and recycle

Ether (considered the best general anesthetic; also an excellent solvent for organic compounds) is made by the dehydration of ethyl alcohol with sulfuric acid at 130° to 140°C. The reaction is

$$2C_2H_5OH \rightarrow C_2H_5-O-C_2H_5 + H_2O$$

The process flow diagram is shown in Figure 4.5.

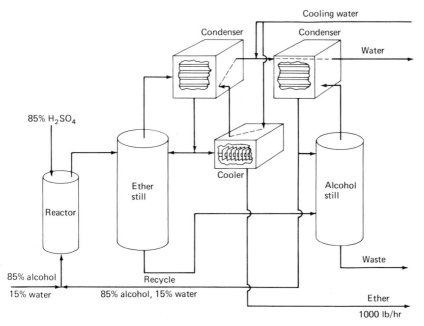

Figure 4.5.   Preparation of ether from ethyl alcohol

Assuming 80% conversion per pass, determine

1. Feed stream

2. Recycle to feed ratio

Solution

Basis: 1000 lb/hr of ether produced.

1.   Moles of ether $= 1000/74 = 13.5$ lb-moles/hr

Moles of C_2H_5OH required $= 13.5 \times 2 = 27$ lb-moles/hr

Mass of C_2H_5OH required $= 27 \times 46 = 1240$ lb/hr

2.   Feed stream $= 1240/0.85 = 1460$ lb/hr

The once-through alcohol balance is

$$(1240 + 0.85R)\, 0.20 = 0.85R$$

$$248 + 0.17R = 0.85R$$

$$0.68R = 248$$

$$R = 365 \text{ lb/hr}$$

$$R/F = 365/1460 = 0.25$$

Example 4.19   Acetaldehyde production from ethane

In the simplified flow diagram shown in Figure 4.6, we see that 0.4 mole each of

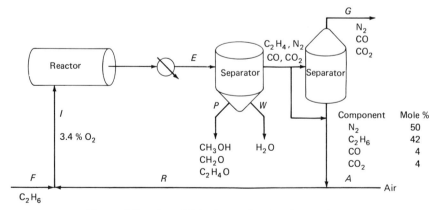

Figure 4.6.   Acetaldehyde production from ethane

ethanol, formaldehyde, and acetaldehyde are produced per mole of ethane when it is oxidized with air, and equimolar amounts of CO and CO_2 are also produced.

If $1000 \, lb_m$/day of acetaldehyde are desired, determine the weight and weight percent composition of each stream.

Solution

$$5C_2H_6 + 7O_2 \rightarrow 2CH_3OH + 2CH_2O + 2C_2H_4O + CO + CO_2 + 5H_2O$$

Basis: $1000 \, lb_m$ acetaldehyde (C_2H_4O).

Since all CH_3OH, CH_2O, and C_2H_4O are removed in the first separator, all of that removed must have been formed in the reaction. By the stoichiometry, stream P must be

$$1000 \, lb_m \, C_2H_4O \times \frac{1 \text{ lb-mole}}{44 \, lb_m} = 22.75 \text{ lb-moles } C_2H_4O$$

Component	lb-mole	MW	lb_m	Weight %
CH_3OH	22.75	32	728	30.2
CH_2O	22.75	30	683	28.3
C_2H_4O	22.75	44	1000	41.5
Total			2411	100.0

The same reasoning applies to the water of stream W:

$$22.75 \text{ lb-moles } C_2H_4O \times \frac{5 \text{ lb-moles } H_2O}{2 \text{ lb-moles } C_2H_4O} \times \frac{18 \, lb_m \, H_2O}{\text{lb-mole } H_2O} = 1025 \, lb_m \, H_2O$$

Because the process is steady state, the reaction stoichiometry must apply to the streams entering and leaving the system as a whole. Therefore, stream F must be

$$22.75 \text{ lb-moles } C_2H_4O \times \frac{5 \text{ lb-moles } C_2H_6}{2 \text{ lb-moles } C_2H_4O} \times \frac{30 \, lb_m \, C_2H_6}{\text{lb-mole } C_2H_6} = 1710 \, lb_m \, C_2H_6$$

Stream A must be

$$22.75 \text{ lb-moles } C_2H_4O \times \frac{7 \text{ lb-moles } O_2}{2 \text{ lb moles } C_2H_4O} \times \left(\frac{100 \text{ lb-moles air}}{21 \text{ lb-moles } O_2}\right)$$

$$\times \left(\frac{29.0 \text{ lb}_m \text{ air}}{\text{lb-mole air}}\right) = 11,000 \text{ lb}_m \text{ air}$$

Using N_2 as a tie element, N_2 in stream G is

$$(11,000 \text{ lb}_m \text{ air}) \frac{0.79 \text{ lb-mole } N_2/\text{lb-mole air}}{29.0 \text{ lb}_m \text{ air}/\text{lb-mole air}} = 300 \text{ lb-moles } N_2$$

$$22.75 \text{ lb-moles } C_2H_4O \times \frac{1 \text{ lb-mole } CO}{2 \text{ lb-moles } C_2H_4O} = 11.375 \text{ lb-moles } CO$$

Component	lb-mole	Mole %	MW	lb$_m$
N_2	300.000	93.0	28	8400
CO	11.375	3.5	28	318
CO_2	11.375	3.5	44	500
Total	322.75	100.0		9218

Since the stream into which the air (stream A) is injected contains no oxygen, all oxygen in stream I must come from the injected air. Find streams R and I:

$$80 \text{ lb-moles } O_2 \times \frac{100 \text{ lb-moles total in } I}{3.4 \text{ lb-moles } O_2 \text{ in } I} = 2350 \text{ lb-moles total in } I$$

Total lb-moles in I	2350
lb-moles from F	−57
lb-moles from A	−380
	1913

The stream into which the air is injected contains

Component	Mole %	lb-moles
N_2	50	956.5
C_2H_6	42	803.5
CO	4	76.5
CO_2	4	76.5
Total	100	1913.0

and therefore stream R is

Component	lb-moles	Mole %	MW	lb_m
N_2	1256.5	54.8	28	35,200
C_2H_6	803.5	35.1	30	24,100
CO	76.5	3.3	28	2,140
CO_2	76.5	3.3	44	3,370
O_2	80.0	3.5	32	2,560
Total	2292.0	100.0		67,370

and stream I is

Component	lb-moles	Mole %	MW	lb_m
N_2	1256.5	53.50	28	35,200
C_2H_6	860.5	36.60	30	25,800
CO	76.5	3.25	28	2,140
CO_2	76.5	3.25	44	3,370
O_2	80.0	3.40	32	2,560
Total	2349.0	100.00		69,070

Since all 80 lb-moles of oxygen react in the reactor, the composition of E can be determined from the reaction stoichiometry:

Component	lb-moles	Mole %	MW	lb_m
N_2	1256.500	53.5	28	35,200
C_2H_6	803.500	34.0	30	24,100
CO	87.875	3.7	28	2,464
CO_2	87.875	3.7	44	3,870
O_2	–	–	32	–
H_2O	57.000	2.4	18	1,025
CH_3OH	22.750	1.0	32	728
CH_2O	22.750	1.0	30	683
C_2H_4O	22.750	1.0	44	1,000
Total	2361.000	100.0		69,070

Example 4.20 Recycle in a toluene-to-benzene catalytic reformer (reactor)

Determine recycles, purge, and makeup for the system shown in Figure 4.7, using 100 moles of toluene in the combined feed to the reactor. Given:

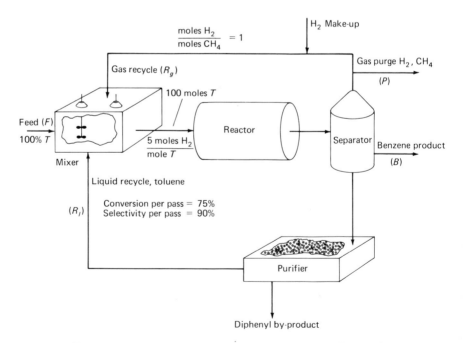

Figure 4.7. Toluene-to-benzene catalytic reformer (reactor)

Main reaction:

toluene   hydrogen   benzene   methane

Side reaction:

toluene   hydrogen   diphenyl   methane

Conversion: Percent of toluene reacted.

Selectivity: Percent of toluene reacted to form benzene only.

$$100 - \text{selectivity} = \% \text{ toluene reacted to form diphenyl}$$

Solution

Basis: 100 moles of toluene in the combined feed to the reactor.

In general, data are given for the conversion per pass around the reactor; thus it is recommended to start your inventory around the reactor. Since the conversion per pass is 75%, 75 moles of toluene have reacted per pass.

$$\text{Toluene out from reactor} = 100 - 75 = 25 \text{ moles}$$

Ninety percent of the reacted toluene goes to benzene, and the rest goes to diphenyl:

$$\text{Toluene to benzene} = 75 \times \frac{90}{100} = 67.5 \text{ moles}$$

$$\text{Toluene to diphenyl} = 75 - 67.5 = 7.5 \text{ moles}$$

$$\text{Benzene produced per pass} = \frac{1 \text{ mole benzene}}{1 \text{ mole toluene}} \times 67.5 \text{ moles toluene}$$

$$= 67.5 \text{ moles}$$

$$\text{Diphenyl produced per pass} = \frac{1 \text{ mole diphenyl}}{2 \text{ moles toluene}} \times 7.5 \text{ moles toluene}$$

$$= 3.75 \text{ moles}$$

H_2 consumed:

Main reaction	67.50	
Side reaction	3.75	
	71.25 moles	

CH$_4$ produced: Main reaction   67.5
                             Side reaction   7.5
                                             ─────
                                             75.0 moles

Since

$$\frac{\text{moles H}_2}{\text{moles toluene}} = 5$$

H$_2$ input to reactor = 5 × 100 = 500 moles
H$_2$ output from reactor = (input − consumption)

$$= 500 - 71.25 = 428.75 \text{ moles}$$

Since we have 1 mole H$_2$/mole CH$_4$,

CH$_4$ input to reactor = 500 moles
CH$_4$ output from reactor = 500 + 75 = 575 moles

Tabulating around the reactor only, we have

Component	MW	Input		Output	
		Moles	Wt (lb)	Moles	Wt (lb)
Hydrogen	2	500	1,000	428.75	857.50
Methane	16	500	8,000	575.00	92,000.00
Benzene	78	0	0	67.50	5,250.00
Toluene	92	100	92,000	25.00	2,300.00
Diphenyl	154	0	0	3.75	578.00

Gas recycle = (input H$_2$ + input CH$_4$) = 1000 + 8000 = 9000 lb

Since only pure toluene is recycled, the unreacted toluene is equal to the liquid recycle:

Liquid recycle = R_l = 25 moles = 25 × 92 = 2300 lb

The toluene balance around the mixer is

$$F + R_l = 100$$

$$F + 25 = 100$$

$$F = 75 \text{ moles} = 6900 \text{ lb}$$

The gas purge is

$$\text{Methane purged} = \text{methane produced}$$

Since this is applied after steady state per pass has been established,

$$75 \text{ moles} = 1200 \text{ lb}$$

H_2 purged with CH_4 must be in the ratio of 428.75 moles H_2/575 moles CH_4

$$H_2 \text{ purged} = \frac{428.75 \text{ moles } H_2}{575 \text{ moles } CH_4} (75 \text{ moles } CH_4) = 55.8 \text{ moles}$$

$$= 111.6 \text{ lb}$$

$$\text{Purge} = 75 + 55.8 = 130.8 \text{ moles} = 1200 + 111.6 = 1311.6 \text{ lb}$$

$$H_2 \text{ make-up} = H_2 \text{ consumed} + H_2 \text{ purged}$$

$$= 71.25 + 55.8 = 127.05 \text{ moles}$$

$$= 254.10 \text{ lb}$$

Check: The overall mass balance for the entire process is

$$F + K = P + B + D$$

$$6900 + 254.1 = 1311.6 + 5250 + 578$$

$$7154.1 = 7139.6$$

This is within slide rule accuracy (if you are nervous, repeat your calculations).

4.4 UNSTEADY STATE OPERATIONS

Whenever operating conditions change with time, one has an unsteady state process. "Unsteady state," which is synonymous with "transient phenomenon," is widely encountered in industry. It is of special interest in plant startup and process control. Unsteady state problems are complex at all levels, and we are limiting this treatment to a simple and elementary approach.

General Case

Consider the process unit shown in Figure 4.8.

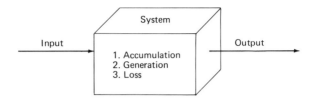

Figure 4.8. Unsteady state process

For this generalized process, the *component* mass balance is

$$\begin{pmatrix} \text{Rate of accumulation} \\ \text{of a component} \\ \text{inside the unit} \end{pmatrix} = \begin{pmatrix} \text{flow rate of} \\ \text{the component} \\ in \end{pmatrix} - \begin{pmatrix} \text{flow rate of} \\ \text{the component} \\ out \end{pmatrix}$$

$$+ \begin{pmatrix} \text{rate of generation of} \\ \text{the component due to} \\ \text{chemical reaction} \end{pmatrix} - \begin{pmatrix} \text{rate of loss of} \\ \text{the component due to} \\ \text{chemical reaction} \end{pmatrix}$$

or, correspondingly,

$$A_C = (I - O + G - L)_C \tag{4.8}$$

This relationship can be simplified to fit the case under consideration. Thus, for a batch process there is no steady flow into and out of the system, and $I = O =$ zero. For a process with no generation, $G =$ zero, and for another with no loss, $L =$ zero. Ultimately, for a steady state operation, $A_C =$ zero. When used for an *overall balance,* the generation and loss of all components must be equivalent, and the unsteady state equation simplifies to

$$A_{\text{overall}} = (I - O)_{\text{overall}} \tag{4.9}$$

Mathematically, the component balance is

$$\rho_C V|_{t + \Delta t} - \rho_C V|_t = [(\rho_C vS)_1 - (\rho_C vS)_2 + R_C] \Delta t \tag{4.10}$$

where

$$\rho_C V|_{t + \Delta t} = \text{mass of material evaluated at time } t + \Delta t$$

$$\rho_C = \text{density of a given component}$$

$$V = \text{volume occupied by the given component in the system}$$

$$t = \text{time}$$

$$\Delta t = \text{time increment}$$

Subscript 1 = evaluated at inlet

Subscript 2 = evaluated at outlet

v = flow velocity

S = cross-sectional area of tube carrying material in and out of volume element V

R_C = Net rate of generation or loss of a given component due to chemical reaction. R_C is positive for generation and negative for loss.

Dividing both sides of the equation by Δt and taking the limit as t approaches zero, we obtain

$$\frac{d(\rho_C V)}{dt} = -\Delta(\rho_C v S) + R_C \qquad (4.11)$$

This is true since the expression

$$\lim_{\Delta t \to 0} \frac{\rho_C V|_{t + \Delta t} - \rho_C V|_t}{\Delta t}$$

is the definition of the derivative. For an *overall* material balance, $R_C = 0$, and this equation reduces to

$$\frac{d(\rho V)}{dt} = -\Delta(\rho v S) \qquad (4.12)$$

where ρ is the density of total mass in volume element V.

The rate of generation or loss of a chemical component is best illustrated through chemical kinetics, which constitutes a course in itself, but for our purpose, it is introduced here.

Chemical Kinetics

Chemical reactions proceed at varying rates. Some are very fast, such as the flameburst of white phosphorus when exposed to air. Others are very slow, such as the rusting of iron in air. But most industrial reactions take place at moderate rates between the two extremes. Chemical kinetics is the study of reaction rates through measurement and the interpretation of these rates. The chemical engineer is concerned about reaction rates because he must understand how rapidly a reaction will proceed and what factors influence its rate so that he can determine the optimal size of needed equipment and be able to bring the reaction under control.

The reaction rate is simply the change in the concentration of a reactant with respect to time. For example, the decomposition of a compound according to the equation

$$2A \rightarrow 2B + C \tag{4.13}$$

has the reaction rate

$$R_A = -\frac{dC_A}{dt} = -\frac{d(N_A/V)}{dt} = -\frac{1}{V}\frac{dN_A}{dt} \tag{4.14}$$

for a reactor of constant volume V, where

$$N_A = \text{number of moles of component } A \text{ at time } t$$

Experimentally, the reaction rate has been found to be a function of concentration; thus for the above reaction we have

$$R_A = -\frac{dC_A}{dt} = k \ C_A{}^2 \tag{4.15}$$

where k is the rate constant or reaction rate constant, determined empirically. Although it is named a constant, it is a strong function of temperature.

For the reaction

$$A + B \rightarrow C + D \tag{4.16}$$

The rate is

$$R_A = k \ C_A C_B \tag{4.17}$$

The two reactions represented by Equations (4.13) and (4.16) are called *elementary reactions,* because the rate equation is obtained directly from a stoichiometric equation representing the step which really took place in the chemical action. In this introduction we shall limit ourselves to problems dealing with simple elementary reactions. Equations 4.15 and 4.17 are second order because the rate is proportional to the second power of the concentration.

In *nonelementary reactions* there is no correspondence between the rate expression and the stoichiometric equation. For example, the reaction of hydrogen and bromine is

$$H_2 + Br_2 \rightarrow 2HBr \tag{4.18}$$

The rate equation is *not*

$$R_{HBr} = C_{H_2} \cdot C_{Br_2} \tag{4.19}$$

but it is found through experimental considerations to be

$$R_{HBr} = \frac{K_1[H_2][Br_2]^{1/2}}{K_2 + [HBr]/[Br_2]} \tag{4.20}$$

where

K_1, K_2 = reaction rate constants

[ ] = indicates concentration of a given compound

The nonelementary reaction of hydrogen and bromine is not really what it appears to be, a single chemical reaction. Rather it is the overall result of a series of elementary reactions. The reaction may be assumed to take the following steps.

$$Br_2 \rightarrow 2Br*$$

$$H_2 + Br* \rightarrow HBr + H*$$

$$H* + Br_2 \rightarrow HBr + Br*$$

$$H* + HBr \rightarrow H_2 + Br* \tag{4.21}$$

$$2Br* \rightarrow Br_2$$

$$\overline{}$$

$$H_2 + Br_2 \rightarrow 2HBr \quad \text{overall reaction}$$

where H* and Br* are reactive intermediates.

As you see, chemical rates and concentrations are all changing with time, and the subject of kinetics is first kin to unsteady state processes.

At this stage, a few illustrations should help clarify the confusion that is usually inherent in unsteady state problems.

Example 4.21 Unsteady state in a coal-oil slurry tank

Consider a tank containing 500 gal of a coal-oil slurry. This slurry has initially 200 lb of fine coal particles. (Coal particles are kept in suspension by a mixer.) If pure oil enters the tank at the rate of 10 gal/min, and the coal-oil slurry leaves the tank at the same rate so that the tank contains 500 gal of a slurry of changing concentration, determine the amount of coal left in the tank after 20 min. Make any logical assumptions.

Solution

Assume ideal mixing, so that the slurry leaving the tank has the same coal concentration as that of the slurry in the tank at any instant.

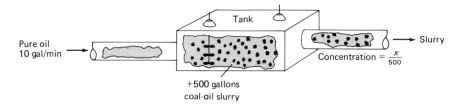

Since there is no chemical reaction,

$$\text{Accumulation} = \text{input} - \text{output}$$

To make a material balance on the *solids,* let

$$X = \text{mass of solids (lb}_m) \text{ in the tank at a given time } t$$

and

$$X|_{t + \Delta t} - X|_t = (0 - 10 \text{ gal/min} \times \frac{X}{500 \text{ gal}}) \Delta t$$

Divide both sides by Δt and take the limit as $\Delta t \to 0$:

$$\lim_{\Delta t \to 0} \frac{X|_{t + \Delta t} - X|_t}{\Delta t} = -0.02 \, X$$

or

$$\frac{dX}{dt} = -0.02 \, X$$

The quantity dX/dt is the rate of change of the mass of solids, or the variation of the amount of solids with time. Now solve the differential equation by separating the variables:

$$dX/X = -0.02 \, dt$$

To integrate this equation, use the limits

$$t = 0 \qquad X = 200$$

$$t = 20 \qquad X = X$$

or

$$\int_{200}^{X} \frac{dX}{X} = -0.02 \int_{0}^{20} dt$$

$$\ln X - \ln (200) = \ln \frac{X}{200} = -0.02 (20 - 0) = -0.4$$

$$X = 200e^{-0.4} = 200 (0.671) = 134.2 \text{ lb}_m$$

Example 4.22   Unsteady state in a tank of NaOH solution

A 500-gal tank has an unknown quantity of 50% NaOH solution. This tank receives, steadily, 19.2 gal/min of dilution water. As soon as the tank is full, the exit stream has a concentration of 10% NaOH and a flow rate of 19.2 gal/min. Determine the time required for the exit stream concentration to become 8% NaOH. You can assume good mixing, and that the specific gravity of 8% and 10% NaOH solutions is 1.10.

Solution

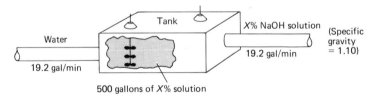

Basis: 19.2 gal/min of dilution water.

Input $= 19.2$ gal/min $\times 8.33 \text{ lb}_m$/gal $= 160 \text{ lb}_m$/min of dilution water

Output $= 19.2$ gal/min $\times 8.33 \times 1.10 \text{ lb}_m$/gal $= 176 \text{ lb}_m$/min of solution

Mass of solution in tank $= 500$ gal $\times 8.33 \times 1.10 \text{ lb}_m$/gal $= 4580 \text{ lb}_m$

To set up the differential equation, it seems logical to use NaOH in setting up the *transient balance,* namely,

$$\text{Accumulation} = \text{input} - \text{output}$$

Accumulation corresponds to the change in the mass of NaOH in the tank. Let

t = time at which the NaOH concentration becomes 8%

X = concentration of NaOH in the tank or exit stream (lb NaOH/lb solution)

Now

$$(4580) \, X|_{t + \Delta t} - (4580) \, X|_t = (0 - 176 \, X) \, \Delta t$$

Divide by Δt and take the limit as Δt approaches zero.

$$4580 \, dX/dt = -176 \, X$$

Separate the variables:

$$\left[\frac{4580}{176} \right] \frac{dX}{X} = -dt$$

Use these limits of integration:

$$t = 0 \qquad X = 0.10$$
$$t = t \qquad X = 0.08$$

Thus

$$\frac{4580}{176} \int_{0.10}^{0.08} \frac{dX}{X} = - \int_{0}^{t} dt$$

or

$$t = -\frac{4580}{176} \ln \frac{0.08}{0.10} = 26.02 \ln \frac{0.10}{0.08} = 5.83 \text{ min} \quad \triangleleft$$

Example 4.23 Rate of a chemical reaction

Given the reaction

$$A \rightarrow B$$

and the rate of loss of A

$$R_A = k \, C_A$$

where

R_A = rate at which A disappears, moles of A/hr-ft^3

k = constant

C_A = concentration of A at any time t, moles of A/ft^3

Find an expression for the concentration of A as a function of time. Assume the reactor volume is V and the initial concentration of A is C_{A_i}.

Solution

The material balance on A is

$$\text{Accumulation} = I - O + G - L$$

There is no input, output, or generation. Thus

$$\text{Accumulation} = -L = -R$$

or

$$\text{MW}_A \, V \, C_A |_{t + \Delta t} - \text{MW}_A \, V \, C_A |_t = [-V(kC_A) \, \text{MW}_A] \, \Delta t$$

where MW_A is the molecular weight of A. Divide by Δt and take the limit as Δt approaches zero; then cancel the constant volume V and the molecular weight of A:

$$\frac{d(\text{MW}_A V C_A)}{dt} = -V \, kC_A \text{MW}_A$$

or

$$\frac{dC_A}{dt} = -k \, C_A$$

Separate the variables and integrate:

$$\int_{C_{A_i}}^{C_A} \frac{dC_A}{C_A} = \int_0^t -k \, dt$$

This gives

$$\ln \frac{C_A}{C_{A_i}} = -kt$$

$$\frac{C_A}{C_{A_i}} = e^{-kt}$$

and

$$C_A = C_{A_i} e^{-kt}$$

This is the expression that gives the concentration of A at any time t.

Example 4.24   Decomposition of nitrous oxide

The decomposition of nitrous oxide may be represented by the elementary reaction

$$2N_2O \xrightarrow{k} 2N_2 + O_2$$

or symbolically as

$$2A \xrightarrow{k} 2B + C$$

Develop an expression for the concentration of N_2O as a function of time.

Solution

The rate of decomposition of N_2O is

$$R = -\frac{d(N_2O)}{dt} = k[N_2O]^2$$

or

$$R = -\frac{dC_A}{dt} = k\ C_A^2$$

Separate the variables to get

$$-\frac{dC_A}{C_A^2} = k\ dt$$

and integrate:

$$-\int_{C_{A_i}}^{C_A} \frac{dC_A}{C_A^2} = -\int_0^t k\ dt$$

where C_{A_i} is the initial concentration of N_2O.

In other words, at time $t = 0$, the initial concentration of N_2O is C_{A_i}, and after proceeding with the reaction, the concentration becomes C_A at the elapsed time t. Then

$$\frac{1}{C_A} - \frac{1}{C_{A_i}} = kt$$

or

$$\frac{1}{C_A} = \frac{1}{C_{A_i}} + kt \quad \triangleleft$$

You can tell your boss the concentration of N_2O at any given time, once you have the rate constant k and the initial concentration.

Example 4.25   Equilibrium constant in reversible reactions

Acetic acid and alcohol react in a constant temperature reactor according to the reversible elementary reaction

$$CH_3COOH + C_2H_5OH \underset{K_2}{\overset{K_1}{\rightleftharpoons}} CH_3COOC_2H_5 + H_2O$$

or

$$A + B \underset{K_2}{\overset{K_1}{\rightleftharpoons}} C + D$$

What is the rate equation and what is the expression for the equilibrium constant?

Solution

The rate of disappearance of A is equal to the rate of formation of C. Thus

$$R_A = -\frac{dC_A}{dt} = +\frac{dC_C}{dt}$$

The concentration of A is decreasing with time, while the concentration of C is equally increasing with time:

$$R_A = -\frac{dC_A}{dt} = K_1\, C_A C_B - K_2\, C_C C_D \quad \triangleleft$$

At equilibrium, concentrations are no longer a function of time, and

$$R_A = 0$$

and

$$0 = K_1 \, C_A C_B - K_2 \, C_C C_D$$
$$K_1 \, C_A C_B = K_2 \, C_C C_D$$

or

$$k_e = \frac{K_1}{K_2} = \frac{C_C C_D}{C_A C_B} \qquad \triangleleft$$

where k_e is the equilibrium constant previously encountered in general chemistry.

Example 4.26   Flow from a conical tank

A cone with a base diameter of 1 ft and a height of 1.5 ft is initially full of a certain fluid. If this fluid is pumped from the cone at the rate of 2 in.^{3}/sec, find the rate at which the fluid level is dropping when the fluid is 6 in. from the base.

Solution

Initially, the volume of fluid in the cone is equal to the volume of the cone.

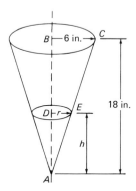

For a given time t let

$$r = \text{radius of fluid surface}$$
$$h = \text{height of fluid surface}$$
$$V = \text{volume of fluid in the cone}$$

By the similitude of the two triangles ABC and ADE, we get

$$r/6 = h/18$$

$$r = 6h/18 = h/3$$

$$\text{Volume of a cone} = V = \tfrac{1}{3}\pi r^2 h$$

Replace r by $h/3$ to get

$$V = \tfrac{1}{3}\pi \frac{h^2}{9} h = \frac{\pi h^3}{27}$$

Take the derivative of both sides with respect to time:

$$\frac{dV}{dt} = \frac{3\pi}{27} h^2 \frac{dh}{dt} = \frac{\pi}{9} h^2 \frac{dh}{dt}$$

We are seeking the rate (dh/dt) when

$$(dV/dt) = -2 \text{ in.}^3/\text{sec} \quad \text{and} \quad h = 18 - 6 = 12 \text{ in.}$$

Thus

$$-2 = \tfrac{\pi}{9}(12)^2 \frac{dh}{dt}$$

$$\frac{dh}{dt} = -\frac{18}{\pi(12)^2} = -0.04 \text{ in./sec}$$

4.5   USE OF THE COMPUTER IN MATERIAL BALANCES

The development, growth, and acceptance of large electronic digital computers in modern sciences have been dramatic and rapid. Chemical engineering is by no means an exception. In this particular field of engineering, the powerful tools of high-speed digital computers are applied by process engineers in large-scale chemical plants for calculation of individual unit operations, simulation and control processes, and many other purposes.

This general involvement of computers in engineering work requires the engineer to be familiar with the basic functioning of the machine and to acquire techniques in programming, so that he will be able to accept assistance in computer usage for work like development, experimentation, problem formulation, and management. At the same time, since a computer requires precise definitions and logical organization, and allows no ambiguity, the training should be of value to the engineer in all of his work.

A general discussion of computerized process control is beyond the scope of this book. Yet it would be interesting to show how computer programming can be utilized in solving problems at our present level of studies. The following examples will serve this purpose. They have been written in standard Fortran IV language. A fundamental understanding of the language, which is commonly employed in scientific work, is assumed.

Example 4.27 Computer solution to example 4.14

Let us see how Example 4.14 could be solved by a simple Fortran IV program. With the inserted comments the statements should be self-explanatory. The program was processed by the Univac 1108 Multi-processing Computer at Illinois Institute of Technology.

```
 1*   C      *************************************************
 2*   C      *                                               *
 3*   C      *  THIS IS A COMPUTER PROGRAM WHICH SHOWS HOW    *
 4*   C      *  EXAMPLE 4.14 CAN BE CALCULATED BY THE USE     *
 5*   C      *              OF A COMPUTER                     *
 6*   C      *                                               *
 7*   C      *************************************************
 8*   C
 9*          REAL MCO,MCO2,MC7,MC8,MN2,MO2,MACO,MACO2,MAC7,MAC8,MAN2,MAO2
10*          REAL MTOTAL
11*          WRITE(6,100)
12*      100 FORMAT('1')
13*   C      ASSIGN MOLE % VALUES TO EACH COMPONENT
14*          MCO=0.020
15*          MCO2=4.50
16*          MC7=7.0
17*          MC8=7.480
18*          MN2=65.0
19*          MO2=16.0
20*   C      ASSIGN MOLECULAR WEIGHTS
21*          WCO=28.0
22*          WCO2=44.0
23*          WC7=12.0*7.0+1.0*16.0
24*          WC8=8.0*12.0+18.0
25*          WN2=28.0
26*          WO2=32.0
27*   C      CALCULATE MASS(LBM) OF EACH COMPONENT
28*          MACO=MCO*WCO
29*          MACO2=MCO2*WCO2
30*          MAC7=MC7*WC7
31*          MAC8=MC8*WC8
32*          MAN2=MN2*WN2
33*          MAO2=MO2*WO2
34*   C      CALCULATE TOTAL MASS
35*          MTOTAL=MACO+MACO2+MAC7+MAC8+MAN2+MAO2
36*   C      CALCULATE PPM OF EACH COMPONENT
37*          PPMCO=MACO/MTOTAL*10**6
```

```
38*          PPMCO2=MACO2/MTOTAL*10**6
39*          PPMC7=MAC7/MTOTAL*10**6
40*          PPMC8=MAC8/MTOTAL*10**6
41*          PPMN2=MAN2/MTOTAL*10**6
42*          PPMO2=MAO2/MTOTAL*10**6
43*     C    PRINT HEADINGS
44*          WRITE(6,1)
45*        1 FORMAT(8X,'COMPONENT',3X,'MOLE %',7X,'M.W.',6X,'MASS',11X,'PPM')
46*     C    PRINT RESULTS IN TABLE FORM
47*          WRITE(6,2) MCO,WCO,MACO,PPMCO
48*        2 FORMAT(/11X,'CO',5X,F8.3,3X,F8.2,5X,F6.2,6X,F11.4)
49*          WRITE(6,3) MCO2,WCO2,MACO2,PPMCO2
50*        3 FORMAT(/11X,'CO2',4X,F8.3,3X,F8.2,5X,F6.2,6X,F11.4)
51*          WRITE(6,4) MC7,WC7,MAC7,PPMC7
52*        4 FORMAT(/11X,'C7',5X,F8.3,3X,F8.2,5X,F6.2,6X,F11.4)
53*          WRITE(6,5) MC8,WC8,MAC8,PPMC8
54*        5 FORMAT(/11X,'C8',5X,F8.3,3X,F8.2,5X,F6.2,6X,F11.4)
55*          WRITE(6,6) MN2,WN2,MAN2,PPMN2
56*        6 FORMAT(/11X,'N2',5X,F8.3,3X,F8.2,4X,F7.2,6X,F11.4)
57*          WRITE(6,7) MO2,WO2,MAO2,PPMO2
58*        7 FORMAT(/11X,'O2',5X,F8.3,3X,F8.2,5X,F6.2,6X,F11.4)
59*          STOP
60*          END
```

END OF COMPILATION: NO   DIAGNOSTICS.

For the sake of clarity, the program has been written in a straightforward manner. (An advanced technique, often referred to as the DO loop method, which is much more efficient, will be employed in the next example.) The following is the "output" of the same program with proper headings in each column.

COMPONENT	MOLE %	M.W.	MASS	PPM
CO	.020	28.00	.56	137.1446
CO2	4.500	44.00	198.00	48490.4292
C7	7.000	100.00	700.00	171430.8105
C8	7.480	114.00	852.72	208832.1133
N2	65.000	28.00	1820.00	445720.1094
O2	16.000	32.00	512.00	125389.3926

"C7" and "C8" have been used in place of C_7H_{16} and C_8H_{18}, respectively. This simple example makes one thing clear: no matter how fast the computer can do the work (CPU, central processing unit, time of the above program was 1.217 seconds!), it will not do so unless it is told *how* to do it. In other words, the programmer cannot make the computer print out the results just by typing in the question as it is in Example 4.14. The programmer has to analyze the problem with his own knowledge of chemistry, physics, and mathematics before making up the logic of the computer program.

At this point the student should know that the total time required for making up the program is much longer than that of solving the problem by hand. This is in fact true, because it does take time to have the program written and the cards punched, and very often it takes several runs before the program works the way it should. But don't give up yet. The following example, which is the solution to a slightly modified form of Example 4.14, will definitely show the beauty of the high computational speed of a computer.

Example 4.28   Modification of Example 4.14 for optimum use of computer

Suppose you are working in a laboratory and every day you have to compute the analysis of samples of gases like the one you breathe in that tent in Example 4.14. You are given the mole percent and the molecular weight of each of the components in the samples; and in your report you have to put down the mass and concentration in ppm of each component. The following program is written in such a way that it can handle the analysis of any number of samples.

A (-1) mole percent denotes the end of file of data of one sample (test executed in statement 7 in the program), and a (-2) mole percent denotes the end of file of all data to be processed (lines 8 and 25).

```
 1*              REAL M(10),W(10), MA(10),X(10),MTOTAL
 2*              WRITE(6,100)
 3*        100 FORMAT('1')
 4*          1 J=1
 5*          2 READ(5,3) M(J), W(J)
 6*          3 FORMAT(F7.3,F6.2)
 7*              IF(M(J)+1.0) 4,6,4
 8*          4 IF(M(J)+2.0) 5,12,5
 9*          5 J=J+1
10*              GO TO 2
11*          6 K=J-1
12*              MTOTAL=0.0
13*              DO 7 J=1,K
14*              MA(J)=M(J)*W(J)
15*          7 MTOTAL=MTOTAL+MA(J)
16*              DO 8 J=1,K
17*          8 X(J)=MA(J)/MTOTAL*10**6
18*              WRITE(6,9)
19*          9 FORMAT(////8X,'COMPONENT',3X,'MOLE %',9X,'M.W.'9X,
20*             1'MASS',13X,'PPM')
21*              DO 10 J=1,K
22*         10 WRITE(6,11) J,M(J),W(J),MA(J),X(J)
23*         11 FORMAT(/11X,'C',I1,6X,F7.3,6X,F8.3,6X,F7.2,7X,F11.4)
24*              GO TO 1
25*         12 STOP
26*              END
```

```
END OF COMPILATION:       NO  DIAGNOSTICS.
```

The two samples given in Example 4.14 were run with this program. The following is the arrangement of the deck of data cards, physically located at the end of the program. Data are read by the statement in line 5, according to the format specified in line 6:

0.020	28.00	0.020	28.00
4.500	44.00	1.000	44.00
7.000	100.00	0.007	100.00
7.480	114.00	0.005	114.00
65.000	28.00	79.968	28.00
16.000	32.00	19.000	32.00
−1.000		−1.000	
		−2.000	

The following is the printed output.

COMPONENT	MOLE %	M.W.	MASS	PPM
C1	.020	28.000	.56	137.1446
C2	4.500	44.000	198.00	48490.4292
C3	7.000	100.000	700.00	171430.8105
C4	7.480	114.000	852.72	208832.1133
C5	65.000	28.000	1820.00	445720.1094
C6	16.000	32.000	512.00	125389.3926

COMPONENT	MOLE %	M.W.	MASS	PPM
C1	.020	28.000	.56	193.5751
C2	1.000	44.000	44.00	15209.4725
C3	.007	100.000	.70	241.9689
C4	.005	114.000	.57	197.0318
C5	79.968	28.000	2239.10	773990.6875
C6	19.000	32.000	608.00	210167.2559

If desired, a test statement may be inserted in the program to test whether the concentration of a particular component exceeds a certain pre-set limit or not. You were supposed to calculate the concentration of heptane in the second part of Example 4.14. Check whether your answer agrees with that calculated by the computer.

It is this kind of *general program* in computer usage that finds tremendous application in scientific work. To gain further familiarity with it, we shall look at another, similar program.

Example 4.29   Computer solution for a modified version of Example 4.18

Let us write a computer program to find the ethyl alcohol required, the feed stream, the recycle, and the recycle-to-feed ratios for the following compositions of alcohol in the feed streams, and lb/hr ether required as product.

Mass fraction of alcohol in feed stream	lb/hr of ether (desired product)
0.85	1000.00
0.99	2000.00
0.50	2000.00
0.75	3000.00
0.05	5000.00
0.15	8000.00
0.95	8000.00
0.45	9000.00
0.80	10000.00

Assume that the composition of the recycle stream in each case is the same as that of the feed stream, referring to Figure 4.5 earlier in this chapter for the diagram.

A list of the needed statements is given below:

```
 1*          REAL ELBPHR(10),PERALO(10),LBC2(10),FEEDST(10),R(10),RATIO(10)
 2*          WRITE(6,1)
 3*        1 FORMAT('1',11X,'ELBPHR',6X,'PERALO',8X,'LBC2',9X,'FEEDST',11X,
 4*          1'R',8X,'RATIO')
 5*        2 J=1
 6*        3 READ(5,4) ELBPHR(J),PERALO(J)
 7*        4 FORMAT(F7.1,F4.2)
 8*          IF(ELBPHR(J)+1.0)5,6,5
 9*        5 J=J+1
10*          GO TO 3
11*        6 K=J-1
12*          DO 7 J=1,K
```

```
13*          LBC2(J)=(ELBPHR(J)*2*46)/74
14*          FEEDST(J)=LBC2(J)/PERALO(J)
15*          R(J)=(0.20*LBC2(J))/(0.80*PERALO(J))
16*          RATIO(J)=R(J)/FEEDST(J)
17*          WRITE(6,7)ELBPHR(J),PERALO(J),LBC2(J),FEEDST(J),R(J),RATIO(J)
18*        7 FORMAT(/11X,F7.1,6X,F4.2,6X,F9.2,6X,F9.2,6X,F8.2,5X,F4.2)
19*          STOP
20*          END
```

END OF COMPILATION: NO DIAGNOSTICS.

The nomenclature should be interpreted as follows.

$$ELBPHR = \text{ether, lb/hr}$$

$$PERALO = \text{percentage of alcohol}$$

$$LBC2 \quad = \text{pound of } C_2H_5OH \text{ required}$$

$$FEEDST = \text{feedstream}$$

$$RATIO \quad = \text{recycle-to-feed ratio}$$

Data cards for this program are as follows. Note the READ format in statement 3 (line 6).

$$1000.00.85$$
$$2000.00.99$$
$$2000.00.50$$
$$3000.00.75$$
$$5000.00.05$$
$$8000.00.15$$
$$8000.00.95$$
$$9000.00.45$$
$$10000.00.80$$

Note that the relations in lines 13 to 16 are slightly modified from those in Example 4.18 to fit the format of Fortran IV.

The computer output is shown below:

ELBPHR	PERALO	LBC2	FEEDST	R	RATIO
1000.0	.85	1243.24	1462.64	365.66	.25
2000.0	.99	2486.49	2511.60	627.90	.25
2000.0	.50	2486.49	4972.97	1243.24	.25
3000.0	.75	3729.73	4972.97	1243.24	.25

5000.0	.05	6216.22	124324.32	31081.08	.25
8000.0	.15	9945.95	66306.31	16576.58	.25
8000.0	.95	9945.95	10469.42	2617.35	.25
9000.0	.45	11189.19	24864.86	6216.22	.25
10000.0	.80	12432.43	15540.54	3885.14	.25

It is easy to see that with a slight modification of the dimension statement (line 1) the program may be changed to handle any number of pairs of data given. Try to write a program yourself which, besides finding the feed streams and re-cycle ratios, also prints out as output the cost of producing a certain quantity of product. Assume that the costs of alcohol and water are $150.00 and $0.13 per 1000 lb, respectively, and that it costs $5.00 to recycle every pound of material in the recycle stream. It is likely that you will have to use this program when you become a plant engineer!

Example 4.30   Computer solution to a trial-and-error problem

```
C******************************************************************
C        COMPUTER SOLUTION TO A TRIAL AND ERROR PROBLEM
C        ---------------------------------------------------------
C        NITROGEN GAS OCCUPIES A VOLUME OF 240 FT3, AT 68F AND ONE ATM.
C        1. USE A DIGITAL COMPUTER TO FIND THE VOLUME OF THIS GAS UNDER
C        ISOTHERMAL CONDITIONS AND AT A PRESSURE OF 2300 PSIG.
C        2. CHECK YOUR ANSWER WITH EXAMPLE 3.10
C******************************************************************
```

The problem described above can be solved by a simple, straightforward Fortran IV program. With the inserted comment statements, the program should be self-explanatory. It was processed by an IBM 1130 system computer.

Solution

```
C-----------------------IDENTIFICATION SECTION---------------------
C      R       =0.7302(FT3 ATM/LBMOLE OR)
C      PN      = NUMBER OF LB-MOLES OF THE GAS(0.62 LB-MOLES)
C      INITIAL CONDITIONS
C      ------------------
C      V1      =240 FT3
C      P1      =1 ATM
C      T1      =T2= 68F= 528 OR (ISOTHERMAL CONDITIONS)
C      P2      =2300 PSIG=156.5 ATM
C      VI      =1.53 FT3 (IDEAL GAS VOLUME ATTHE GIVEN CONDITIONS)
C----------------------------------------------------------------
C      VIP     =2.47 FT3/LB-MOLE(FIRST ESTIMATE OF THE VOLUME PER LBMOLE
C                      OF THE GAS AT THE GIVEN CONDITIONS(IDEAL VOLUME)
C      T       =TOLERANCE FOR CALCULATING THE VOLUME OF THE GAS
```

```
C      J  =COUNTER FOR THE NUMBER OF TRIALS
C      DV      = THE TOLERANCE FOR VPM
C      VPM     =CALCULATED VALUE OF THE GAS VOLUME USING VANDER WAALS
C      VPP     =VPM*PN
C              EQUATION GIVEN AS
C      (P+(A/V**2))(V-B)=RT
C      WHERE   A=346 ATM(FT3/LB-MOLE)**2
C              B=0.62(FT3/LB-MOLE)
C      A + B ARE CONSTANTS IN VANDER WAALS EQUATION
C      P=THE VALUE PRESSURE AT P2
C*********************************************************************
C-------------------------------------------------------------------
C      THE FORM OF THE ABOVE EQUATION USED TO SOLVE THIS PROBLEM IS
C      VPM**3-VPM**2(B+RT/P)+VPM*A/P-A*B/P=FV
C      FV STANDS FOR THE VALUE OF THE FUNCTION ON THE RIGHT SIDE OF THE EQUATION
C*********************************************************************
C-------------------------------------------------------------------
C*********************************************************************


       READ(2,4) A,B,VIP
  4    FORMAT(2F6.2,F8.5)
       WRITE(3,5)
  5    FORMAT(1H1,20X,'A',8X,'B',8X,'VIP')
       WRITE(3,7) A, B, VIP
  7    FORMAT(1H ,//,19X,F7.2,3X,F7.2,3X,F8.5)
       J       =0
       VPM     =VIP
       R       =0.7302
       TMP     =528.
       PN      =0.62
       RT      =R*TMP
       P       =156.5
       DV      =0.001
       T       =0.1E-05
       WRITE(3,77)
  77   FORMAT(1H1,30X,'J',9X,'VIP')
  14   FV      =VPM**3.-VPM**2.*(B+(RT/P))+VPM*(A/P)-A*B/P
       VPP     =VPM*PN
       IF(FV-T)25,25,22
  22   WRITE(3,15) J,VPP
  15   FORMAT(1H ,27X,I4,5X,F8.4)
       J       =J+1
       VPM     =VPM-DV
       GO TO 14
  25   WRITE(3,15) J,VPP
       CALL EXIT
       END

FEATURES SUPPORTED
 ONE WORD INTEGERS
 IOCS

CORE REQUIREMENTS FOR
 COMMON      0 VARIABLES      36 PROGRAM      246

END OF COMPILATION
```

The program can be modified by reading the constants instead of using Fortran statements to define them. The constants of the van der Waals equation and the first trial of volume (the ideal volume) are listed below in the "output" as the input data.

A	B	VIP
346.00	0.62	2.47000

The second part of the "output" shows the number of trials and the volume for each trial. The output of this part is listed below; this part of the total "output" is presented here for illustration. The total number of trials of this program is 70. A change in the increment of decrease in the volume will change this number of trials.

J	VIP	J	VIP	J	VIP
0	1.5313	16	1.5214	32	1.5115
1	1.5307	17	1.5208	33	1.5109
2	1.5301	18	1.5202	34	1.5103
3	1.5295	19	1.5196	35	1.5096
4	1.5289	20	1.5189	36	1.5090
5	1.5282	21	1.5183	37	1.5084
6	1.5276	22	1.5177	38	1.5078
7	1.5270	23	1.5171	39	1.5072
8	1.5264	24	1.5165	40	1.5065
9	1.5258	25	1.5158	41	1.5059
10	1.5251	26	1.5152	42	1.5053
11	1.5245	27	1.5146	43	1.5047
12	1.5239	28	1.5140	44	1.5041
13	1.5233	29	1.5134	45	1.5034
14	1.5227	30	1.5127	46	1.5028
15	1.5220	31	1.5121	47	1.5022

Example 4.31 Predicting the growth in desalination demand

```
C**************************************************************************
C        HOW TO PREDICT THE GROWTH IN DESALINATION DEMAND
C        -------------------------------------------------------
C**************************************************************************
C        SALINE WATER CONVERSION HAS BEEN PLAYING AN IMPORTANT ROLE IN THE
C        WORLD OF SCIENCE FOR THE LAST TWO DECADES. THE AMOUNT OF FRESH
C        WATER PRODUCED FROM SEA WATER BY DISTILLATION IS SHOWN AS FOLLOWS
```

```
C               MGPD OF
C               FRESH WATER
C               FROM SEA WATER          YEAR              YEARS SINCE 1935
C               ----------              --------          ------------
C                 0.40                  1935                    0
C                 0.50                  1940                    5
C                 0.80                  1945                   10
C                 1.80                  1948                   13
C                 2.50                  1951                   16
C                 4.50                  1954                   19
C                 5.20                  1955                   20
C                 7.20                  1957                   22
C                12.40                  1960                   25
C                23.00                  1965                   30
C               ----------------------------------------------------------------
C       REQUIRED- USE DIGITAL COMPUTER TO DEVELOP AN EMPIRICAL EXPRESSION
C       FOR PREDICTING THE AMOUNT OF FRESH WATER PRODUCED FROM SEA WATER
C       AS A FUNCTION OF YEARS
C               ----------------------------------------------------------------
```

Solution

The problem described above could be solved by using Fortran IV programming and the basic linear regression method, known as curve-fitting in numerical analysis. The program uses some powerful and advanced techniques to speed up the calculation and reduce the time consumed by the computer. This technique is called the DO loop; another technique is the DIMENSION statement for storing values read by the computer. The comment statements are self-explanatory.

```
C*******************************************************************************
C***    PROGRAM FOR LEAST SQUARE CURVE FITTING
C***    THE CHOSEN CURVE IS Y=A0+A1*X+A2*X**2+....  ....+A10*X**10
C***    NMBER  IS THE NUMBER OF X,Y DATA PAIRS MAXIMUM OF 200
C***    M   IS THE DEGREE OF THE POLYNOMIAL
C***    N   IS THE NUMBER OF EQUATIONS  (=M+1)
C***    X,Y  ARRAYA FOR THE DATA PAIRS
C***    A   ARRAY FOR THE SUM WHICH BECOME THE COEFFICIENTS OF THE EQUATIONS
C***    B   ARRAY FOR THE CONSTANT TERM IN THE SIMULTANEOUS EQUATIONS
C***    C   ARRAY FOR THE UNKNOWNS WHICH BECOME COEFFICIENTS OF THE POLYNOMIAL
C***    P   ARRAY FOR THE POWERS OF THE X(I) FROM 1 TO 2M
C***    INSTRUCTIONS TO USE THE PROGRAM
C***    PUNCH ON THE FIRST DATA CARD THE DEGREE OF THE POLYNOMIAL FORMAT  I2
C***    PUNCH ON EACH DATA CARD A PAIR OF DATA
C***    PUNCH ON EACH DATA CARD A PAIR9 F DATAX,Y   FORMAT F10.3
C***    X CANNOT HAVE THE VALUE ZERO
C***    THE LAST CARD OF THE DATA DECK IS FILLED WITH ZERO
C*******************************************************************************
C***    THE STATEMENT  10  TO  160 FROM THE POWERS OF X PLACE THEM IN THE ARRAY P
        DIMENSION X(205),Y(205),A(15,15),B(15)                        EIS   10
        DIMENSION C(11),P(20)
        READ(2,20) M,NMBER
   20   FORMAT(I2,I3)
        DO 11 I=1,NMBER
        READ(2,10) X(I), Y(I)
   10   FORMAT(2F10.3)
        IF(X(I)) 11, 12, 11
```

```
      11    CONTINUE
            CALL EXIT
      12    NMBER = I-1
            MX2 = M*2
            DO 13 I=1,MX2
            P(I)=0.0
            DO 13 J=1,NMBER
C***  THE STATEMENTS 160 TO 320 TRANSFORM THE ARRAY P INTO A 2 DIMENSION ARRAY
C***  THIS ARRAY IS THE MATRIX OF THE COEFFICIENTS OF THE SIMULTANEOUS EQUATIONS
      13    P(I) = P(I)+X(J)**I
            N = M+1
            DO 30 I=1,N
            DO 30 J=1,N
            K = I+J-2
            IF(K) 29, 29, 28
      28    A(I,J) = P(K)
            GO TO 30
      29    A(1,1) = NMBER
      30    CONTINUE
            B(1) =0.0
            DO 21 J=1,NMBER
      21    B(1) = B(1)+Y(J)
            DO 22 I=2,N
            B(I) =0.0
            DO 22 J=1,NMBER
      22    B(I)=B(I)+Y(J)*X(J)**(I-1)
C***  STATEMENTS 330 TO 480 BEGIN THE GAUSS ELIMINATION WITH ROW INTERCHANGE
            NM1=N-1
            DO 300 K=1,NM1
            KP1=K+1
            L=K
            DO 400 I=KP1,N
            IF(ABS(A(I,K))-ABS(A(L,K))) 400, 400, 401
      401   L=I
      400   CONTINUE
            IF(L-K) 500, 500, 405
      405   DO 410 J=K,N
            TEMP=A(K,J)
            A(K,J)=A(L,J)
      410   A(L,J)=TEMP
            TEMP=B(K)
            B(K)=B(L)
            B(L)=TEMP
C***  THE BACK SUBSTITUTION IS DONE FROM STATEMENT 490 TO 610
      500   DO 300 I=KP1,N
            FACT=A(I,K)/A(K,K)
            A(I,K)=0.0
            DO 301 J=KP1,N
      301   A(I,J)=A(I,J)-FACT*A(K,J)
      300   B(I)=B(I)-FACT*B(K)
            C(N)=B(N)/A(N,N)
            I=NM1
      710   IP1 = I+1
            SUM=0.0
            DO 700 J=IP1,N
      700   SUM = SUM+A(I,J)*C(J)
            C(I) = (B(I)-SUM) / A(I,I)
C***  THE REMAINING STATEMENTS PRINT THE VALUE OF THE COEFFICIENTS OF THE
C***  POLYNOMIAL   THE ORDER IS A0,A1,A2,...      ...A10
```

```
      I=I-1
      IF(I) 800, 800, 710
800   WRITE(3,44)
44    FORMAT(1H1,40X,'MGPD OF',/,40X,'FRESH WATER',/,40X,'FROM SEA WATER
     1',2X,'YEARS SINCE 1935')
      DO 33 I=1,NMBER
      WRITE(3,19) X(I),Y(I)
19    FORMAT(1H ,40X,2F10.3)
33    CONTINUE
      WRITE(3,777)
777   FORMAT(1H1)
      WRITE(3,888) M
888   FORMAT(1H ,5X,'M=',I3)
      DO 900 I=1,N
900   WRITE(3,901) I, C(I)
901   FORMAT(1H ,40X,'C(',I3,')=',1X,F15.7)
999   STOP
      END

UNREFERENCED STATEMENTS
 999

FEATURES SUPPORTED
 ONE WORD INTEGERS
 IOCS

CORE REQUIREMENTS FOR
 COMMON        0  VARIABLES      1386  PROGRAM      814

 END OF COMPILATION

// XEQ
```

The first part of the "output" lists the given data.

```
       MGPD OF
       FRESH WATER
       FROM SEA WATER      YEARS SINCE 1935
              0.400       0.000
              0.500       5.000
              0.800      10.000
              1.800      13.000
              2.500      16.000
              4.500      19.000
              5.200      20.000
              7.200      22.000
             12.400      25.000
             23.000      30.000
```

The second part of the "output" lists the coefficients of the polynomial of order M that gives the best fit for the data. These coefficients are substituted in the general equation of the polynomial, which was shown previously in the program:

$$Y = A_0 + A_1 X + A_2 X^2 + \cdots + A_n X^n$$

where X is time in years and Y the amount of distilled water from sea water in mgpd units (million gallons per day).

M= 2

C(1)=	5.5441074
C(2)=	2.9093146
C(3)=	-0.0820943

Thus

$$Y = 5.544 + 2.909X - 0.082 X^2$$

Example 4.32   Plotting with a computer

```
C        USING COMPUTER FOR MAKING A PLOT
C------------------------------------------------------
C        PLOT GIVEN DATA IN EXAMPLE 4.31 BY USING A DIGITAL COMPUTER
```

Solution

The student is asked to solve the problem described above. The program uses the ordinary Fortran IV techniques, but the programmer must have some practice in programming before he tries to write it. It uses ordinary scaling for the "input data" to determine the range of the X-axis and Y-axis for plotting the data. Also, the DATA statement is used here in addition to the DIMENSION statement. The IFIX subroutine is used also to round the numbers to integer numbers.

```
C        -----------------------------------------------------------------
      DIMENSION NCODE(110),X(110),Y(110),XPLOT(110),POINT(40),XSCAL(110)
      DATA BLNK/' '/,POINT/'1','2','3','4','5','6','7','8','9','A','B','
     1C','D','E','E','G','H','I','J','K','L','M','N','O','P','Q','R','S'
     2,'T','U','V','W','X','Y','Z'/
C*************************************************************************
C234567890123456789012345678901234567890123456789012345678901234567890123456789012
C      1         2         3         4         5         6         7
C
C*************************************************************************
C
C--------------------------IDENTIFICATION SECTION---------------------
C        XSUM          = SUM OF ALL VALUES OF X
C        YSUM          = SUM OF ALL VALUES OF Y
C        XAVRG         = AVERAGE VALUE OF X
C        YAVRG         = AVERAGE VALUE OF Y
C        NDATA         = NO. OF DATA CARDS
C*************************************************************************
```

```
         JIN                =  2
         JOUT               =  3
   READ                     (JIN,1000) YAXS
         NDATA              =0
         I=0
10       I                  =I+1
         NDATA              =NDATA+1
   READ                     (JIN,2000) NCODE(I), X(I), Y(I)
   IF                       (NCODE(I))20,20,10
20 WRITE(JOUT,2500)
   WRITE                    (JOUT,3000)(J,NCODE(J),X(J),Y(J),J=1,NDATA
   1)
C***************************************************************

         NND                =NDATA-1
   DO 40 J                  =1,NND
         IP                 =J+1
   DO 40 K                  =IP,NDATA
   IF                       (X(J)-X(K)) 30, 30, 40
30       TT                 =X(J)
         X(J)               =X(K)
         X(K)               =TT
         TP                 =Y(J)
         Y(J)               =Y(K)
         Y(K)               =TP
         TS                 =NCODE(J)
         NCODE(J)           =NCODE(K)
         NCODE(K)           =TS
40 CONTINUE
C***************************************************************

         XSUM               =0.0
         YSUM               =0.0
   WRITE(JOUT,4000)
   DO 50 I                  =1,NDATA
         XSUM               =XSUM+X(I)
50       YSUM               =YSUM+Y(I)
         XAVRG              =XSUM/NDATA
         YAVRG              =YSUM/NDATA
   DO 60 I                  =1,NDATA
         XBAR               =X(I)-XAVRG
         XBSQ               =XBAR**2.
         YBAR               =Y(I)-YAVRG
         YBSQ               =YBAR**2.
60 WRITE                    (JOUT,5000)I,NCODE(I),X(I),XBAR,XBSQ,Y(I),Y
   1                        BAR,YBSQ
         XMAX               =X(1)
         XMIN               =X(NDATA)
   WRITE                    (JOUT,6000)
   DO 80 L                  =1,NND
         IP                 =I+1
   DO 80 M                  =IP,NDATA
   IF(   Y(L)-Y(M)          )70,70,80
70       SS                 =Y(I)
         Y(L)               =Y(M)
         Y(J)               =SS
         SS                 =X(L)
         X(L)               =X(M)
         X(M)               =SS
         RR                 =NCODE(L)
         NCODE(L)           =NCODE(M)
```

```
80              NCODE(M)        =RR
                M               =1
                XAXS            =100.0
                KYAXS           =YAXS
                LINE            =KYAXS
                JY              =KYAXS
                L               =1
                K               =1
        DO 90   I               =1,100
90              XPLOT(I)        =BLNK
100             PY              =((Y(K)-Y(NDATA))/(Y(1)-Y(NDATA)))*YAXS+0.5
                IY              =IFIX(PY)
                PX              =((X(K)-XMIN)/(XMAX-XMIN))*XAXS+0.5
                IX              =IFIX(PX) + 1
        IF(     IY-LINE         )910,200,980
200     IF(     K-L             )300,600,300
300     IF(     IX-MX           )600,400,600
400             M               =M+1
        IF(     M-30            )500,500,600
500             XPLOT(IX)       =POINT(M)
        GO TO   700
600             MX              =IX
                XPLOT(IX)       =POINT(1)
700             K               =K+1
800     IF(     (K-1)-NDATA     )100,900,960
900             JY              =LINE
910     IF(     LINE-JY         )980,930,920
920     WRITE                   (JOUT,7000)(XPLOT(J),J=1,100)
        GO TO   940
930             YSCAL           =(Y(1)-Y(NDATA))*(LINE/YAXS) + Y(NDATA)
        WRITE                   (JOUT,8000)YSCAL,(XPLOT(J),J=1,100)
                JY              =JY-10
940             L               =K
                M               =1
                LINE            =LINE-1
        DO 950  I               = 1,100
950             XPLOT(I)        =BLNK
        IF(     LINE            )960,800,800
960     WRITE                   (JOUT,9000)
                N               =0
        DO 970  II              =10,100,10
                N               =N+1
970             XSCAL(N)        =(XMAX-XMIN)*(II/XAXS)+XMIN
        WRITE                   (JOUT,9500)(XSCAL(I),I=1,10)
1000    FORMAT(F8.1)
2000    FORMAT(I4,2F8.1)
2500    FORMAT(1H1,44X,'I',7X,'NCODE',7X,'X',12X,'Y'///)
3000    FORMAT(42X,I5,8X,I5,4X,F10.5,3X,F10.5)
4000    FORMAT(1H1,12X,'I',8X,'NCODE',10X,'X',9X,'XBAR',8X,'XBSQ',10X,'Y',
     1  19X,'YBAR',8X,'YBSQ',///)
5000    FORMAT(1H ,11X,I3,8X,I4,3X,6(2X,F10.2))
6000    FORMAT(1H1,44X,'PROBLEM NO 7',/,)
7000    FORMAT(1H ,19X,'Y',100A1)
8000    FORMAT(1H ,9X,E10.3,'-',100A1)
9000    FORMAT(1H ,19X,1HX,10(10HIXXXXXXXXXX))
9500    FORMAT(1H ,17X,10(F6.1,4X))
980     CALL    EXIT
        END

FEATURES SUPPORTED
```

The first part of the "output" lists the data X and Y as read by the computer:

I	NCODE	X	Y
1	10	5.00000	0.50000
2	10	10.00000	0.80000
3	10	13.00000	1.80000
4	10	16.00000	2.50000
5	10	19.00000	4.50000
6	10	20.00000	5.20000
7	10	22.00000	7.20000
8	10	25.00000	12.40000
9	10	30.00000	23.00000
10	0	0.00000	0.40000

The second part of the "output" (see below) lists the values of X and Y in descending order in addition to their mean values, square values, and the code number for reading them. This is done to prepare the X and Y values for plotting. The technique used in programming this part is ordinary sorting.

I	NCODE	X	XBAR	XBSQ	Y	YBAR	YBSQ
1	10	30.00	14.00	195.99	23.00	17.17	294.80
2	10	25.00	9.00	80.99	12.40	6.57	43.16
3	10	22.00	6.00	35.99	7.20	1.37	1.87
4	10	20.00	4.00	15.99	5.20	-0.62	0.39
5	10	19.00	3.00	8.99	4.50	-1.32	1.76
6	10	16.00	0.00	0.00	2.50	-3.32	11.08
7	10	13.00	-3.00	8.99	1.80	-4.02	16.24
8	10	10.00	-6.00	35.99	0.80	-5.02	25.30
9	10	5.00	-11.00	120.99	0.50	-5.32	28.40
10	0	0.00	-16.00	255.99	0.40	-5.42	29.48

The last part of the "output" is the plot of X and Y values and the scaling of the X and Y axes at the same time. The plot is just the points, and they have to be connected as shown on the following page. Why don't you improve on this program, the plot and its scale?

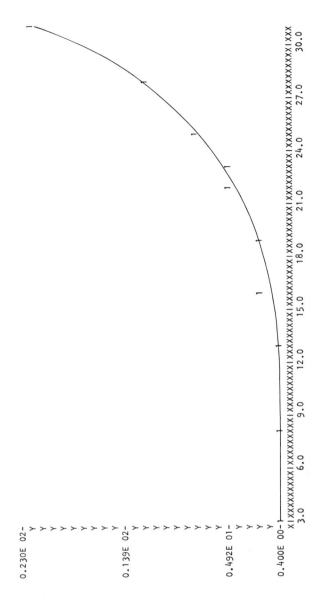

NOMENCLATURE

Symbol	Meaning
A_C	Rate of accumulation of component C inside the system
C_A	Concentration of component A, moles/ft^3
C_{A_i}	Initial concentration of component A, moles/ft^3
F	Feed
G	Rate of generation of a component due to chemical reaction
h	Height (or depth)
I	Flow rate of a component into the system input
k, K_1, K_2	Reaction rate constants
k_e	Equilibrium constant
L	Rate of loss of a component due to chemical reaction
MW	Molecular weight
m	Mass
N	Normality
n	Number of moles
O	Flow rate of a component out of the system output
P	Pressure
R_A	Net rate of generation or loss of component A due to chemical reaction
R_C	Net rate of generation or loss of a component due to chemical reaction
r	Radius
S	Cross-sectional area
T	Absolute temperature, $^\circ$K or $^\circ$R
t	Time
V	Volume
v	Average flow velocity
X	Concentration or mole fraction in liquid
Y	Mole fraction

Greek letters	Meaning
ρ_C	Average density of component C
ρ_w	Density of pure water

REFERENCES

1. Garner, H. G. 1963. Steady state heat and material balances. *Chemical Engineering* 20(9):116.

2. Henley, E. J., and Rosen, E. M. 1969. *Material and energy balance computations.* New York: John Wiley.

3. Himmelblau, D. M. 1962. *Basic principles and calculations in chemical engineering.* Englewood Cliffs, N. J.: Prentice-Hall.

4. Hougen, O. A., Watson, K. M., and Ragatz, R. A. 1954. *Chemical process principles: Part I, Material and energy balances.* New York: John Wiley.

5. Lee, W., and Rudd, D. F. 1966. On the ordering of recycle calculations. *American Institute of Chemical Engineer's Journal* 12(6):1184.

6. Naphtali, L. M. 1964. Process heat and material balances. *Chemical Engineering Progress* 60(9): 70.

7. Nash, L. 1966. *Stoichiometry.* Reading, Mass.: Addison-Wesley.

8. Peters, M. S. 1954. *Elementary chemical engineering.* New York: McGraw-Hill.

9. Rosen, E. M. 1962. A machine computation method for performing material balances. *Chemical Engineering Progress* 58(10):69.

10. Schmidt, A. X., and List, H. L. 1962. *Material and energy balances.* Englewood Cliffs, N. J.: Prentice-Hall.

11. Shreve, R. N. 1967. *Chemical process industries.* New York: McGraw-Hill.

12. Thatcher, C. M. 1962. *Fundamentals of chemical engineering.* Columbus: Charles E. Merrill.

13. Tyner, M. 1960. *Process engineering calculations: Material and energy balances.* New York: Ronald Press.

PROBLEMS

4.1 Stoichiometry in the Preparation of Chloroform

1. How many liters of chlorine at $25°C$ and 760 mm Hg are necessary to transform 32 g of methane into chloroform?

2. What is the weight of chloroform?

4.2 Stoichiometry in the Neutralization of NaOH

An unknown mass of sodium hydroxide is dissolved in 500 g of water. This solution is neutralized by adding successively: 18 g of CH_3COOH, 25.2 g HNO_3, and 29.4 g of H_2SO_4. Determine

1. The mass of NaOH
2. The mass of H_2O in the neutral solution

4.3 Precipitation of AgCl

We add 7.3 cm^3 of HCl solution to 100 cm^3 of $AgNO_3$ solution. The HCl solution has 50 g/liter of HCl. Such an addition caused all the silver to precipitate as AgCl.

1. What is the mass of AgCl precipitated in pounds?

2. What is the number of $\dfrac{\text{lb-moles AgNO}_3}{\text{liter of solution}}$?

4.4 Acetic Acid Concentration in Vinegar

Your job is to determine the acetic acid (CH_3COOH) content of a sample of commercial vinegar. For this purpose you take 100 cm^3 of this vinegar and add a few drops of phenolphthalein indicator. You titrate this volume with a 1 M solution of NaOH. You notice a change in color after using 50 cm^3 of NaOH solution. What is the concentration of vinegar in g/liter?

4.5 Excess Reactant in the Preparation of Nylon

Nylon (a manmade fiber) is produced by reacting adipic acid with hexamethylene diamine:

$$xHOOC(CH_2)_4COOH + xH_2N(CH_2)_6NH_2$$

      (adipic acid)   (hexamethylene diamine)

$$\to x[-H_3N(CH_2)_6NH_3OOC(CH_2)_4COO-]$$

(hexamethylene diammonium adipate, or nylon salt)

$$\to x[-HN(CH_2)_6NHOC(CH_2)_4CO-] + 2x\cdot H_2O$$

(polyhexamethylene adipamide, or nylon)

We have 5 moles of acid, 10 moles of amine, and 80% conversion. Determine

1. Excess reactant
2. Percent excess acid if $x = 3$
3. Percent excess amine if $x = 3$

4.6 Limiting Reactant in the Preparation of Bleaching Powder

Bleaching powder is made from contacting chlorine gas with showered calcium hydroxide in a rotating steel cylinder. The chemical reaction is

$$Ca(OH)_2 + Cl_2 \rightarrow CaOCl_2 \cdot H_2O$$

You have 100 lb of chlorine and 150 lb of calcium hydroxide.

1. Determine the limiting reactant
2. Assuming 90% conversion, determine
   a. Percent excess $Ca(OH)_2$
   b. Percent excess Cl_2
3. Amount of bleaching powder produced

4.7 Limiting Reactant and the Production of Superphosphate

Superphosphate is to be produced by reacting H_2SO_4 (92%) with calcium phosphate (86%) according to the reaction

$$Ca_3(PO_4)_2 + 2H_2SO_4 \rightarrow CaH_4(PO_4)_2 + 2CaSO_4$$

If 40,000 lb of the impure calcium phosphate and 30,000 lb of the dilute H_2SO_4 are reacted per day,

1. What is the limiting reactant?
2. If the reaction goes to 90% completion, how many pounds of superphosphate are produced per day?
3. How many pounds of $Ca_3(PO_4)_2$ are unreacted per day?

4.8 Limiting and Excess Reactants

Given the following equation:

$$H_2SO_4 + 2NaOH \rightarrow Na_2SO_4 + 2H_2O$$

1. If 5 lb of a 70% (by weight) NaOH solution and 10 lb of 80% (by weight) sulfuric acid are mixed together, how much sodium sulfate will be formed?

2. What is the limiting reactant?

3. What is the excess reactant? What is the percent excess?

4. Does this reaction go to completion?

5. What is the percentage conversion of the limiting reactant?

4.9   Roasting of Pyrite to Produce SO_2

An iron pyrite ore contains 90% FeS_2 and 10% inert matter by weight. This material is roasted with 25% excess air according to the reaction

$$4FeS_2 + 11O_2 \rightarrow 2Fe_2O_3 + 8SO_2$$

The solid mixture leaving the roaster contains 13% inert matter by weight, the remainder being Fe_2O_3 and unreacted FeS_2.

Assuming 100 lb of pyrites charged, compute

1. The weight of solids leaving the roaster

2. The percentage conversion, based on FeS_2

3. The Orsat analysis of the gas produced

4.10   Excess Air and Incomplete Reaction

Chlorine is produced by the reaction

$$4HCl + O_2 \rightarrow 2Cl_2 + 2H_2O$$

Calculate

1. The molar composition of product gases on a dry basis, if 50% excess air is used and the reaction is 75% complete.

2. The volume of chlorine produced per $100 \, ft^3$ of HCl fed if both are metered at the same conditions.

4.11   Saturation in a Barium Nitrate Solution

The solubility of barium nitrate at $100°C$ is 34 g/100 g H_2O, and at $0°C$ the solubility is 5.0 g/100 g H_2O. If you start with 100 g of Ba $(NO_3)_2$ and make a saturated solution in water at $100°C$,

1. How much water is required (in grams)?

2. If this solution is cooled to $0°C$, how much $Ba(NO_3)_2$ is precipitated out of solution (in grams)?

4.12 Oxidation of FeS in a Converter

Suppose that 1.4×10^5 lb of matter containing 50% FeS is placed in a copper converter. The iron sulfide is oxidized by blowing oxygen into the converter. The chemical reaction is

$$2FeS + 3O_2 \rightarrow 2FeO + 2SO_2$$

Find

1. Volume (ft^3) of air necessary

2. Mass of FeO formed

3. Volume of SO_2 formed

4. Mass of slag formed if FeO constitutes 70% of the slag

4.13 Concentration of a Zinc Sulfate Solution

A certain zinc sulfate solution contains 30% $ZnSO_4$ by weight. Some of the water is evaporated and then the solution is cooled to $10°C$. This process concentrates $ZnSO_4$ to 45% by weight. Crystals of zinc sulfate hepta hydrate are formed. If we have 1000 lb of original solution, what is the mass of water evaporated and weight of crystals obtained? Given:

$$\text{Solubility of } ZnSO_4 \text{ at } 10°C = 47.6 \text{ g}/100 \text{ ml } H_2O$$

4.14 Composition of a Water-Alcohol Mixture

The density of pure ethyl alcohol is 0.791 g/cm^3 and that of water is 0.995 g/cm^3, both at $30°C$. Equal volumes of the two are mixed together, and the resulting solution is found to have a density of 0.919 g/cm^3 at $30°C$. Calculate the composition of the mixture in

1. Weight percent   2. Mole percent

4.15 Average Molecular Weight and Composition of a Gas Mixture

A gas has the following composition.

Component	Mole %
CH_4	60.0
O_2	10.0
N_2	10.0
H_2	20.0

1. What is the average molecular weight?
2. What is the composition in volume percent?
3. Find the composition in weight fractions.

4.16   Removal of Acetone from Air

Acetone is removed completely from air by passing the acetone-air stream counter-currently to a pure water stream in a contacting tower. From the information given in Figure P4.16, calculate

1. X and Y
2. Composition of exit water stream
3. Amount of acetone removed per hour

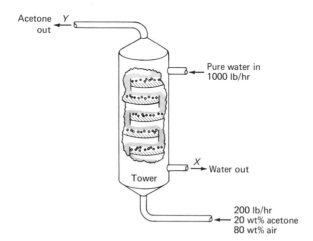

Figure P4.16.

4.17 Combustion of Butane in Air

Butane is burned in a combustion chamber with 30% excess air. Gaseous products leave at 175°F. Calculate

1. Weight percent composition of stack gas
2. Volume of stack gas at STP per ft^3 of C_4H_{10}

4.18 Combustion of Propane in Air

Ten moles of propane are burnt with 400 moles of air such that 3 moles of carbon monoxide are formed along with some carbon dioxide. The chemical reactions are

$$C_3H_8 + 5O_2 \rightarrow 3CO_2 + 4H_2O$$

$$C_3H_8 + \frac{7}{2}O_2 \rightarrow 3CO + 4H_2O$$

Determine

1. Moles of CO_2 obtained
2. Percent excess air

4.19 Analysis of an Unknown Gaseous Mixture

We have 100 cm^3 of a gaseous mixture of CH_4, C_2H_2, C_2H_4, and CO_2 (assume all volumes in this problem are measured at STP). After treatment with a KOH solution, the gas contracts by 32 cm^3; after treatment with a CuCl ammoniacal solution, it contracts by 18 cm^3.

We add an excess of oxygen to the remaining gaseous mixture (50 cm^3). After ignition, the new mixture is mixed with KOH solution and cooled. The new mixture contracts by 70 cm^3. Determine

1. Molar composition of the initial gaseous mixture
2. Mass fraction of CO_2

4.20 Combustion of Hydrogen in Air

Five pounds of dry hydrogen are burnt with 60% excess air. Determine the product gas analysis.

4.21 Combustion of Sulfur in Air

Sulfur dioxide is being produced by burning S with 20% excess air. Determine weight, volume, and mole % composition of flue gas products.

4.22 Combustion of a Gas Mixture in Air

A certain gas is burned with 80% excess air under a boiler. The initial gas analysis is

Component	Mole %
CH_4	65
C_2H_4	10
CS_3	8
CO	5
CO_2	2
N_2	5
O_2	5
	100

1. Determine the Orsat analysis of the product gas
2. Give the flue gas analysis on an SO_2-free basis

4.23 Fuel Combustion in Air-Product Analysis

A liquid fuel is burned in an engine with 25% excess air. The fuel has the composition

Component	Mole %
C_5H_{12}	40
C_6H_{14}	60

If 75% of the carbon goes to CO_2, then 20% goes to CO and 5% is unburned. Find

1. Flue gas analysis
2. Mole fraction of water vapor in the gaseous product

4.24 Incomplete Combustion of Coal, Product Analysis

A certain coal has the composition

Component	Weight %
C	72
H_2	5
H_2O	6
N_2	2
O_2	9
Ash	6
	100

After this coal was burned in a furnace, the ashes had 18% carbon and the flue gases contained 12% oxygen. Calculate

1. Theoretical air required per 100 lb of coal

2. Percent excess air

3. Molar composition of the stack gas

4.25 Analysis of an Unknown Substance by Combustion

Burning 0.88 g of an unknown organic substance, one obtains 1.76 g CO_2 and 0.72 g H_2O.

1. Determine the composition by weight of the organic substance.

2. What is its simplest formula?

4.26 Analysis of an Unknown Gas Mixture

A gas mixture contains CO, CO_2, O_2, N_2, CH_4, and unsaturated hydrocarbons. With 100 cm^3 of this gas, the Orsat analysis gives

Treatment with	Volume contraction (cm^3)
Bromide water	11.0
Cuprous solution	27.5
Alkaline pyrogallol	2.5
Potassium hydroxide solution	3.0

Suppose that 15 cm³ of the residue is mixed with 65 cm³ of oxygen and ignited. Upon cooling the contraction was 20.1 cm³, and after treating with KOH, the additional contraction was 5.2 cm³. What was the composition of the initial gas mixture?

4.27 Excess Air in Burning Illuminating Gas

The burning of illuminating gas gives a flue gas analysis of 9.2% CO_2, 5.3% O_2, and 85.5% N_2. Calculate the amount of excess air.

4.28 Combustion of a CH_4-C_2H_6 Mixture with Excess Air

A mixture of 80 mole % CH_4 and 20 mole % C_2H_6 is burned with an excess of air. The hot flue gas has a dry-basis analysis of

Component	Mole %
CO_2	7.90
CO	1.58
O_2	5.30
N_2	85.22
	100.00

1. What percent excess air was supplied? (The excess air is based on the theoretical requirement for all carbon to go to CO_2.)
2. How many moles of flue gas are produced per mole of fuel gas consumed?

4.29 Combustion of Coal in Excess Air

A coal containing 92 weight percent total carbon and 6 weight percent of unoxidized hydrogen (the remainder is inert ash) is burned with 40% excess air. Calculate:

1. The pounds of air used per pound of coal if C and H are completely oxidized to CO_2 and H_2O, respectively
2. The molal composition of the flue gas, dry basis

4.30 Stack Gas and Molal Humidity

A pure saturated paraffin hydrocarbon is burned with air to produce a stack gas whose Orsat analysis is

Component	Mole %
CO_2	8.86
CO	2.22
O_2	5.54
N_2	83.38

Assuming that dry air is supplied to the furnace, compute

1. Percent excess air

2. Percent excess oxygen

3. Molal humidity of the stack gas (moles H_2O per mole of dry flue gas)

4.31   Flue Gases from a Furnace Fired with Hydrogen-Free Coke

The flue gases from a furnace fired with hydrogen-free coke contain on a molar basis 14.0% CO_2, 1.0% CO, and 6.4% O_2. These gases enter the stack at 750°F. The air used for combustion, which is substantially dry, also enters the furnace at 750°F.

1. What is the volume in cubic feet of the flue gases leaving this furnace for each pound of carbon burnt?

2. What is the volume of air in cubic feet entering the furnace per pound of carbon burnt?

3. What percentage excess air is used in this furnace?

4.32   Production of SO_2 from Sulfur

Crude sulfur, analyzing 95 wt % S and 5 wt % noncombustible, is burned to produce SO_2 as the desired product. The analysis of the burner gases shows

Component	Volume %
SO_2	14.7
O_2	5.4
N_2	79.9

Any SO_3 formed would not show up in the analysis (just as H_2O does not show up in a flue gas analysis). Burner gases leave the burner at $1040°F$ and 750 mm Hg. Determine

1. The percent of the sulfur in the crude that is burned to SO_3
2. The percent excess air (based on burning to SO_2 being 100%)
3. The volume of burner gases $(SO_2 + SO_3 + O_2 + N_2)$ produced per pound of crude sulfur

4.33 Gas-Fired Furnace

Hydrogen gas, obtained as a by-product in the electrolytic decomposition of salt to produce caustic and chlorine, is burnt in a gas-fired furnace. The flue gases from this furnace are collected in a sampling device and analyzed in an Orsat. They are found to contain 5.4% O_2, and the rest N_2. The fuel enters the furnace dry, at $80°F$ and 820 mm Hg absolute pressure. The barometer is 750 mm Hg. The flue gases go to the stack at $700°F$.

1. If the flue gases from this furnace were cooled to $80°F$, dried and measured at the same pressure as the original hydrogen, what volume of dry flue gases would be obtained per 100 ft^3 of fuel fed to the furnace?
2. What is the actual volume of flue gas going to stack per 100 ft^3 of fuel fed to the furnace?
3. What percent excess air is used in burning this gas?

4.34 Oxidation of Impurities in a Bessemer Steel Converter

A Bessemer steel converter is fed with 5000 kg of molten iron containing

Component	Weight %
Carbon	4.0
Silicon	1.6
Manganese	1.2

The impurities are oxidized and removed from the iron by blowing 25% excess air into the converter. Of the carbon, 30% goes to CO_2 and 70% goes to CO. The reactions are

$$C + O_2 \rightarrow CO_2$$

$$C + \tfrac{1}{2}O_2 \rightarrow CO$$

$$Si + O_2 \rightarrow SiO_2$$

$$Mn + \tfrac{1}{2}O_2 \rightarrow MnO$$

Calculate

1. The molar composition of the total product of these reactions
2. Volume (ft^3) of air used at STP

4.35   Extraction of Oil from Soybean Flakes

Soybean, which is used nowadays for making textured vegetable proteins (meat analogs), contains 15% by weight of oil. Suppose that 300 lb of solvent containing 2% oil is used to extract oil from 500 lb of soybean. The solvent and soybean flakes are mixed thoroughly, and the solution is drained. The flakes are still wet with solution, and the oil in this solution is 2 lb. Find the weight and oil composition of the solution.

4.36   Catalytic Dehydrogenation of Ethyl Alcohol
to Produce Acetaldehyde

A batch experiment was carried out on the catalytic dehydrogenation of ethyl alcohol to produce acetaldehyde, ethyl acetate, and hydrogen by these two reactions:

$$C_2H_5OH \rightarrow CH_3CHO + H_2$$
acetaldehyde

$$2C_2H_5OH \rightarrow CH_3COOC_2H_5 + 2H_2$$
ethyl acetate

The reaction product mixture was found to contain 0.11 lb-mole unreacted ethyl alcohol, 2.2 lb-mole acetaldehyde, and 0.15 lb-mole ethyl acetate. Calculate

1. Pound moles of hydrogen produced
2. Pounds of ethyl alcohol charged to the reactor
3. Percentage conversion of the alcohol to the acetaldehyde

Molecular weights:

$$C_2H_5OH = 46 \text{ lb}_m/\text{lb-mole}$$

$$CH_3CHO = 44 \text{ lb}_m/\text{lb-mole}$$

$$CH_3COOC_2H_5 = 88 \text{ lb}_m/\text{lb-mole}$$

4.37 Extraction of Naphthalene-Diamine with Ethyl Ether

Naphthalene-diamine is recovered from a 3.00% by weight aqueous solution by extraction with ethyl ether containing 1.25% water, the remainder being ether. The ether extract is found to contain 15.2% naphthalene-diamine, 3.67% water by weight. The extracted aqueous solution contains a negligible amount of the naphthalene-diamine but contains 3.24% ether by weight. For the recovery of 1000 lb of naphthalene-diamine, calculate

1. Pounds of naphthalene-diamine solution extracted

2. Pounds of ether solution used for the extraction

3. Percentage of the inlet ether contained in the extracted aqueous solution

4.38 Mass Balance in a Fractionating System

The feed to a fractionating system that operates continuously is 30,000 lb/hr of a mixture containing 50% benzene, 30% toluene, and 20% xylene by weight. The fractionating system consists of two towers, No. I and No. II. The liquid described is fed to I, and the overhead from I is X lb/hr of a mixture containing 95% benzene, 3% toluene, and 2% xylene. The bottoms from I are fed to II, resulting in an overhead from II of Y lb/hr of a mixture containing 3% benzene, 95% toluene, and 2% xylene, while the bottoms from II, flowing at the rate Z lb/hr, contain 1% benzene, 4% toluene, and 95% xylene. See Figure P4.38, and find X, Y, and Z in lb/hr.

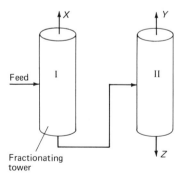

Figure P4.38.

4.39   Scrubbing of NH_3 with an Acid Solution

A gas mixture containing 25% CO_2 by volume and 75% NH_3 is being scrubbed with an acid solution to remove the ammonia. What percentage of the original ammonia has been removed, assuming that the gas mixture behaves according to the ideal gas law, that the CO_2 remains unaffected, and that no part of the acid solution vaporizes? (The exit gas mixture contains 37.5% NH_3 by volume).

4.40   Recovery of Acetone from a Gaseous Mixture

A gaseous mixture containing 80 mole percent N_2 and 20 mole percent acetone (CH_3OCH_3) at $540°F$ and 1.46 atm enters a heat exchanger where some of the acetone is condensed and removed as a liquid. The gases, which leave the heat exchanger at $540°F$ and 0.70 atm, contain acetone at a partial pressure of 0.035 atm. Assume that all gases behave ideally and calculate

1. The moles of acetone removed per 1000 ft^3 of entering mixture
2. Number of cubic feet of gas leaving the heat exchanger (at exit T and P) per 1000 ft^3 of entering mixture
3. The percent recovery of the entering acetone

4.41   Absorption Tower for Removal of HCl

A gas stream contains 30% HCl and 70% air by volume. The gas enters an absorption tower at $120°F$ and 743 mm Hg. Suppose that 96% of the HCl is removed in the column and that the gases leave at $75°F$, 740 mm Hg. Calculate

1. The pounds of HCl removed per 100 ft^3 of entering gases
2. The exit volume of gases per 100 ft^3 of entering gases
3. The percent by volume composition of the exit gases
4. The partial pressure of HCl in the entering and exit gases
5. The average molecular weight of the entering gases

4.42   Condensation of NH_3 from a Gaseous Mixture

The volumetric composition of a gas is 54% H_2, 18% N_2, and 28% NH_3. This gas leaves a reactor at $210°F$, 200 psia and is sent to a condenser where 95% of the NH_3 is condensed. The gas leaves the condenser at $115°F$, 200 psia. Assuming that 200 tons/day of NH_3 is condensed, calculate

1. Average molecular weight of the gas entering the condenser
2. Tons/day of gas entering the condenser
3. NH_3 partial pressure of gas entering the condenser
4. Volumetric flow rate (ft^3/min) of gas leaving the condenser

4.43   Removal of Benzene from a Gaseous Mixture

A gaseous mixture of benzene, C_6H_6 (MW = 78), and nitrogen, N_2 (MW = 28), containing 0.3 lb_m of C_6H_6 per lb_m of N_2 is treated to recover the benzene. A total of 10,000 ft^3 of the mixture enters an absorber at 626°R and 1.225 atm. Of this, 9650 ft^3 of gas leaves the absorber at 545°R and 1.02 atm. Only benzene is removed from the gas. Given:

$$R = 0.73 \frac{(ft^3)\,(atm)}{(lb_m\text{-mole})\,(°R)}$$

Assume ideal gas behavior and calculate or do the following:

1. Draw a sketch of the process, labeling each stream and showing the data known about that stream
2. The average molecular weight of the entering gas mixture
3. The pounds of C_6H_6 recovered
4. The mole percent of C_6H_6 in the exit gas
5. The volume percent of C_6H_6 in the exit gas

4.44   Drying a Wet Stock with Recycle

Wet stock containing 1.562 lb H_2O/lb dry solids is to be dried to 0.099 lb H_2O/lb dry solids. For every pound of dry solids, 52.5 lb of dry air passes through the dryer; the air leaves with a humidity of 0.0525 lb H_2O/lb dry air. Some of the air leaving the dryer is recycled and mixed with the fresh air feed. The fresh air has a humidity of 0.0152. Find the fraction of air recycled.

4.45   Preparation of Perchloric Acid:
Incomplete Reaction and Recycle

Perchloric acid is both a very strong acid and a strong oxidizing agent. When brought into contact with strong reducing agents, violent explosions sometimes occur. This acid is made according to the chemical reaction

$$Ba(ClO_4)_2 + H_2SO_4 \rightarrow BaSO_4 + 2HClO_4$$

The process used is indicated in Figure P4.45.

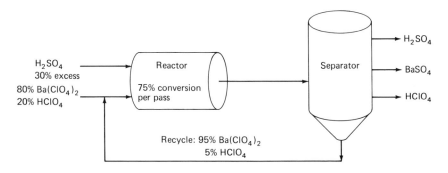

Figure P4.45.

Determine

1. Pounds of perchloric acid leaving separator per 100 lb of feed $[Ba(ClO_4)_2,$ $HClO_4]$

2. Pounds of recycle per 100 lb of feed if one obtains 75% conversion per pass in the reactor

4.46 Preparation of Ether from Ethyl Alcohol: Incomplete Reaction and Recycle

Ether (considered as the best general anesthetic; also an excellent solvent for organic compounds) is made by the dehydration of ethyl alcohol with sulfuric acid at $130°$ to $140°C$. The reaction is

$$2C_2H_5OH \rightarrow C_2H_5-O-C_2H_5 + H_2O$$

The process flow diagram is shown in Figure P4.46.

Assuming 87% conversion per pass, determine

1. Feed stream

2. Recycle-to-feed ratio

3. Waste stream

4.47 Recycle in a Distillation Column

A distillation column is used to separate benzene from a benzene-toluene-xylene

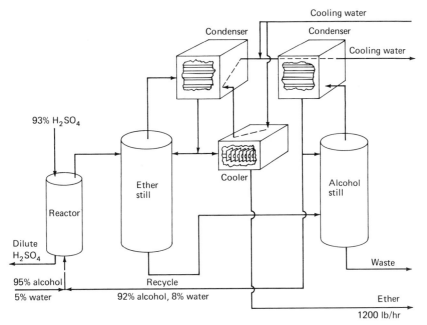

Figure P4.46.

mixture (see Figure P4.47). Certain information about the stream flow rates and composition (mass fractions) is shown in the table on the following page.

1. Complete the table, showing all calculations
2. Find the overhead-recycle to overhead-product ratio, R/P

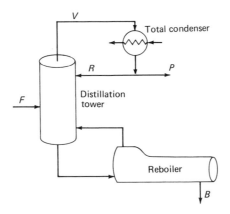

Figure P4.47.

Stream	Flow rate	Benzene	Toluene	Xylene
F	1000 lb/hr	0.420	0.370	0.210
P	–	0.980	–	0.000
B	–	0.000	–	–
V	3600 lb/hr	–	–	–
R	–	–	–	–

4.48 Recycle in a Polymerization Reactor

Reactant A is being polymerized in a reactor by contacting with a recycled catalyst (Figure P4.48). Conversion of A to polymer is 40% per pass. Catalyst is fed to
the reactor at a rate of 0.40 lb G/lb A in H stream. The separator removes 90%
of the catalyst and recycles it as stream S. Also, 15% of the unreacted A remains
in the P stream. Find R/G.

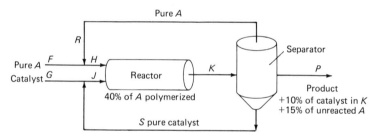

Figure P4.48.

4.49 Recycle in the Polymerization of Ethylene

Pure ethylene is fed to a polymerization reactor. When the polymerization reaction is 60% complete, the reaction mixture is transported to a separator where it

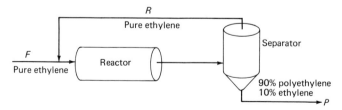

Figure P4.49.

is divided into two streams, the first stream being a product stream containing 90% polyethylene and 10% ethylene, and the second stream containing pure ethylene vapor. This ethylene vapor stream is recycled. Calculate the weight ratio of recycle to feed (see Figure P4.49).

4.50 Polymerization of Ethylene and Recycle of Unreacted Ethylene

One hundred moles/hr of pure ethylene, C_2H_4 (MW = 28), is fed to a polymerization reactor. When the polymerization reaction is 50% complete (i.e., reactor conversion is 50% per pass), the reaction mixture is transported to a separator where it is divided into two streams: a product stream P containing pure polyethylene, and a recycle stream R containing 90 mole percent unreacted ethylene and 10 mole percent polyethylene. The process is operated at steady state (see Figure P4.50) and the reaction is

$$nC_2H_4 \rightarrow (C_2H_4)n$$

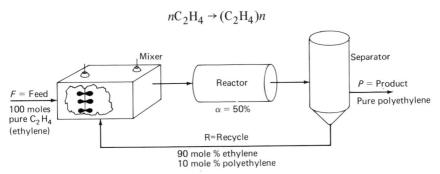

Figure P4.50.

1. Calculate the pounds of product P produced per 100 moles of fresh feed.
2. Calculate the recycle ratio r (moles of recycle/mole of fresh feed).
3. Calculate the recycle ratio if the conversion per pass is reduced to 25%; increased to 75%.
4. Sketch a rough plot of recycle ratio versus conversion per pass using the results from parts 2 and 3 of this problem.

4.51 Recycle in a Hypothetical Process

The fresh feed to a reactor contains equimolal amounts of A and B. These react according to the equation shown in Figure P4.51.

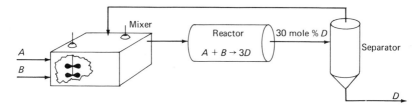

Figure P4.51.

The effluent from the reactor contains 30 mole % D; all the D is removed in a separator and the unreacted A and B are recycled. Calculate

1. The number of moles of D produced per 100 moles of fresh feed

2. The recycle ratio (moles recycled/moles of fresh feed)

3. The total number of moles leaving the reactor per 100 moles of fresh feed

4.52 Preparation of Sulfuric Acid by SO_3 Absorption

Sulfuric acid is made by the contact process shown in Figure P4.52.

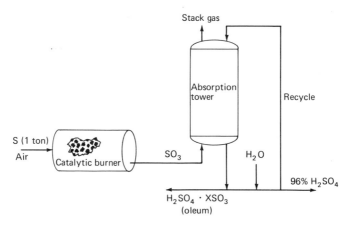

Figure P4.52.

Sulfur is burned to SO_3 over a catalyst and absorbed in a tower, using 96% sulfuric acid as the solvent. The exiting stream of oleum is diluted with water to produce both product 96% H_2SO_4 and solvent. Fifty percent (by weight) of the S is withdrawn as H_2SO_4; given 30-weight SO_3/100-weight H_2SO_4 per ton of S burned. Determine

1. Pounds of water

2. Pounds of oleum

3. Pounds of 96% H_2SO_4

4. Weight of recycle stream

4.53   Manufacture of Adipic Acid by Oxidation of Cyclohexane

Adipic acid is manufactured by oxidation of cyclohexane (C_6H_{12}). The charged cyclohexane is specified to have no more than 0.04% benzene (B) by weight. The reaction is

$$C_6H_{12} \xrightarrow[\substack{\text{Mn-, Co-}}]{\text{air (125°C)}} C_6H_{11}OH + C_6H_{10}O \xrightarrow[\text{aqueous}]{80°C} HOOC(CH_2)_4COOH$$

| cyclo-hexane | acetates | cyclo-hexanol | cyclo-hexanone HNO_3 | adipic acid |

$$+ xN_2O + yNO$$

The conversion of C_6H_{12} per pass is 65%, and the selectivity is 95%. The products from the reactor go to a fractionator to take C_6H_{12} and B overhead and recycle the liquid to the feed. The benzene, which is completely inert, is maintained at 1 mole percent in the reactor feed by purging the recycle liquid. Determine the amount of purge and its composition.

4.54   Filtration and Wash Steps

A slurry of a solid in water has 1 lb solid (S) per 20 lb of mother liquor (ML). The ML contains 18% dissolved salt.

The solid will be recovered by filtering, reslurrying the wet cake with 10 volumes of deionized water a multiple number of times, and drying. The deionized water contains 2 ppm NaCl, and the final product must contain no more than 6 ppm. The wet cake from the filter contains 1 lb of S/1 lb water. Determine the number of wash steps.

4.55   Producing a Gas by Destructive Distillation of Coconut Shells

A gas produced by destructive distillation of coconut shells has the following composition.

Component	Volume %
N_2	10.0
H_2	40.0
H_2O (vapor)	15.0
NH_3	35.0

Suppose that 100,000 ft^3/hr at 850°F and 15 psia are produced. They are cooled to 150°F in a heat exchanger where 90% of the H_2O is removed by condensation. The remaining gases pass into an H_2SO_4 absorber where all the NH_3 and the remaining H_2O are removed (see Figure P4.55). Assume that all gases behave ideally and calculate

1. The average molecular weight of the original gas mixture

2. The weight (pounds) of H_2O condensed in the heat exchanger per hour

3. The volume of gases leaving the heat exchanger at 150°F and 15 psia in ft^3/hr

4. The volumetric analysis of the gas leaving the H_2SO_4 absorber

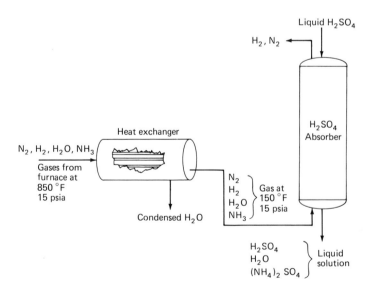

Figure P4.55.

4.56   Getting Acquainted with a Flow Diagram

In the process shown in Figure P4.56, flow rates are given in lb/hr. Find the flow rates of the two streams H and D.

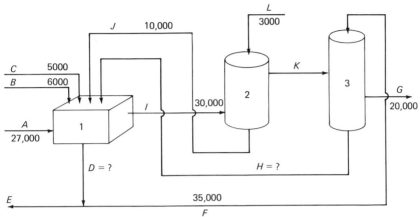

Figure P4.56.

4.57   Separation of Butene and Butadiene by Solvent Extraction

Figure P4.57 summarizes the process for separating butene and butadiene by extraction with cuprous ammonium acetate solution (the solvent). Find the rates and compositions of all streams (A, B, C, D, E).

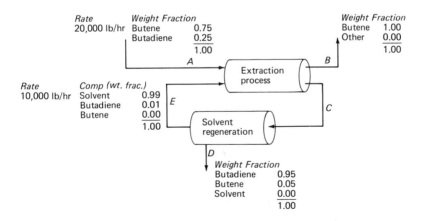

Figure P4.57.

4.58 Recycle in the Production of Ammonia

In the operation of a synthetic ammonia plant, shown in Figure P4.58, a 1:3 nitrogen-hydrogen mixture is fed to the converter, resulting in a 22% conversion to ammonia. The ammonia is separated by condensation and the unconverted gases are recycled to the reactor. The initial nitrogen-hydrogen mixture contains 0.18 part of argon to 100 parts of N_2-H_2 mixture. The tolerance limit of argon in the reactor is assumed to be 4.5 parts to 100 parts of N_2-H_2 mixture.

Assuming the applicability of the ideal gas law and steady state operation, compute

1. Pound moles of N_2-H_2 recycle per 10,000 pounds of NH_3 produced
2. Pound moles of fresh feed required
3. Pound moles of N_2-H_2 mixture that must be continuously purged
4. Cubic feet of purge stream at $180°F$ and 2 atm total pressure

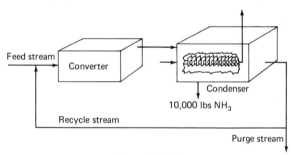

Figure P4.58.

4.59 Synthetic Production of Ammonia

A synthetic ammonia plant contains three catalytic converters operated in series with a feed gas consisting of 1% argon, 24.75% nitrogen, and 74.25% hydrogen. The plant is operated continuously, and the ammonia produced in each converter is separated and condensed as pure NH_3 in rectifier-condenser units. For the steady operating conditions shown in Figure P4.59, calculate

1. Percentage of fresh feed gas converted to ammonia in the first converter.
2. Percent yield of ammonia in the whole system based on the amount of fresh feed gas, assuming that the percentage of ammonia in the recycle gas from each of the rectifier-condenser units is the same.

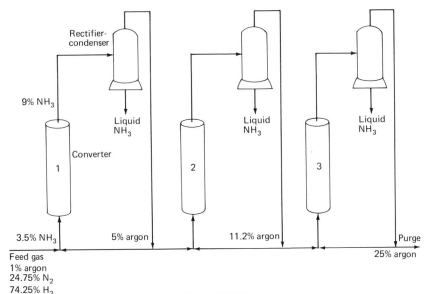

9% NH₃

Rectifier-condenser

Liquid
NH₃

Converter

1

2

3

Liquid
NH₃

Liquid
NH₃

3.5% NH₃   5% argon   11.2% argon   Purge
                                                25% argon
Feed gas
1% argon
24.75% N₂
74.25% H₂

Figure P4.59.

4.60 Process for Making Benzene from Toluene

A process for making benzene (B) from toluene (T) takes place according to the reaction

$$C_6H_5CH_3 + H_2 \rightarrow C_6H_6 + CH_4$$

toluene hydrogen benzene methane

At 1150°C, the conversion of T to B is 90% per pass through the reactor as designed. However, the selectivity to form B is only 90%. That is, 10% of B reacts further to form diphinyl (D):

$$2C_6H_6 \rightarrow C_6H_5-C_6H_5 + H_2$$

benzene   diphinyl   hydrogen

Given: The B loss from the system is 2 mole percent of T fed to reactor; the B product is 100% B; the D present in the bottoms is 99%; the recycle gas is 20% methane and negligible B and T; the recycle liquid is 25% D (and therefore 75% T); the mole ratio of H_2 to $T + D$ is 6 at the entrance to the reactor; and the toluene feed is 100% T. See Figure P4.60.

Find the following:

1. The composition in and out of the reactor per 100 moles of T into the reactor

2. Overall mole percent yield of B

3. Moles purge gas from stabilizer, neglecting hydrogen and methane

4. Moles makeup gas, using 100% hydrogen

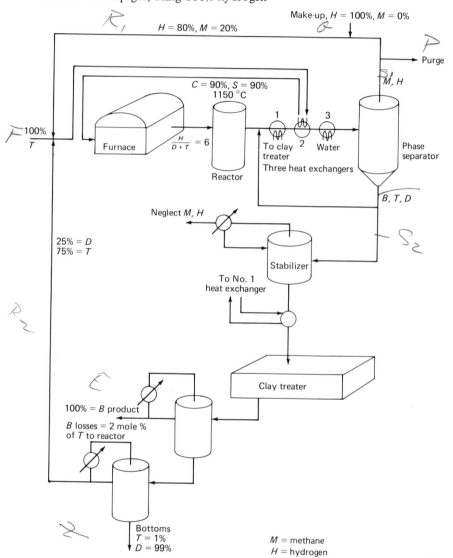

Figure P4.60.

4.61 Crystallization and the Use of a Phase Diagram

One hundred pounds of 25% Na_2CO_3 in water is heated until boiling sets in. As boiling proceeds, water vapor is removed. The process is continued until 45 lb of water have been removed. The whole process is carried out at 1 atm.

1. How many pounds of solution and of solid crystals remain at the final temperature?

2. What is the composition (weight percent Na_2CO_3) of each phase?

3. What is the final temperature? See Figure P4.61.

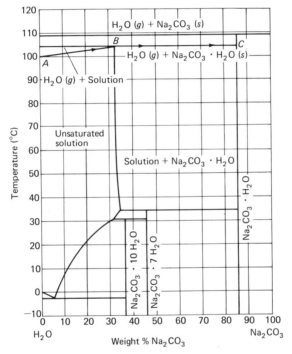

Figure P4.61. Solubility diagram for $Na_2CO_3 - H_2O$ system at 1 atm (g = gas, s = solids)

4.62 Production of Iso-Octane

Iso-octane is to be produced by the catalytic alkylation of butylene with iso-butane, according to the reaction

$$i\text{-}C_4H_{10} + C_4H_8 \rightarrow C_8H_{18}$$

The reaction is carried out by emulsifying the liquid hydrocarbons in strong sulfuric acid followed by separating the emulsion and recycling the acid to be used with fresh hydrocarbon. The flow diagram for such a plant is shown in Figure P4.62.

The process requirements are

1. The fresh feed is to consist of 40,000 lb of liquid hydrocarbon containing 25 mole percent *i*-butane, 25 mole percent butylene, and 50 mole percent *n*-butane.

2. The fresh feed is to be mixed with *i*-butane recycle from the fractionator so that the combined feed will contain 5.0 moles *i*-butane per mole of butylene.

3. There is sufficient recycle from the reactor effluent stream to maintain 200 moles of *i*-butane per mole of butylene at the reactor entrance.

4. The reaction proceeds to completion in the reactor.

5. There are to be 2 pounds of sulfuric acid per pound of hydrocarbon entering the reactor.

6. The fractionation is to be carried out so that the plant product is free of *i*-butane.

Compute the quantity of material that is to flow through each unit in this process.

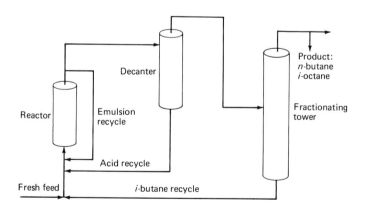

Figure P4.62.

4.63 Unsteady State Dissolution of Solid Salt by a Water Stream

One hundred pounds of salt (specific gravity, 2.165) in the form of 1-in. cubes is exposed to a stream of running water. At the end of 10 min, 90 lb of NaCl has dissolved. Assume that the salt remains as cubes. If the salt was in the form of 2-in. cubes initially, how much would dissolve in 5 min?

4.64 Change in KCl Concentration with Time

A tank holds 100 gal of KCl solution containing 50 lb KCl. This tank is to be purged of KCl by displacement with fresh water at a rate of 10 gal/min. The exit stream is 5 gal/min. Assuming perfect mixing, calculate the amount of KCl at the end of 30 minutes.

4.65 Change in Brine Concentration with Time

A tank containing 75 ft^3 of water receives 3 ft^3/min of brine with a concentration of 1 lb of salt/1 ft^3 of brine. Given that the exit stream is 1 ft^3/min, determine its brine concentration when the tank has 200 ft^3 of material.

4.66 Kinetics in a Simple Reaction

The reaction $2A \rightarrow B$ takes place in a reactor of constant volume V. Reactant A disappears at a rate

$$R = k \ C_A{}^2$$

where

R = rate of disappearance of A, moles/hr-ft^3 of reactor

k = constant

C_A = concentration of A at any time

Initial concentrations of A and B are, respectively, A_i and B_i. Find an expression for the concentration of A as a function of time.

4.67 Rise of Water in a Conical Reservoir: Unsteady State

A conical reservoir 30 ft in depth and 15 ft in diameter receives water at the rate of 1.5 ft^3/min. Assuming that the water has reached 15 ft in depth, determine

1. The rate at which the water level rises.
2. The rate at which the area of the water surface increases.

5.
Energy Balances in Physical and Thermochemical Processes

Part I: Energy and Material Balances in Physical Processes

Energy is the capacity to do work and liberate heat. Energy requirements play an important role in designing for the chemical process industries; an engineer who is concerned with material balances finds that he is continually dealing with energy balances. In conveying solids or liquids, carrying out a chemical reaction, or dealing with any chemical process, the engineer must account for all forms of energy, whether internal, kinetic, potential, or work. Experience gained in working problems is a necessary tool for grasping the basic knowledge in setting up energy balances.

5.1 COMMON TERMS

Let us begin by defining essential terms and then proceed to the heart of the matter.

System

A system is a limited portion of space that is under observation. Consider a vessel half full of gasoline (Figure 5.1). If you wish to devote your interest to the gasoline (G) only, then gasoline is your system; however, you could choose the vapor (V) in the vessel, or the liquid and vapor in the vessel $(G + V)$. To avoid confusion the boundaries of a system must be clearly understood. For example, the gasoline system is bounded by $DEFC$, where EF is the liquid-vapor interface.

In a *nonflow* or closed system (Figure 5.2), matter does not cross the boundaries, but energy does. In a *flow* or open system (Figure 5.3), matter and energy both cross the boundaries. One has an *isolated* system (Figure 5.4) when neither matter nor energy cross the boundaries.

Surroundings are, essentially, anything not included in the system, and they are separated from the system by the boundaries.

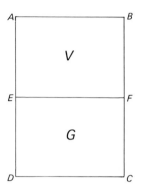

Figure 5.1.   System and boundaries

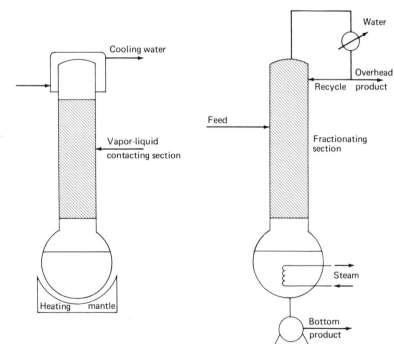

Figure 5.2.   Nonflow or closed system, distillation at total reflux (boundary is the still walls)

Figure 5.3.   Flow or open system, continuous distillation unit

A system may be *homogeneous,* in which the properties are the same throughout, like gasoline in a vessel; or a system may be *heterogeneous,* wherein some discontinuity exists, like coal-in-oil slurry. This slurry, if colloidal and well dispersed, can be considered and treated as a homogeneous system.

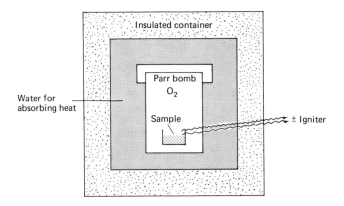

**Figure 5.4.   Isolated system, Parr oxygen bomb test for measuring
gross heat of combustion**

Property

This is a distinctive attribute or characteristic of a system or material, for example, density or volume. An extensive property is one that depends on the size of the system, such as volume or mass. An *intensive property* is one that is *independent* of the size of the system, such as pressure, temperature, specific volume, or density. Is heat an intensive property? Is it a property?

The State of a System

The state of a system is defined as a set of attributes or properties that characterizes it. One must fix certain physically measurable quantities in order to completely characterize the system; such properties could be pressure, temperature, density, and so on. With some experience, the student will develop an intuition that allows him to discard properties that are redundant or extraneous. For example, you can find the kinetic energy of a moving block without reference to its temperature; and given the mass, volume, and pressure of an ideal gas, you can find its temperature.

Equilibrium

A system is in a state of equilibrium when, after exposure to a momentary slight disturbance, it returns slowly or rapidly to its initial state. A system may be in apparent equilibrium when its resistance to change is so great that, essentially, no change can take place.

Thermodynamics deals mainly with systems in thermodynamic equilibrium or with those where the departure from equilibrium can be neglected.

Process

A process is the path or mechanism by which a system changes from one state to another. A flow process is associated with an open system, and a batch process is usually associated with a closed system. An isobaric process takes place at constant pressure, an isothermal process takes place at constant temperature, and an isochoric or isometric process takes place at constant volume. An adiabatic process occurs when there is no net heat interchange between the system and

Table 5.1 IMPORTANT PROCESSES

Type of process	Conditions imposed
Flow	Open system
Batch	Closed system
Isobaric or isopiestic	Constant pressure
Isothermal	Constant temperature
Isochoric, isometric, isovolumetric or isovolumic	Constant volume
Adiabatic	No heat interchange between system and surroundings
Isenthalpic	Constant enthalpy
Cyclic	Change from initial state to intermediate and back to initial
Quasistatic	System is almost static, approximated equilibrium (kinetic energy can be neglected)
Reversible	Infinitesimal change in the independent variable could reverse the process

the surroundings. A cyclic process exists when a system undergoes change from an initial state to another one and back to its initial state. A process that causes a system to depart infinitesimally from equilibrium is called a quasistatic process (meaning "almost static"). If departures from the equilibrium state are finite, the process is nonquasistatic. The various processes discussed here are summarized in Table 5.1. A process is reversible if an infinitesimal change in the independent variable can reverse the process.

Example 5.1   Intensive and extensive properties

List the following as intensive or extensive properties:

> pressure, temperature, volume, specific volume,
> potential energy, friction, enthalpy, heat, work,
> kilowatt-hours, surface tension, motor-horsepower.

Solution

Intensive property	Extensive property	Not a property
Pressure	Volume	Friction
Temperature	Potential energy	Heat
Specific volume	Enthalpy	Work
Surface tension	Motor-horsepower	Kilowatt-hours

Check your imagination, and you will see that this listing is correct!

5.2   THE FIRST LAW OF THERMODYNAMICS AND THE TOTAL ENERGY BALANCE

The approach here will be to find the total energy balance for a general case, and then to simplify the equation for other specific cases.

Consider an open, or flow, system that is often encountered in practice, for example, the system for transporting fluids in a pipeline (Figure 5.5). This fluid is being heated and pumped through a pipeline with varying cross section and elevation. For this flow system, all energy terms must be accounted for. In order to properly account for potential energy, a datum plane is chosen; sometimes it is taken to pass through plane 1, thus making the potential energy at this plane

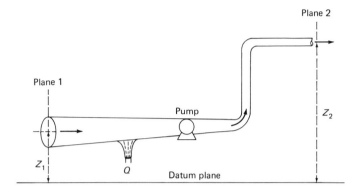

Figure 5.5. Fluid flow system

zero. However, for general purposes, the datum plane in Figure 5.5 was chosen. Since total energy input equals total energy output, a steady-state energy balance written between planes 1 and 2 gives

$$\Delta U + \Delta(\text{K.E.}) + \Delta(\text{P.E.}) + \Delta(PV) = Q - W \qquad (5.1)$$

where

$\Delta U =$ change in internal energy

$\Delta(\text{K.E.}) =$ change in kinetic energy

$\Delta(\text{P.E.}) =$ change in potential energy

$\Delta(PV) =$ change in (PV) work; this (PV) energy is the product of the force exerted by the fluid immediately behind the entrance point times the distance through which it acts

$Q =$ heat added to the system from the surroundings

$W =$ work done by the fluid on the surroundings; this is called shaft work when frictional losses are considered negligible; W is negative, since work is done by the pump

Equivalently, the relationship can be expressed as

$$\Delta H + \Delta\left(\frac{v^2}{2g_c\alpha}\right) + \Delta Z\frac{g}{g_c} = Q - W \qquad (5.2)$$

where

$\Delta H = \Delta U + \Delta(PV)$, change in enthalpy

α = correction factor, taken as $1/2$ or 1 depending on the nature of flow

v = average velocity

Z = elevation from the datum plane

(All terms in Equations 5.1 and 5.2 are expressed in Btu/lb$_m$ or (ft-lb$_f$)/lb$_m$)

Equation 5.2 is the mathematical expression for the first law of thermodynamics for an open system. It is a statement of the principle of conservation of energy.

For a closed system, or nonflow condition, the terms for kinetic energy, potential energy, and PV work are all zero, and the general equation reduces to

$$\Delta U = Q - W \tag{5.3}$$

This is the first law of thermodynamics for a closed system.

Various other forms may be deduced from the total energy equation, depending on the special cases at hand:

No shaft work in the system:

$$\Delta H + \Delta\left(\frac{v^2}{2g_c\alpha}\right) + \Delta Z\frac{g}{g_c} = Q \tag{5.4}$$

No heat added or taken away from the system (adiabatic process):

$$\Delta H + \Delta\left(\frac{v^2}{2g_c\alpha}\right) + \Delta Z\frac{g}{g_c} = -W \tag{5.5}$$

No heat, no work, and no potential energy:

$$\Delta H + \Delta\left(\frac{v^2}{2g_c\alpha}\right) = 0 \tag{5.5a}$$

It is advisable to write the general form of the equation and then to drop out the unnecessary terms as the statement of the problem dictates. Then proceed to solve for the unknown.

The correction factor α accounts for the error introduced in calculating the change in kinetic energy based on average velocity. For flow in tubes, three types of flow are usually encountered:

1. Laminar, or streamline, flow, where the velocity profile is parabolic and α is taken to be $1/2$.

2. Turbulent flow, where eddies and chaotic motion are predominant and the velocity profile is more flat. The factor α is approximately equal to one.

3. Plug flow, where the velocity is constant and equal to one.

These flow regimes are illustrated in Figure 5.6.

The nature of flow is determined by the Reynolds number, since in 1883 Osborne Reynolds demonstrated, by using dye injection, the difference between laminar and turbulent flow. For laminar flow,

$$Re = \frac{Dv\rho}{\mu} \leqslant 2100$$

where

$$Re = \text{Reynolds number, dimensionless}$$
$$D = \text{diameter of tube}$$
$$v = \text{average velocity}$$
$$\rho = \text{density of fluid}$$
$$\mu = \text{viscosity of fluid}$$

For turbulent flow,

$$Re > 2100$$

With some mathematical manipulations (shown in the Appendix) this equation becomes

$$\Delta \left(\frac{v^2}{2g_c\alpha}\right) + \Delta Z \frac{g}{g_c} + \int \frac{1}{\rho} dP + W_f' + \Sigma F = 0 \qquad (5.6)$$

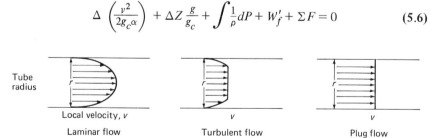

Figure 5.6.   Flow regimes in a tube

where

W_f' = shaft work; it is negative in conformity with the
basic assumption, since work is done by the pump
(surroundings) on the system (fluid).

ΣF = Summation of all frictional losses resulting from
pipe friction, elbows, valves, expansion, contraction,
and so on.

Note that in the American engineering system, the units of each component in
Equation 5.6 are ft-lb$_f$/lb$_m$.

For the flow of an incompressible fluid in a pipe with no shaft work, and
where there is no change in kinetic or potential energy, Equation 5.6 reduces to:

$$-\frac{\Delta P}{\rho} = \Sigma F = \frac{fv^2 \Sigma L}{g_c D} \tag{5.7}$$

where

$$f = \frac{g_c D(-\Delta P)}{2\rho v^2 \Sigma L} \tag{5.8}$$

is the definition of the friction factor (certain books define f as four times the f
given here), and where ΣL is the total length, including straight pipe, equivalent
length of elbows, valves, and so on. (For example, the equivalent length of an
elbow is the length of a given pipe that will give the same friction as the elbow).
A plot of friction factor f versus Reynolds number Re is shown in the Appendix.

The importance of Equations 5.2 and 5.6 arises from the universal occurrence
of flow processes in every phase of engineering practice.

In order to master the use of the energy balance, elaboration on certain functions such as internal energy, enthalpy, entropy, and so on is essential. Thus, prior
to illustrating the energy balance calculations, we will describe some of the important functions and then proceed to the needed examples relating to the overall energy balance and its components.

5.3 POINT FUNCTIONS

A thermodynamic property whose change between two states is independent of
the path is called an exact function, or a point function. Independence of the path
means that the change in the property is unique and the same, no matter which

route is chosen between the initial and final states of the system. Let us summarize the exact functions used in thermodynamics, keeping in mind that this section is a very brief introduction to thermodynamics, a subject that requires many years of study and practice before it is really mastered.

Internal Energy

$$\Delta U = Q - W \tag{5.3}$$

where

$\Delta U =$ change in internal energy

$Q =$ heat added to the system

$W =$ work done by the system on the surroundings; kinetic, potential, and other forces of energy are neglected

In a system carried through a complete cycle, the net quantity of heat added must equal the work delivered. The quantity ΔU was chosen to account for differences between Q and W which arise in actual processes.

Enthalpy

The mathematical definition of enthalpy is:

$$H = U + PV \tag{5.9}$$

where

$H =$ enthalpy

$U =$ internal energy

$P =$ pressure

$V =$ volume

Enthalpy is often called heat content, since it is equal to Q in a constant pressure process:

$$dH = dU + d(PV)$$
$$= dU + PdV + VdP$$

For constant pressure, we have

$$dH = dU + PdV$$

since

$$dU = dQ - dW$$

and

$$W = PdV$$

Thus, at constant pressure,

$$dH = dQ - PdV + PdV = dQ \tag{5.10}$$

Entropy

This is an important concept in thermodynamics, and apparently most difficult to understand intuitively. Simply stated, entropy is a measure of the degree of randomness in a system. For example, a crystal at $0°K$ has a very low entropy since all atoms and even electrons can largely be accounted for. As the temperature increases, the randomness (and likewise the entropy) increases, since the crystal may melt to form a liquid and then a gas. Mathematically, entropy is defined by the equation

$$dS = \frac{dQ_{rev}}{T} \tag{5.11}$$

where

$$dS = \text{change in entropy}$$

$$dQ_{rev} = \text{reversible heat added to the system}$$

$$T = \text{absolute temperature}$$

Equation 5.11 is a mathematical statement of the second law of thermodynamics; the change in entropy is a yardstick for checking the degree of irreversibility.

Helmholtz Function

This function is usually expressed

$$A = U - TS \tag{5.12}$$

where

$$A - \text{Helmholtz free energy}$$

$$S = \text{entropy}$$

Gibbs Free Energy

This function can be expressed

$$G = H - TS \qquad (5.13)$$

where G is Gibbs free energy.

All these functions are arbitrarily chosen for convenience in determining thermodynamic relationships.

Let us rewrite Equation 5.9 in a differential form:

$$dH = dU + PdV + VdP \qquad (5.14)$$

From Equations 5.3 and 5.11 and from $dW = PdV$, we have

$$dU = TdS - PdV \qquad (5.15)$$

Now replace dU by its equivalent in Equation 5.14

$$dH = TdS - PdV + PdV + VdP$$

or

$$dH = TdS + VdP \qquad (5.16)$$

Similarly, we can obtain expressions for dA and dG. Summarizing, we have

$$dU = TdS - PdV \qquad (5.17)$$

$$dH = TdS + VdP \qquad (5.18)$$

$$dA = -SdT - PdV \qquad (5.19)$$

$$dG = -SdT + VdP \qquad (5.20)$$

All these are point functions and equivalently exact differentials. (See Appendix A.5 for a detailed mathematical review.) For the differential

$$dU = Mdx + Ndy \qquad (5.21)$$

the relationship

$$\left(\frac{\partial M}{\partial y}\right)_x = \left(\frac{\partial N}{\partial x}\right)_y \qquad (5.22)$$

is a necessary condition for exactness. Thus from Equations 5.15 to 5.20 we obtain

$$\left(\frac{\partial T}{\partial V}\right)_S = -\left(\frac{\partial P}{\partial S}\right)_V \qquad (5.23)$$

$$\left(\frac{\partial T}{\partial P}\right)_S = \left(\frac{\partial V}{\partial S}\right)_P \qquad (5.24)$$

$$\left(\frac{\partial S}{\partial V}\right)_T = \left(\frac{\partial P}{\partial T}\right)_V \tag{5.25}$$

$$-\left(\frac{\partial S}{\partial P}\right)_T = \left(\frac{\partial V}{\partial T}\right)_P \tag{5.26}$$

These are the *Maxwell relations*, which are used to develop expressions for exact functions using only the variables P, T, V, and heat capacities.

5.4 ENTHALPY AND HEAT CAPACITY

The enthalpy of a pure substance may be completely defined by any two of the three variables—pressure, temperature and volume—since these variables can be related by an equation of state. Selecting temperature and pressure as the independent variables, we have

$$H = f(T, P) \tag{5.27}$$

The total differential is

$$dH = \left(\frac{\partial H}{\partial T}\right)_P dT + \left(\frac{\partial H}{\partial P}\right)_T dP \tag{5.28}$$

The heat capacity at constant pressure is defined by

$$C_p = \left(\frac{\partial H}{\partial T}\right)_P \tag{5.29}$$

Integrating Equation 5.20, we obtain

$$\int_{H_1}^{H_2} dH = \int_{T_1}^{T_2} C_p dT = \Delta H \tag{5.30}$$

For a constant C_p, we have

$$\Delta H = C_p \Delta T = C_p(T_2 - T_1) \tag{5.31}$$

To obtain a general expression for enthalpy that takes into account the effect of pressure, one should evaluate

$$\left(\frac{\partial H}{\partial P}\right)_T$$

which appeared in Equation 5.28. From Equation 5.16,

$$dH = TdS + VdP \tag{5.16}$$

Dividing through by dP, we have

$$\frac{dH}{dP} = T\frac{dS}{dP} + V$$

using the condition of constant temperature,

$$\left(\frac{\partial H}{\partial P}\right)_T = T\left(\frac{\partial S}{\partial P}\right)_T + V$$

From the Maxwell relation (Equation 5.26) this reduces to

$$\left(\frac{\partial H}{\partial P}\right)_T = -T\left(\frac{\partial V}{\partial T}\right)_P + V \tag{5.32}$$

Equation 5.32 allows $(\partial H/\partial P)_T$ to be evaluated using only the quantities P, T, and V, whose relationships are known by some equation of state; these were described in Chapter 3. Using Equations 5.29 and 5.32 in 5.28, we get

$$dH = C_p dT + [V - T(\partial V/\partial T)_p]\, dP \tag{5.33}$$

This equation is better understood from physical intuition by using paths of convenience. Complex and convenience paths are represented in Figure 5.7. It should be obvious that paths 142 and 132 are the simplest to employ. Mathematically these are identical to Equation 5.33:

Path 142:

$$\Delta H = \int_{P_1}^{P_4}\left[V - T_1\left(\frac{\partial V}{\partial T}\right)_P\right]dP + \int_{T_4}^{T_2} C_p dT \tag{5.34}$$

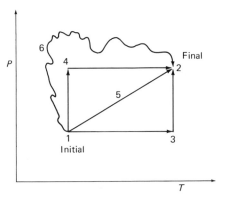

Figure 5.7. Complex paths versus paths of convenience.
Complex: 162 and 152. Convenience: 142 and 132.

Path 132:

$$\Delta H = \int_{T_1}^{T_3} C_p dT + \int_{P_3}^{P_2} \left[V - T_3 \left(\frac{\partial V}{\partial T} \right)_P \right] dP \qquad (5.35)$$

Table 5.2 summarizes the fundamental relationships in thermodynamics. Developing these relationships is left as an exercise for interested students.

Table 5.2   FUNDAMENTAL RELATIONSHIPS IN THERMODYNAMICS

Convenience functions	Exact differentials
$H = U + PV$	$dU = TdS - PdV$
$A = U - TS$	$dH = TdS + VdP$
$G = H - TS$	$dA = -SdT - PdV$
	$dG = -SdT + VdP$
Maxwell relations	General relationships
$\left(\frac{\partial T}{\partial V} \right)_S = -\left(\frac{\partial P}{\partial S} \right)_V$	$dS = C_v \frac{dT}{T} + \left(\frac{\partial P}{\partial T} \right)_V dV$
$\left(\frac{\partial T}{\partial P} \right)_S = \left(\frac{\partial V}{\partial S} \right)_P$	$dS = C_p \frac{dT}{T} - \left(\frac{\partial V}{\partial T} \right)_P dP$
$\left(\frac{\partial S}{\partial V} \right)_T = \left(\frac{\partial P}{\partial T} \right)_V$	$dU = C_v dT + \left[T \left(\frac{\partial P}{\partial T} \right)_V - P \right] dV$
$\left(\frac{\partial S}{\partial P} \right)_T = -\left(\frac{\partial V}{\partial T} \right)_P$	$dH = C_p dT + \left[V - T \left(\frac{\partial V}{\partial T} \right)_P \right] dP$
	$C_p - C_v = T \left(\frac{\partial V}{\partial T} \right)_P \left(\frac{\partial P}{\partial T} \right)_V$
	$\frac{C_p}{C_v} = \frac{\left(\frac{\partial P}{\partial V} \right)_S}{\left(\frac{\partial P}{\partial V} \right)_T}$
	$\left(\frac{\partial C_v}{\partial V} \right)_T = T \left(\frac{\partial^2 P}{\partial T^2} \right)_V$
	$\left(\frac{\partial C_p}{\partial P} \right)_T = -T \left(\frac{\partial^2 V}{\partial T^2} \right)_P$

Source: H.F. Johnson, Professor and Chairman of the Department of Chemical Engineering, University of Tennessee, Knoxville, private communication.

5.5 METHODS FOR FINDING ENTHALPY CHANGES

It is customary to define enthalpy relative to some reference state, since only changes in enthalpy can be determined. For example, in steam tables, liquid water at $32°F$ is the reference state. The reference state is chosen as a matter of convenience and varies widely with different substances. The thermodynamic properties of air are often referred to $0°F$, whereas chemical substances are usually referred to $25°C$. Some of the methods for calculating enthalpy changes follow.

Use of C_p

We are now familiar with the equation:

$$\Delta H = \int C_p dT \tag{5.30}$$

But we must remember that it is true only when no change in pressure or phase occurs.

Constant heat capacity. For ideal gases and when C_p is a constant, we find

$$\Delta H = C_p \Delta T \tag{5.31}$$

Dependence of C_p on temperature. Heat capacity C_p is often expressed as a function of temperature as follows:

$$C_p = a + bT + cT^2 + \cdots \tag{5.36}$$

Using the first three terms of the series and Equations 5.30 and 5.32, we obtain

$$\Delta H = \int_{T_1}^{T_2} (a + bT + cT^2) \, dT$$

$$= \left[aT + \frac{bT^2}{2} + \frac{cT^3}{3} \right]_{T_1}^{T_2}$$

$$= a(T_2 - T_1) + b/2\,(T_2^2 - T_1^2) + c/3\,(T_2^3 - T_1^3) \tag{5.37}$$

Mean heat capacity. This is defined by

$$C_{p\,mean} = \frac{\int_{T_1}^{T_2} C_p dT}{\int_{T_1}^{T_2} dT} \tag{5.38}$$

Using Equation 5.36 we find

$$C_{p\,mean} = \frac{\int_{T_1}^{T_2}(a + bT + cT^2)\,dT}{\int_{T_1}^{T_2} dT}$$

$$= \frac{a(T_2 - T_1) + b/2\,(T_2^{\,2} - T_1^{\,2}) + c/3\,(T_2^{\,3} - T_1^{\,3})}{(T_2 - T_1)} \tag{5.39}$$

Once we have $C_{p\,mean}$ we get

$$\Delta H = C_{p\,mean} \Delta T \tag{5.40}$$

Graphical integration. The expression

$$\Delta H = \int C_p dT \tag{5.30}$$

can be determined graphically by plotting C_p versus T and evaluating the area under the curve. For Figure 5.8 this area is the area of the rectangle $T_1 T_2 BC$.

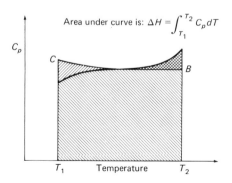

Figure 5.8. Enthalpy change by graphical integration

Kopp's rule, law of Dulong et Petit. Kopp's rule states that at room temperature the specific heat of solids on a molar basis is equal to 6.2 times the number of atoms present:

$$C_v = 6.2 \, N \qquad (5.41)$$

where

C_v = specific heat at constant volume, cal/g-mole-°C

N = number of g-atoms

Dulong and Petit formulated the original rule, which applied to solid elements and not compounds. The theoretical considerations for these rules pertain to C_v rather than C_p. However, since $\Delta(PV)$ for solids is small, the difference between C_p and C_v for solids is less than 5% and can be neglected in the application of the rule.

Boltzman showed from kinetic energy considerations that the atomic value should be $3R$ or 6 cal/g-atom-°C. Some examples of actual values are given in Table 5.3 below. The values will all approach zero as the temperature approaches absolute zero.

Table 5.3   SPECIFIC HEAT OF SOLIDS AT ROOM TEMPERATURE

Component	Actual	Specific heat Cal/g-mole-°C or cal/g-atom-°C Kopp's rule	Deviation
NaCl	12.8	12.4	0.4
SiC	6.4	12.4	−6.0
KI	13.6	12.4	1.2
PbCl$_2$	18.5	18.6	−0.1
Li	6.1	6.2	−0.1
K	7.5	6.2	1.3
Na	6.9	6.2	0.7
Fe	6.0	6.2	−0.2
Au	6.2	6.2	0.0
Pb	6.2	6.2	0.0

Use of Steam Tables

When dealing with water, the steam tables are very useful and give a quick answer for ΔH. Remember, the reference substance is liquid H_2O at $32°F$ and under its own vapor pressure of 0.088 psia. For further information, see Appendix 6, Steam Tables.

Tabulated Data for Specific Substances

When dealing with substances other than water, enthalpy data may be obtained from

1. Standard handbooks, e.g., Perry's *Chemical Engineers' Handbook.*

2. Technical journals that are abstracted in chemical abstracts, e.g., *Industrial and Engineering Chemistry, Journal of Physical Chemistry.*

3. Government publications available through the Clearinghouse for Federal Scientific and Technical Information.

4. Company data, which are sometimes made available to the public.

5. *Engineering Data Book,* Natural Gas Processors Suppliers Association.

Enthalpy Change in Phase Transition and the Clausius-Clapeyron Equation

Phase transitions that take place at constant temperature involve a special type of enthalpy, latent heat, meaning hidden or dormant, in the sense that such heat is needed to cause a change in phase but is not manifested by a temperature increase (see Figure 5.9). Latent heat contrasts with what we call sensible heat,

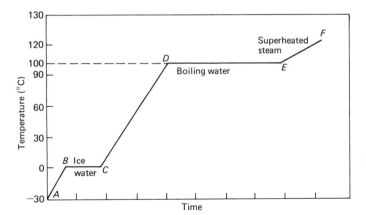

Figure 5.9.   Qualitative plot for phase changes in taking ice from $-30°C$ to $130°C$

which is sensed by a rise in temperature. For example, if we heat water from 75°F to 212°F at 1 atm, the heat supplied up to the boiling point is the sensible heat; if we continue to supply energy, the temperature will remain 212°F until all the water has evaporated; energy used per pound mass of water evaporated is called the normal or latent heat of vaporization at 212°F.

Let us survey enthalpies in phase transitions as shown in Table 5.4.

Table 5.4   ENTHALPIES IN PHASE TRANSITION FOR WATER

Type	Phase change	Description and value
Vaporization	Liquid → Vapor	Water to steam at 212°F and 14.7 psia, 970 Btu/lb$_m$
Condensation	Vapor → Liquid	Steam to water at 212°F and 14.7 psia, −970 Btu/lb$_m$
Sublimation	Solid → Vapor	Ice to steam at 32°F and 0.088 psia, 1220 Btu/lb$_m$
Fusion	Solid → Liquid	Ice to water at 32°F and >0.088 psia, 144 Btu/lb$_m$

The *Clausius-Clapeyron equation* is most widely used for processes where phase changes take place under equilibrium conditions. It is applied to vaporization, condensation, freezing, melting, sublimination, and crystallization processes.

Let us derive the Clausius-Clapeyron Equation. Consider an equilibrium process, vaporization or otherwise, where we have two distinct phases, 1 and 2, which could be vapor and liquid, solid and vapor, liquid$_1$-liquid$_2$ (extraction), solid$_1$-solid$_2$ (metallurgy), and so forth. Let us apply Equation 5.11:

$$dG = -SdT + VdP$$

At equilibrium, by definition, dP and dT must equal zero. Therefore,

$$dG = 0 \qquad (5.42)$$

This condition of equilibrium is universally true for any system that is completely defined by P, V, and T. Thus we know that

$$G_1 = G_2 \qquad (5.43)$$

and

$$dG_1 = dG_2 \qquad (5.44)$$

$$dG_1 = -S_1 dT + V_1 dP \qquad (5.45)$$

$$dG_2 = -S_2 dT + V_2 dP \qquad (5.46)$$

After rearranging, we get

$$\frac{dP}{dT} = \frac{S_2 - S_1}{V_2 - V_1} = \frac{\Delta S}{V_2 - V_1} \tag{5.47}$$

From Table 5.2, we have

$$\Delta G = \Delta H - T\Delta S = 0 \qquad \text{at equilibrium} \tag{5.48}$$

and

$$\Delta S = \Delta H/T \tag{5.49}$$

Equation 5.45 becomes the well-known Clapeyron equation:

$$\frac{dP}{dT} = \frac{\Delta H}{T\Delta V} \tag{5.50}$$

For the phase transition of liquid to vapor, Equation 5.50 is integrated, using these simplifying assumptions:

1. ΔH is constant over the range of temperature under consideration.
2. The volume of liquid is negligible relative to the volume of vapor.
3. The vapor behaves like an ideal gas; that is, for one mole,

$$V_2 = V_g = \frac{RT}{P}$$

Equation 5.50 becomes:

$$\frac{dP}{dT} = \frac{\Delta H}{TV_2} = \frac{\Delta H}{TV_g} = \frac{\Delta H}{T(RT/P)} \tag{5.51}$$

or

$$\frac{dP}{dT} = \frac{\Delta H}{RT^2} P \tag{5.52}$$

Separate the variables to get

$$\frac{dP}{P} = \frac{\Delta H}{RT^2} dT \tag{5.53}$$

Integrate the above equation:

$$\int_{P_1}^{P_2} \frac{dP}{P} = \int_{T_1}^{T_2} \frac{\Delta H}{RT^2} dT \tag{5.54}$$

or

$$\ln \frac{P_2}{P_1} = \frac{\Delta H}{R} \int_{T_1}^{T_2} \frac{dT}{T^2} = \frac{\Delta H}{R} \left[-\frac{1}{T} \right]_{T_1}^{T_2} \tag{5.55}$$

and,

$$2.303 \log_{10} \left(\frac{P_2}{P_1} \right) = -\frac{\Delta H}{R} \left[\frac{1}{T_2} - \frac{1}{T_1} \right]$$

or,

$$2.303 \log_{10} \left(\frac{P_1}{P_2} \right) = \frac{\Delta H}{R} \left[\frac{T_1 - T_2}{T_1 T_2} \right] \tag{5.56}$$

This is the celebrated Clausius-Clapeyron equation. It is most widely used to determine vapor pressure as a function of temperature.

Heat of Vaporization by Trouton's Rule

This is defined by the equation

$$\frac{\Delta H_v}{T_b} = C_1 \tag{5.57}$$

where

ΔH_v = heat of vaporization, cal/g-mole

T_b = normal boiling point temperature, $^\circ$K

C_1 = constant = 26, for H_2O and low molecular weight alcohols

or

C_1 = constant = 21, for nonpolar liquids like heptane and octane

For the Heat of Fusion Use Honda's Rule

$$\frac{\Delta H_f}{T_f} = C_2 \tag{5.58}$$

where

$$\Delta H_f = \text{heat of fusion, cal/g-mole}$$

$$T_f = \text{melting point, } °K$$

$$C_2 = \text{constant} = 6, \text{ for inorganic compounds}$$

$$= 10, \text{ for organic compounds}$$

$$= 2.5, \text{ for elements}$$

These methods show a wide variety for obtaining changes in enthalpy; other methods such as the Cox chart, the Othmer plot, reference-substance plots, and Duhring lines are described elsewhere.

Example 5.2 Independence of the path

A given gas follows the equation of state:

$$P = \frac{RT}{V} - \frac{a}{V^2}$$

This gas is expanded at constant enthalpy from

$$P_1 = 30 \text{ atm}$$

$$V_1 = 10 \text{ ft}^3/\text{lb-mole}$$

to

$$P_3 = 1 \text{ atm}$$

$$V_3 = ?$$

What is the final specific volume V_3? Given:

$$a = 1600 \text{ atm-ft}^3/(\text{lb-mole})^2$$

$$C_{p \text{ (avg)}} = 7.0 \text{ Btu/lb-mole-}°F$$

Solution

Let us choose this path of convenience:

1. Assume isothermal expansion from 30 atm to 1 atm.
2. Heat or cool to final state such that overall $\Delta H = 0$.

This path is shown in Figure 5.10.

Path 1 → 2:

From Table 5.2 we find

$$dU = C_v dT + \left[T \left(\frac{\partial P}{\partial T} \right)_V - P \right] dV$$

Since this is an isothermal path,

$$dU = \left[T \left(\frac{\partial P}{\partial T} \right)_V - P \right] dV$$

or

$$\left(\frac{\partial U}{\partial V} \right)_T = T \left(\frac{R}{V} \right) - \left(\frac{RT}{V} - \frac{a}{V^2} \right)$$

$$= \frac{a}{V^2}$$

$$\Delta U_T = \int_{V_1}^{V_2} \frac{a}{V^2} dV = a \left(\frac{V_2 - V_1}{V_1 V_2} \right)$$

Solve the equation of state for temperature

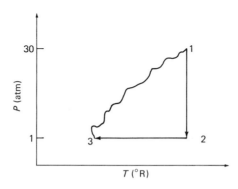

Figure 5.10. Path of convenience for an isenthalpic expansion

$$T_1 = T_2 \quad \text{(isothermal)}$$

or

$$T_1 = T_2 = \frac{1}{R}\left(PV_1 + \frac{a}{V_1}\right)$$

$$T_1 = T_2 = \frac{30 \times 10 + 1600/10}{0.73} = 630°R$$

From the equation of state we find

$$P = \frac{RT_2}{V_2} - \frac{a}{V_2{}^2}$$

or

$$V_2 = 460 \text{ ft}^3/\text{lb-mole}$$

Then

$$\Delta U_T = \frac{a(V_2 - V_1)}{V_1 V_2} = 1600\left(\frac{450}{10\,(460)}\right)$$

$$= 156.5 \frac{\text{atm-ft}^3}{\text{lb-mole}}$$

$$\Delta H_T = \Delta U + \Delta(PV) = 156.5 + [1(460) - 30(10)]$$

$$= 156.5 + 460 - 300$$

$$= 316.5 \text{ atm-ft}^3/\text{lb-mole}$$

$$= \frac{(316.5)\,(14.7)\,(144)}{778} = 863 \text{ Btu/lb-mole}$$

This is the enthalpy change for path $1 \to 2$. For path $1 \to 3$ we have

$$\Delta H_{1\to3} = \Delta H_{1\to2} + \Delta H_{2\to3}$$

Since overall ΔH is zero, we get

$$0 = \Delta H_{1\to2} + \Delta H_{2\to3}$$

or

$$\Delta H_{2\to3} = -\Delta H_{1\to2} = -\Delta H_T = -863 \text{ Btu/lb-mole}$$

and

$$C_p(T_3 - T_2) = -863 = 7\,(T_3 - 630)$$

Thus

$$T_3 = 507^\circ \text{R}$$

Now we can solve for the final volume V_3 from the equation of state, since

$$P_3 = 1 \text{ atm}$$

$$T_3 = 507^\circ \text{R}$$

We find

$$V_3 = 370 \text{ ft}^3/\text{lb-mole}$$

Example 5.3 $C_p - C_v$ for an ideal gas

Find $C_p - C_v$ for an ideal gas, using the proper expression in Table 5.2.

Solution

First method:

Use the expression

$$C_p - C_v = T \left(\frac{\partial V}{\partial T}\right)_P \left(\frac{\partial P}{\partial T}\right)_V$$

and the ideal gas law for one mole

$$PV = RT$$

$$V = \frac{RT}{P}$$

$$\left(\frac{\partial V}{\partial T}\right)_P = \frac{R}{P}$$

$$P = \frac{RT}{V}$$

$$\left(\frac{\partial P}{\partial T}\right)_V = \frac{R}{V}$$

Replace these partials in the original equation:

$$C_p - C_v = T\left(\frac{R}{P}\right)\frac{R}{V} = \frac{TR^2}{RT}$$

and

$$C_p - C_v = R$$

Second method:

H and U are functions of temperature only, and

$$H = U + PV$$
$$= U + RT$$

or

$$C_p T = C_v T + RT$$

Thus

$$C_p - C_v = R$$

Example 5.4   Use of the Clausius-Clapeyron equation

One-half g-mole of vaporized gaseous benzene is placed in a 50-liter vessel. If the temperature is dropped to 27°C, what is the amount of benzene condensed? Given: Boiling point of benzene is 80°C at 1 atm; enthalpy of vaporization is 7600 cal/g-mole

Solution

Let us find the vapor pressure of benzene at 27°C by using the Clausius-Clapeyron equation:

$$\ln\frac{P_2}{P_1} = \frac{\Delta H}{R}\left(\frac{T_2 - T_1}{T_2 T_1}\right)$$

or

$$\ln\frac{P_{300}}{1} = \frac{7600}{1.98}\left(\frac{300 - 353}{(300)(353)}\right) = -1.90$$

$$P_{300} = 0.15 \text{ atm}$$

Apply the ideal gas law

$$PV = nRT$$

where n is moles of vapor. Then

$$n = \frac{PV}{RT} = \frac{(0.15)\,(50)}{(0.082)\,(300)} = \frac{(0.15 \text{ atm})\,(50 \text{ liters})}{(273 + 27)^\circ \text{K}\, \dfrac{(1 \text{ atm})\,(22.4 \text{ liters})}{(1 \text{ g-mole})\,273^\circ \text{K}}}$$

$$= 0.3 \text{ g-mole of benzene vapor}$$

$$\text{Condensed benzene} = (0.5 - 0.3) \text{ g-mole}$$

$$= 0.20 \text{ g-mole} \quad \diamond$$

Example 5.5   Temperature in a pressure cooker

The wife of an engineer shows her scientific interest when she asks,

1. What is the temperature in our pressure cooker?
2. Why does it cook faster than an ordinary saucepan?

Given: Pressure regulator weighs 78 g and sits on a 3/8" O.D. opening; ΔH_V for water at 212°F and 1 atm is 9700 cal/g-mole

Solution

1. Cross-sectional area of opening $= \pi r^2 = 3.14 \times [(3/8)/2]^2 = 0.11 \text{ in}^2$

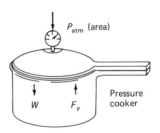

Make a force balance around the pressure regulator:

$$F_y = P_{atm} \text{ (area)} - \text{weight} = 0$$

$$F_y = P_{atm} \text{ (area)} + W$$

$$F_y = 78 \text{ g} \left(\frac{lb_m}{454 \text{ g}}\right) \left(32.2 \frac{ft}{sec^2}\right) \left(\frac{1}{32.2} \frac{lb_f}{lb_m} \frac{sec^2}{ft}\right) + 14.7 \frac{lb_f}{in^2} (0.11 \text{ in}^2)$$

$$= 0.172 + 1.620 = 1.79 \text{ lb}_f$$

$$\text{Pressure in the cooker} = \frac{1.79 \text{ lb}_f}{0.11 \text{ in}^2} = 16.3 \frac{lb_f}{in^2}$$

Use the Clausius-Clapeyron equation to find the temperature in the cooker:

$$2.303 \log_{10}\left(\frac{P_1}{P_2}\right) = \frac{\Delta H}{R}\left[\frac{T_1 - T_2}{T_1 T_2}\right]$$

or

$$2.303 \log_{10}\left(\frac{P_2}{P_1}\right) = \frac{\Delta H}{R}\left[\frac{T_2 - T_1}{T_1 T_2}\right]$$

where

$$P_1 = 14.7 \text{ psia}$$

$$P_2 = 16.3 \text{ psia}$$

$$\Delta H = 9700 \text{ cal/g-mole}$$

$$R = 1.99 \text{ cal/g-mole-}°K$$

$$T_1 = 100 + 273 = 373°R$$

$$T_2 = ?$$

Replace in the above equation:

$$2.303 \log_{10}\left(\frac{16.3}{14.7}\right) = \frac{9700}{1.99}\left[\frac{T_2 - 373}{373 \, T_2}\right]$$

$$2.303 \log_{10}(1.11) = \frac{4870}{373} - \frac{4870}{T_2} = 13.1 - \frac{4870}{T_2}$$

$$2.303 \, (0.0453) = 13.1 - \frac{4870}{T_2} = 0.104$$

and

$$T_2 = \frac{4870}{12.996} = 375°K = 102°C \quad \triangleleft$$

2. The higher pressure raises the boiling point of the water and thus causes the cooking to occur faster than under normal pressure. The opposite of this happens when you drive your car up a mountain road; at the higher elevation the pressure is lower than normal atmospheric, and the water coolant in your car boils at a lower temperature than 100°C; if your luck is as good as mine, the water will spill out and you must cool it, meditate, and come down the slopes.

Example 5.6   The energy equation in superheating steam

Saturated steam at $P_1 = 200$ psia ($T_1 = 382°F$) is being superheated to $T_2 = 600°F$ at $P_2 = 200$ psia. See Figure 5.11.

1. What is the amount of heat needed per pound of steam if $C_{p\text{ mean}} = 18.0$ Btu/lb-mole-°K?

2. Compare your answer with that from steam tables.

Solution

1. Apply Equation 5.2 between points 1 and 2:

$$\Delta H + \frac{\Delta v^2}{2g_c\alpha} + \Delta Z \frac{g}{g_c} = Q - W$$

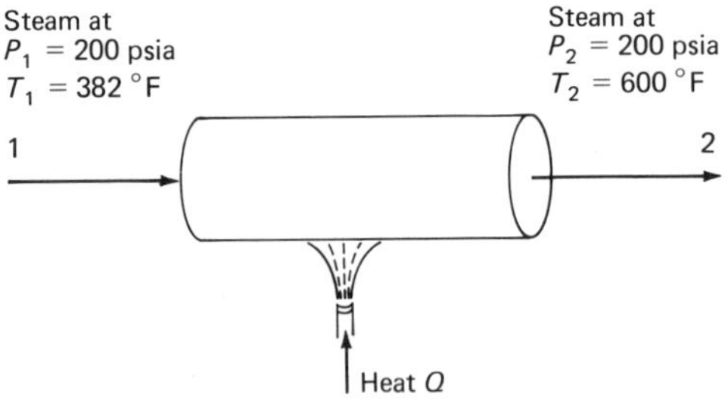

Figure 5.11.   Superheating steam

For this process, there is no change in elevation ($\Delta Z = 0$), and there is no work ($W = 0$). Assuming that kinetic energy is negligible, we get

$$\Delta H = Q = C_{p\text{ mean}} \Delta T$$

$$= 18.0 \frac{\text{Btu}}{\text{lb-mole-}^\circ\text{K}} (588 - 467)^\circ\text{K}$$

$$= 18 \,(121) = 2180 \frac{\text{Btu}}{\text{lb-mole}}$$

$$= 2180 \frac{\text{Btu}}{\text{lb-mole}} \times \frac{\text{lb-mole}}{18 \text{ lb}_m}$$

$$= 121 \text{ Btu/lb}_m \;\triangleleft$$

2. From steam tables, we get

$$\Delta H = 1322.1 - 1198.4$$

$$= 123.7 \text{ Btu/lb}_m \;\triangleleft$$

Example 5.7   Flow of air in a vertical heat exchanger

Air enters the bottom of a vertical pipe at 75°F and leaves at 180°F. Heat is supplied externally and the pipe is used as a heat exchanger. The pressure drop per 100 ft of pipe is 3 psia, and the average air velocity at the entrance is 25 ft/sec. What is the total heat added to the air?

Solution

Basis: 1 lb$_m$ of air.

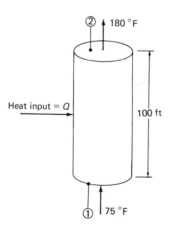

Apply the energy equation between points 1 and 2:

$$\Delta H + \Delta \left(\frac{v^2}{2g_c\alpha} \right) + \Delta Z \frac{g}{g_c} = Q - W$$

Since there is no shaft work, $W = 0$

$$C_p \Delta t + \left(\frac{v_2^2 - v_1^2}{2g_c\alpha} \right) + \Delta Z \frac{g}{g_c} = Q$$

Assume turbulent flow, $\alpha = 1$, and average heat capacity for air as

$$C_p = 0.24 \text{ Btu/lb}_m \cdot °F$$

Then calculate as follows:

$$v_1 = 25 \text{ ft/sec}$$

$$v_2 = 25 \frac{\text{ft}}{\text{sec}} \times \frac{460 + 180}{460 + 75} \times \frac{14.7}{14.7 - 3}$$

$$v_2 = 25 \times \frac{640}{535} \times \frac{14.7}{11.7} = 37.6 \text{ ft/sec}$$

$$Q = 0.24 \frac{\text{Btu}}{\text{lb}_m \cdot °F} (180 - 75)°F$$

$$+ \left[\frac{(37.6)^2 - (25)^2}{2(32.2)1} + 100 \times \frac{32.2}{32.2} \right] \frac{\text{ft-lb}_f}{\text{lb}_m} \times \frac{1 \text{ Btu}}{778 \text{ ft-lb}_f}$$

$$= 0.24(105) + \frac{1414 - 625}{64.4} \times \frac{1}{778}$$

$$= 25.2 + 0.016 + 0.129$$

$$Q = 25.35 \text{ Btu/lb}_m \;\triangleleft$$

The kinetic energy contribution is negligible, as is the potential energy contribution.

Example 5.8 Power requirement in oil transport

Oil is transported in a cross-country pipeline at a rate of 5000 bbl/day. The pressure at the outlet of station 1 is 250 psig, and at the inlet to station 2 the pressure is 115 psig; the number 2 station is 57 ft above station 1. See Figure 5.12. Given:

$$\rho_{oil} = 48 \text{ lb/ft}^3$$

$$1 \text{ bbl} = 42 \text{ gal}$$

Find the energy loss due to friction in the pipe.

Solution

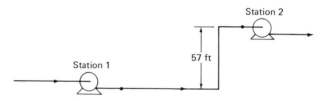

Figure 5.12. Pumping stations in oil transport

Apply the energy equation (5.6) between the two pumping stations:

$$\Delta\left(\frac{v^2}{2g_c\alpha}\right) + \Delta Z\frac{g}{g_c} + \int_{}^{}\frac{1}{\rho}dP + W_f' + \Sigma F = 0$$

Since there is no change in cross section,

$$\Delta\left(\frac{v^2}{2g_c\alpha}\right) = 0 \qquad v_1 = v_2$$

$$W_f' = 0 \qquad \text{no shaft work}$$

and the energy equation reduces to

$$\Delta Z\frac{g}{g_c} + \frac{\Delta P}{\rho} + \Sigma F = 0$$

$$\Sigma F = -\Delta Z\frac{g}{g_c} - \frac{\Delta P}{\rho}$$

$$\Sigma F = -57\,\frac{\text{ft-lb}_f}{\text{lb}_m} - (115 - 250)\frac{114}{48}\,\frac{\text{ft-lb}_f}{\text{lb}_m}$$

$$= -57 + 405 = 348\,\frac{\text{ft-lb}_f}{\text{lb}_m} \quad \triangleleft$$

To express this in horsepower, we need the flow rate:

$$w = \frac{5000\,(42)\,(48)}{(7.5)\,(24)\,(3600)} = 15.6 \; \text{lb}_m/\text{sec}$$

and

$$\Sigma F = \frac{(348)\,\text{ft-lb}_f/\text{lb}_m\,(15.6\,\text{lb}_m/\text{sec})\;1\;\text{HP}}{550\;\text{ft-lb}_f/\text{sec}} = 9.9 \; \text{HP} \quad \triangleleft$$

Example 5.9   Atmospheric pressure varying with altitude

Atmospheric temperature is expressed as a function of altitude by the relation

$$T = T_0(1 - Z/a)$$

where

$$T = \text{temperature at altitude } Z, \,^\circ\text{R}$$

$$T_0 = \text{ground temperature}, \,^\circ\text{R}$$

$$Z = \text{altitude, ft}$$

$$a = \text{constant} = 50,000 \; \text{ft}$$

1. Find an expression for atmospheric pressure as a function of altitude. Make any logical assumptions.

2. What is the atmospheric pressure at an elevation of 25,000 ft, if the pressure at a point on the earth's surface is $P_0 = 14.7$ psia and the corresponding temperature is $T_0 = 70^\circ\text{F} + 460 = 530^\circ\text{R}$?

Solution

1. Apply the energy equation (5.6):

$$\Delta\left(\frac{v^2}{2g_c\alpha}\right) + \Delta Z\frac{g}{g_c} + \int^1\frac{1}{\rho}\,dP + W_f' + \Sigma F = 0$$

There is no shaft or pump work and friction and kinetic energy changes are negligible. Thus

$$\Delta Z\frac{g}{g_c} + \int\frac{1}{\rho}\,dP = 0$$

and

$$\int dZ \frac{g}{g_c} + \int \frac{1}{\rho} dP = 0$$

or

$$\frac{g}{g_c} dZ + \frac{1}{\rho} dP = 0$$

Assume ideal gas behavior:

$$PV = nRT$$

$$P = \frac{n}{V} RT$$

or

$$PM = \frac{nM}{V} RT = \rho RT$$

where M is molecular weight. Then

$$\frac{1}{\rho} = \frac{RT}{PM} = \frac{RT_0(1 - Z/a)}{PM}$$

Now we get

$$\frac{g}{g_c} dZ + \frac{RT_0(1 - Z/a)}{PM} dP = 0$$

Separate the variables:

$$\frac{g}{g_c} \int_0^Z \frac{dZ}{(1 - Z/a)} + \frac{RT_0}{M} \int_{P_0}^P \frac{dP}{P} = 0$$

$$= \left[-\frac{g}{g_c} a \ln \left(1 - \frac{Z}{a} \right) \right]_0^Z + \left[\frac{RT_0}{M} \ln P \right]_{P_0}^P$$

The required expression is

$$P = P_0(1 - Z/a)^{c'} \quad \triangleleft$$

where

$$c' = \frac{g}{g_c} \frac{aM}{RT_0}$$

2. $$P = 14.7\,(1/2) \left[\frac{(1)\,(50{,}000)\,(29)}{(1545)\,(530)} \right]$$

$P = 4.3$ psia

5.6 EVAPORATION

Evaporation is a process for concentrating a solution that is made of nonvolatile solute and a volatile solvent. Water is the volatile solvent in most evaporation processes. For example, to concentrate a glycerol solution at 1 atm, evaporation is used because of the wide difference in the normal boiling points of the two components; namely, at 1 atm, water boils at 212°F while glycerol boils at 555°F. If the boiling points were closer, distillation or some other processes of separation would have to be used.

It is necessary to distinguish between evaporation and other similar processes, such as drying, distillation, and crystallization. In drying, the residue is a solid, while in evaporation it is a concentrated solution or thick liquor. In distillation, the vapor is a mixture, while in evaporation the vapor is usually one component, and if this vapor is a mixture, no attempt is made to separate it into its components as is done in distillation. Evaporation differs from crystallization in that the interest is to concentrate a solution, not to build crystals. However, the demarcation line is not very sharp between evaporation and crystallization, especially in the production of salt from brine solutions.

In many industrial situations, the vapor formed in an evaporation process is not the desired product, but in desalination, where fresh water is made from sea water, the desired product is the condensed vapors. The boiling of sea water to give potable water is sometimes called distillation, but it should properly be called evaporation.

Evaporators of various designs encountered in industry are a physical variation of the simplest type, which we will consider here. A simple schematic diagram of an evaporator is shown in Figure 5.13 for the purpose of illustrating material and energy balances.

Under steady state conditions, the feed enters the evaporator, where it is heated by steam. The area available for heat transfer from the steam to the feed is represented by a coil; thus there is no direct contact between the steam and the

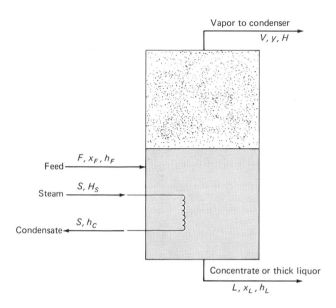

Vapor to condenser
V, y, H

Feed F, x_F, h_F

Steam S, H_S

Condensate S, h_c

Concentrate or thick liquor
L, x_L, h_L

Figure 5.13. Simple schematic diagram of a single-effect evaporator

feed. The vapor formed escapes from the top of the evaporator, where it is received by a condenser. The thick liquor, or concentrated solution, is withdrawn
from the bottom. The area available for heat transfer, such as the area of the
steam coil, is obtained from the relationship

$$Q = U\, A\Delta t \tag{5.59}$$

where

$Q =$ total heat transferred from the steam to the feed, Btu/hr

$U =$ overall heat transfer coefficient Btu/hr-ft^2-°F

$A =$ available area for heat transfer, ft^2

$\Delta t =$ temperature gradient $=$ (steam temperature) $-$ (boiling point of solution)

This heat transfer area A is very important in evaporator design. The overall
material balance around the evaporator is

$$F = L + V \tag{5.60}$$

and the component material balance is

$$Fx_F = Lx_L + Vy \tag{5.61}$$

where

F, L, V = feed, thick liquor, and vapor streams, respectively, lb/hr

x_F, x_L = mass fraction of solute in feed and thick liquor, respectively

y = mass fraction of solute in the vapor

Since the vapor stream is usually pure water, we can write

$$y = 0 \qquad (5.62)$$

and

$$Fx_F = Lx_L \qquad (5.63)$$

The energy balance around the evaporator is

$$\text{Heat input} = \text{heat output}$$

or, equivalently,

(Heat in feed) + (heat in steam) = (heat in vapor)

+ (heat in condensate)

+ (heat in thick liquor)

+ (heat loss to surroundings)

Assuming there is no heat loss, we get correspondingly

$$Fh_F + SH_S = VH + Sh_C + Lh_L \qquad (5.64)$$

where

$$S = \text{flow rate of steam, lb}_m/\text{hr}$$

$$h_F, H_S, H_V, h_C, h_L = \text{enthalpy of feed, steam, vapor,}$$
condensate, and thick liquor,
respectively, Btu/lb$_m$

Let us now illustrate the application of material and energy balances in evaporation.

Example 5.10 Long-tube vertical evaporator in desalination

Long-tube vertical evaporators are used in converting sea water into fresh water. As many as twelve evaporators have been used; let us concentrate on the first evaporator and apply material and energy balances. The feed is 1×10^6 gal/day of saline water at 115°F and 3.5% by weight NaCl. The feed is to be concentrated to 4.0% by weight NaCl. Assume that the boiling point rise due to concentration is negligible and that the vapor pressure in the evaporator is 1 atm. The heating surface of the evaporator is supplied with saturated steam at 30 psia. Determine

1. Weight of thick liquor and vapor produced, lb_m/hr
2. Weight of steam needed, lb_m/hr
3. The heating area of the steam coil, given that the overall heat transfer coefficient is $U = 650$ Btu/ft^2-hr-°F.

Solution

Basis: One hour of operation.

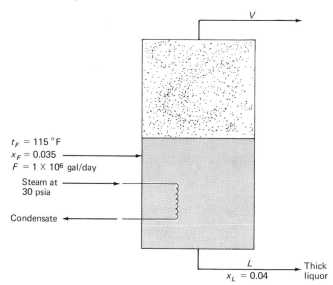

$t_F = 115\,°F$
$x_F = 0.035$
$F = 1 \times 10^6$ gal/day

Steam at 30 psia

Condensate

L

$x_L = 0.04$

Thick liquor

V

1. The overall material balance around the evaporator is

$$F = V + L$$

The salt balance is

$$Fx_F = Lx_L \qquad \text{vapor is pure water}$$

Replace these terms by their values:

$$F = 1 \times 10^6\ \frac{gal}{day} \times \frac{1\ day}{24\ hrs} \times 61.8\frac{lb_m}{ft^3} \times \frac{1\ ft^3}{7.48\ gal}$$

$$= 3.44 \times 10^5\ lb_m/hr$$

From the second equation we find

$$(3.44 \times 10^5)\,(0.035) \;=\; L(0.04)$$

$$L \;=\; 3.02 \times 10^5 \; \text{lb}_m/\text{hr} \; \lhd$$

and

$$3.44 \times 10^5 \;=\; V + 3.02 \times 10^5$$

$$V \;=\; 4.2 \times 10^4 \; \text{lb}_m/\text{hr} \; \lhd$$

2. To determine the weight of steam needed, we need to write an overall energy balance. Assuming there is no heat loss we get

$$Fh_F + SH_S \;=\; VH + Sh_C + Lh_L$$

From the steam tables we find

$h_F = 82.9 \; \text{Btu/lb}_m$ at $155°\text{F}$

$H_S = 1164 \; \text{Btu/lb}_m$ at $t_S = 250°\text{F}$, corresponding to a saturated vapor pressure of 30 psia

$H = 1150.4 \; \text{Btu/lb}_m$ for saturated vapor at $212°\text{F}$

$h_C = 218.5 \; \text{Btu/lb}_m$ for steam condensate, assuming that it leaves at the condensing temperature, $250°\text{F}$

$h_L = 180.1 \; \text{Btu/lb}_m$ for saturated liquid at $212°\text{F}$

Thus

$$(3.44 \times 10^5)\,(82.9) + S(11.64) = 4.2 \times 10^4 \,(1150.4)$$

$$+ \, 5(218.5) + (3.02 \times 10^5)\,(180.1)$$

and

$$S = \frac{745 \times 10^5}{945.5}$$

$$\text{Steam needed} = S = 7.9 \times 10^4 \; \text{lb}_m/\text{hr} \; \lhd$$

3. The total heat transferred is

$$Q = UA \; \Delta t$$

$$Q = S(H_S - h_C) = 7.9 \times 10^4 \,(1164 - 218.5)$$

$$Q = 7.45 \times 10^7 \; \text{Btu/hr}$$

$$A = \frac{Q}{U\Delta t} = \frac{7.45 \times 10^7 \text{ Btu/hr}}{(650 \text{ Btu/hr-ft}^2\text{-}^\circ\text{F}) (250 - 212)^\circ\text{F}}$$

$$A = 3.02 \times 10^3 \text{ ft}^2 \ \ \triangleleft$$

Again, note that the temperature gradient which is the driving force is the difference between the steam temperature and the boiling point of the solution. If the solution is highly concentrated, corrections must be made to account for the rise in boiling point; such corrections will involve Δt and enthalpy values.

Example 5.11   Use of waste gas to produce steam

In a chemical plant, a new plan calls for using a waste gas that has been discarded at 800°F for supplying a waste-heat boiler; it will exit at 500°F. This boiler receives feed water at 80°F and produces saturated steam at 450°F. The average heat capacity of the gas is 7.75 Btu/lb-mole-°F. Determine the weight of steam produced per 100 lb-moles of gas.

Solution

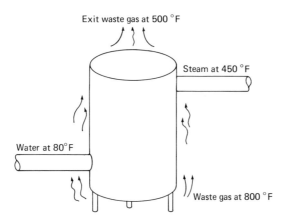

Basis: 100 lb-moles of waste gas. A heat balance around the boiler gives

Heat lost by waste gas = heat gained in heating water
and making steam

or

$$(mC_p\Delta t)_{\text{waste gas}} = w(H_S - h_{\text{H}_2\text{O}})$$

where w is the weight of the steam produced. Then

$$100 \text{ lb-mole } (7.75 \frac{\text{Btu}}{\text{lb-mole-}^\circ\text{F}}) (800 - 500)^\circ\text{F} = w(1204.6 - 48) \text{ Btu}$$

$$100 (7.75) 300 = 1156.6 \, w$$

$$w = \frac{100 (7.75) 300}{1156.6}$$

$$\text{Weight of steam produced} = \frac{201 \text{ lb}_m}{100 \text{ lb-moles of waste gas}}$$

Example 5.12 Warm-hearted students taking a make-up exam
(combined material and energy balances)

Fresh air at 95°F and 90% humidity is cooled to 72°F and 35% humidity and then admitted to a room with two students taking a make-up exam. The rate of heat emission is 700 Btu/person-hr, and the rate of fresh air is 16,000 ft^3/hr.

1. Draw a schematic flow diagram of the process.

2. Determine the weight of condensed water in the cooler after 1 hr.

3. Find the weight of the air stream leaving the room each hour.

4. Is the exit temperature of the air stream leaving the room going to affect their comfort and blood pressure?

5. What is the amount of heat removed in the cooler every hour?

Solution

1.

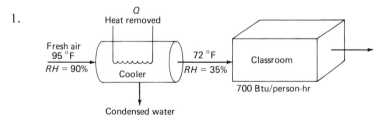

2. Basis: 16,000 ft^3/hr of fresh air at 95°F and 90% RH. From the humidity chart the absolute humidity of fresh air is

$$H_1 = 0.033 \frac{\text{lb}_m \text{ water vapor}}{\text{lb}_m \text{ dry air}}$$

After the cooler, at $72°F$ and 35% humidity,

$$H_2 = 0.006 \frac{\text{lb}_m \text{ water vapor}}{\text{lb}_m \text{ dry air}}$$

Now we should find the mass flow rate of fresh air. Let

Mass of H_2O vapor $= x$

$$\text{Volume of } H_2O \text{ vapor} = \frac{x}{\rho_{H_2O \text{ vapor}}}$$

$$\text{Volume of dry air} = 16{,}000 - \frac{x}{\rho_{H_2O \text{ vapor}}}$$

$$\text{Mass of dry air} = \left(16{,}000 - \frac{x}{\rho_{H_2O \text{ vapor}}}\right) \rho_{\text{air}}$$

$$\begin{array}{c} \text{Mass ratio of water vapor} \\ \text{to dry air} \end{array} = \frac{x}{\left(16{,}000 - \frac{x}{\rho_{H_2O \text{ vapor}}}\right) \rho_{\text{air}}}$$

$$= 0.033 \text{ in the fresh air stream}$$

We find ρ_{air} and $\rho_{H_2O \text{ vapor}}$ through the ideal gas law:

$$PV = nRT$$

or

$$P = \frac{MW}{MW} \frac{nRT}{V}$$

where MW is molecular weight and n is number of moles. But

$$(MW)n = \text{weight}$$

$$\frac{(MW)n}{V} = \rho = \text{density}$$

Thus

$$P = \frac{\rho R T}{MW}$$

and

$$\rho = \frac{PMW}{RT}$$

at 95°F and 1 atm:

$$\rho_{H_2O \ vapor} = \frac{1 \ atm \left(18 \frac{lb_m}{lb\text{-mole}}\right)}{0.73 \frac{ft^3\text{-atm}}{lb\text{-mole-}°R} (95 + 460)°R}$$

$$= \frac{1 \times 18}{0.73 \times 555} = 0.0445 \ lb_m/ft^3$$

$$\rho_{air} = \frac{(1 \ atm) \left(29 \frac{lb_m}{lb\text{-mole}}\right)}{0.73 \frac{ft^3\text{-atm}}{lb\text{-mole-}°R} (95 + 460)°R}$$

or

$$\rho_{air} = \rho_{H_2O \ vapor} \times \frac{29}{18} = 0.0445 \times \frac{29}{18} = 0.0719 \ lb_m/ft^3$$

Thus

$$\frac{x}{\left(16{,}000 - \frac{x}{0.0445}\right) 0.0719} = 0.033$$

$$(0.033)(0.0719) \left(16{,}000 - \frac{x}{0.0445}\right) = x$$

$$37.90 - 0.0533x = x$$

$$37.90 = 1.0533x$$

$$x = \frac{37.90}{1.0533} = 35.90 \ lb_m \ H_2O \text{ vapor in} \atop \text{fresh air stream}$$

$$\text{Mass of dry air} = \left(16{,}000 - \frac{35.90}{0.0445}\right)0.0719$$

$$= 1150 - 58.0 = 1092 \text{ lb}_m$$

$$\text{Total mass of fresh air} = 35.90 + 1092 = 1127.90 \text{ lb}_m$$

The air stream after the cooler contains

$$0.006 \frac{\text{lb}_m \text{ water vapor}}{\text{lb}_m \text{ dry air}} \times 1092 \text{ lb}_m \text{ dry air} = 6.56 \text{ lb}_m \text{ water vapor}$$

$$\text{Weight of condensed water} = 35.90 - 6.56$$

$$= 29.34 \text{ lb}_m$$

3. A mass balance around the classroom gives

$$\text{Air input} = \text{air output}$$

or

$$(1092 \text{ lb}_m \text{ dry air}) + (6.56 \text{ lb}_m \text{ H}_2\text{O vapor})$$

$$= 1098.56 \text{ lb}_m \text{ of air leaving the room}$$

4. Heat given by people in the room = heat gained by air stream
leaving cooler

$$mC_p \Delta t = 700(2) = 1400 \text{ Btu/hr}$$

The heat capacity of the air stream entering the classroom is found from the humidity chart:

$$C_p = 0.242 \text{ Btu/lb}_m \text{ dry air} - {}^{\circ}\text{F}$$

Thus

$$\left(1092 \frac{\text{lb}_m \text{ dry air}}{\text{hr}}\right)\left(0.242 \frac{\text{Btu}}{\text{lb}_m \text{ dry air-}{}^{\circ}\text{F}}\right)(t - 72){}^{\circ}\text{F} = 1400 \text{ Btu/hr}$$

$$264.2t - 19{,}040 = 1400$$

Exit temperature of air stream leaving room $= t$

$$= \frac{19{,}040 + 1400}{264.2} = 77.2{}^{\circ}\text{F}$$

The students should be comfortable; however, their blood pressure
may be upset if they are not doing well in their make-up examination.

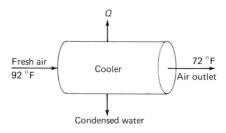

5. Heat removed in the cooler = heat given in lowering the fresh air
                                temperature from 95°F to 72°F
                              + heat given in condensing water vapor

$$Q = (1092)(0.25)(95 - 72) + (35.9)(0.445)(95 - 72) + 29.34(1053)$$

$$= 6290 + 368 + 30,900$$

Thus the heat removed in the cooler is

$$Q = 37,558 \text{ Btu/hr}$$

5.7 DISTILLATION

Distillation processes are widely used in industry for separating components of
liquid mixtures. This separation makes use of the difference in the volatilities
or vapor pressures of the respective components. Various types of distillation
exist, but fractional distillation is most often used, especially in the petroleum
refining industry. The basic unit in this process is the distillation tower, or fractionating column. The liquid mixture is usually fed to the column as shown in
Figure 5.14. A reboiler is used to supply energy for generating vapor. The vapor
moves upward and passes through a total condenser where it is all condensed.
This condensed vapor, which is rich in the more volatile component, is divided
into a reflux stream and a product stream. The liquid reflux returns to the column,
where it contacts the ascending vapor. The reflux becomes richer with the less
volatile substance and the vapor stream becomes richer with the more volatile
substance. The reflux is always cooler than the ascending vapor, and the top of the
column is cooler than the bottom. Thus the reflux acts as a coolant for the ascending vapor, and while it is gaining heat a portion of itself is vaporized; this
portion comes from the more volatile component, and the product will become
more enriched with the desired substance.

    The intimate contact between liquid and vapor is accomplished by using sieve
plates or bubble caps at specified positions in the tower.

Distillation towers are ideal for demonstrating material and energy balances in combined mass and heat transfer operations. Consider Figure 5.14c with the following nomenclature; keep in mind that a subscript indicates a given stream:

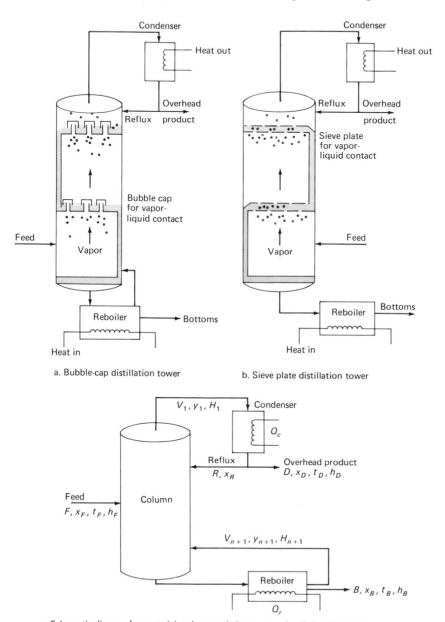

a. Bubble-cap distillation tower

b. Sieve plate distillation tower

c. Schematic diagram for material and energy balance around a distillation tower

Figure 5.14.   Distillation towers

B, F, V_1, D, and $R =$ bottoms, feed, top vapor, distillate or overhead product, and reflux, lb_m/hr

$x =$ mass fraction in liquid

$y =$ mass fraction in vapor

$t =$ temperature, $°F$

$h =$ enthalpy of liquid, Btu/lb_m

$H =$ enthalpy of vapor, Btu/lb_m

$Q_r =$ heat added in the still or reboiler, Btu/hr

$Q_c =$ heat removed in the condenser, Btu/hr

For steady-state operations, we can write the following material and energy balances, assuming no heat losses from the system to the surroundings.

Balances Around the Distillation Tower

The overall material balance is

$$F = D + B \tag{5.65}$$

The component balance is

$$Fx_F = Dx_D + Bx_B \tag{5.66}$$

If we have a two-component system we will have two component balances. In the feed, for example, the mass fraction of one component is x_F and the mass fraction of the other component is $(1 - x_F)$. Remember that for a two-component system, the number of independent equations is only two; the third equation can be used to check the results.

The overall energy balance is

$$Fh_F + Q_r = Dh_D + Bh_B + Q_c \tag{5.67}$$

The heat removed at the condenser may be obtained from

$$Q_c = mC_p(t_2 - t_1) \tag{5.68}$$

where

$m =$ mass flow rate of coolant, lb_m/hr

$C_p =$ heat capacity of coolant, $Btu/lb_m\text{-}°F$

$$t_1 = \text{inlet temperature of cooling medium}$$

$$t_2 = \text{outlet temperature}$$

The heat added at the reboiler may be obtained from condensing steam:

$$Q_r = SH_S \tag{5.69}$$

where

$$S = \text{steam flow rate, lb}_m/\text{hr}$$

$$H_S = \text{enthalpy of steam, Btu/lb}_m$$

Balances Around the Total Condenser

The overall material balance is

$$V_1 = D + R \tag{5.70}$$

The component balance is

$$V_1 y_1 = Dx_D + Rx_R \tag{5.71}$$

In general

$$x_D = x_R$$

The overall energy balance is

$$V_1 H_1 = Dh_D + Rh_R + Q_c \tag{5.72}$$

Making use of these equations, we obtain

$$\frac{Q_c}{D} = \left(\frac{R}{D} + 1\right)(H_1 - h_D) \tag{5.73}$$

Balances Around the Reboiler

The overall material balance is

$$L_n = V_{n+1} + B \tag{5.74}$$

The subscripts n and $n + 1$ indicate the number of the plate or stage from which the stream originates (very often the reboiler is counted as an ideal stage).

The component balance is

$$L_n x_n = V_{n+1} y_{n+1} + Bx_B \tag{5.75}$$

The overall energy balance is

$$L_n h_n + Q_r = V_{n+1} H_{n+1} + B h_B \qquad (5.76)$$

Specifying the feed rate and certain stream compositions renders tower calculations relatively simple. Here is an illustration.

Example 5.13   Mass and energy balances in a distillation tower

A distillation tower operating at atmospheric pressure is used to fractionate a benzene-toluene solution. The feed, at 40,000 lb_m/hr, contains 50% benzene by weight and 50% toluene. The overhead product contains 0.98 mass fraction benzene and the bottoms contain 0.96 mass fraction toluene. The feed is liquid at its boiling point and $R/D = 4.0$. The recycle and distillate are at 125°F.

Determine

1. Mass of the distillate

2. Mass of the bottoms

3. Condenser duty

4. Heat input to the reboiler

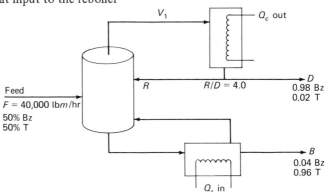

Solution

Basis: One hour.

Write an overall material balance around the distillation tower:

$$F = B + D$$

or

$$40,000 = B + D$$

The component balances are
for benzene:

$$0.50\,(40,000) = 0.04B + 0.98D$$

and for toluene:

$$0.50\,(40{,}000) = 0.96B + 0.02D$$

Solving any two of these equations gives

1. $$D = 1.96 \times 10^4 \ \mathrm{lb}_m/\mathrm{hr}$$

2. $$B = 2.04 \times 10^4 \ \mathrm{lb}_m/\mathrm{hr}$$

$$\mathrm{Total} = 4.00 \times 10^4 \ \mathrm{lb}_m/\mathrm{hr}$$

3. To solve for the condenser duty we consider the condenser alone. In the previous section, a combination of material and energy balances provided an equation for finding the condenser duty:

$$\frac{Q_c}{D} = \left(\frac{R}{D} + 1\right)(H_1 - h_D)$$

Q_c, the heat taken out, is the condenser duty.

From the enthalpy concentration diagram for benzene-toluene (Figure 5.15), the enthalpy of the saturated vapor leaving the tower is

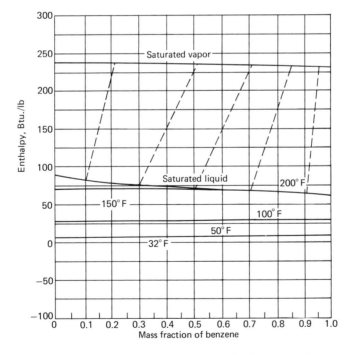

Figure 5.15. Enthalpy-concentration diagram for benzene-toluene system at 1 atm (reference state, 32°F)

$$H_1 = 232.0 \text{ Btu/lb}_m \quad \text{reference temperature, } 32°\text{F}$$

and the enthalpy of the distillate is taken at $125°\text{F}$:

$$h_D = 37.0 \text{ Btu/lb}_m$$

Thus

$$\frac{Q_c}{19{,}600} = (4.0 + 1)(232.0 - 37.0)$$

$$Q_c = 5(195.0) \, 19{,}600$$

$$Q_c = \text{condenser duty} = 1.91 \times 10^7 \text{ Btu/hr} \;\lhd$$

4. The heat input to the reboiler is found by applying an overall energy balance around the distillation tower:

$$Fh_F + Q_r = Dh_D + Bh_B + Q_c$$

For liquid feed at its boiling point,

$$h_F = 71.5 \text{ Btu/lb}_m$$

The bottoms stream is a saturated liquid with

$$x_B = 0.04 \text{ Bz}$$

and from the enthalpy concentration diagram, we have

$$h_B = 85.5 \text{ Btu/lb}_m$$

and the energy equation gives

$$40{,}000 \,(71.5) + Q_r = 19{,}600 \,(37.0) + 2.04 \times 10^4 \,(85.5) + 1.91 \times 10^7$$

$$Q_r = 19{,}600 \,(37.0) + 2.04 \times 10^4 \,(85.5) + 1.91 \times 10^7 - 40{,}000 \,(71.5)$$

$$= 0.725 \times 10^6 + 1.743 \times 10^6 + 19.100 \times 10^6 - 2.860 \times 10^6$$

$$\text{Heat input to the reboiler} = Q_r = 1.87 \times 10^7 \text{ Btu/hr} \;\lhd$$

Part II: Thermochemical Systems and Heats of Reaction

Thermochemical systems deal with enthalpy changes that accompany a chemical reaction. These changes are usually studied with the aid of a calorimeter (Figure 5.4). A calorimeter is essentially an insulated tank filled with water in which the reaction chamber is placed; the heat of reaction is determined by means of a heat balance.

The amount of heat absorbed or given off in a reaction taking place at constant pressure, and under such conditions as to do no useful work, is called the heat of reaction. Heats of reaction are usually indicated in the thermochemical equations under consideration.

The physical state of reactants and products affects the heat of reaction. Thus it is necessary to define the state of each substance entering into the reaction. A subscript is usually used to define such states as gas, solid, liquid, amorphous, and so on.

Various types of heats of reaction are found in thermochemical systems. These include heats of: formation, combustion, neutralization, solution, dilution, dissociation, polymerization, and others. All these are particular types of the broader topic of heats of reaction, and they are all subject to similar treatments and thermodynamic requirements.

5.8   THERMOCHEMICAL EQUATIONS

What are they?   These equations represent the changes in a chemical reaction. For example, the combustion of carbon at $25°C$ gives

$$C_{(s)} + O_{2(g)} \rightarrow CO_{2(g)} \qquad \Delta H_{25°C} = -94{,}050 \text{ cal/g-mole} \qquad (5.77)$$

This equation tells us that when solid carbon and gaseous oxygen react at $25°C$ and the carbon dioxide is cooled to $25°C$, the heat liberated is 94,050 cal/g-mole CO_2; a reaction like this that gives off heat is called *exothermic*. An *endothermic* reaction is one that absorbs heat; for example,

$$CO_{2(g)} \rightarrow CO_{(g)} + 1/2\ O_{2(g)} \qquad \Delta H = +67{,}600 \text{ cal/g-mole} \qquad (5.78)$$

The signs are arbitrarily chosen to be positive for exothermic reactions and negative for endothermic reactions.

Hess's law of heat summation.   Hess showed in 1840 that the overall heat evolved or absorbed in a chemical reaction proceeding in several steps is equal to the algebraic sum of the enthalpies of the various stages. These chemical equations may be treated like ordinary algebraic equations.

5.9   HEAT OF FORMATION

The heat of formation of a compound is the change in enthalpy of the reaction through which one mole of the compound is made from its elements.

The heat of formation of the elements, at a pressure of 1 atm and a temperature of 25°C, is conveniently chosen to be zero. This convention gives the standard heat of formation (ΔH^0_f) of all desired compounds. The *standard heat of reaction* (ΔH^0) is found from the standard heats of formation of the reactants and products, as follows:

$$\Delta H^0{}_{\text{reaction}} = \Delta H^0_{f\,\text{products}} - \Delta H^0_{f\,\text{reactants}}$$

5.10   HEAT OF COMBUSTION

The heats of combustion for many organic compounds are available for determining heats of reaction and formation. The usual heat of combustion refers to oxidation of all carbon to $CO_{2(g)}$ and all hydrogen to $H_2O_{(l)}$. If other products are present, their final form must be specified, such as sulfur to SO_2, SO_3, or the corresponding acids. The measurement is ordinarily made in a Parr combustion bomb.

5.11   HEATS OF NEUTRALIZATION, SOLUTION, AND DILUTION

Dilute solutions of strong acids react with dilute solutions of strong bases, and the neutralization reaction, which is

$$H^+ + OH^- \rightarrow H_2O \qquad (5.79)$$

gives off, essentially, a constant amount of heat per mole of H_2O formed. The heat given off per mole of H_2O formed at infinite dilution is called heat of neutralization. The standard value is $-13,360$ cal/mole, as shown in these two reactions of dilute solutions:

$$HNO_3 + NaOH \rightarrow KNO_3 + H_2O \quad \Delta H = -13,870 \text{ cal/mole } H_2O \quad (5.80)$$

$$HCl + NaOH \rightarrow NaCl + H_2O \qquad \Delta H = -13,680 \text{ cal/mole } H_2O \quad (5.81)$$

The heat will vary with the concentration and degree of ionization of the acids and bases involved. Representative values for various compounds are given in Table 5.5.

The solution of a substance in a solvent is usually accompanied by absorption or evolution of heat.

This thermal action is called heat of solution; it is a direct function of the number of moles of solvent used, as shown in Table 5.6.

Table 5.5   HEATS OF NEUTRALIZATION FOR ACIDS AND BASES IN INFINITELY DILUTE SOLUTIONS AT 25°C

Acid	Base	ΔH, cal/g-mole H_2O formed
HCl	NaOH	−13,680
HCl	NH_4OH	−12,400
CH_3COOH	NaOH	−13,300
CH_3COOH	NH_4OH	−12,000
HCN	NaOH	−2,900
HCN	NH_4OH	−1,300

The heat of dilution is equal to the difference between any two heats of solution. For example, the heat of dilution evolved in going from the addition of 1 mole H_2O to the addition of 4 moles H_2O to sulfuric acid is

$$\Delta H_{dilution} = \left(\begin{array}{c} \text{heat of solution} \\ \text{with 4 moles } H_2O \end{array} \right) - \left(\begin{array}{c} \text{heat of solution} \\ \text{with 1 mole } H_2O \end{array} \right)$$

$$= [(-13,010) - (-6740)] \text{ cal/mole } H_2SO_4$$

$$= -6270 \text{ cal/mole } H_2SO_4$$

5.12   HEAT OF REACTION AS A FUNCTION OF TEMPERATURE

We have seen that the heat of reaction at a given temperature, usually 25°C, is well tabulated in the literature. However, we often need to know this heat of

Table 5.6   HEATS OF SOLUTION OF ONE g-MOLE H_2SO_4 IN H_2O AT 18°C

Moles of H_2O	ΔH, cal/g-mole of dissolved substance
0.00	0
0.11	−920
0.43	−3,300
1.00	−6,740
4.00	−13,010

reaction, which is a function of temperature, at temperatures other than 25°C. We know that, for a chemical reaction,

$$\Delta H = H_{\text{products}} - H_{\text{reactants}} \tag{5.82}$$

Differentiating the above equation with respect to temperature at constant pressure, we get

$$\left[\frac{\partial(\Delta H)}{\partial T}\right]_P = \left[\frac{\partial(H_{\text{products}})}{\partial T}\right]_P - \left[\frac{\partial(H_{\text{reactants}})}{\partial T}\right]_P \tag{5.83}$$

From the definition of C_p we get

$$\left[\frac{\partial(\Delta H)}{\partial T}\right]_P = \left[C_{p\,(\text{products})} - C_{p\,(\text{reactants})}\right]$$

$$= \Delta C_p \tag{5.84}$$

Let us integrate this equation:

$$\int_{\Delta H_0}^{\Delta H_T} d(\Delta H) = \int_{T_0}^T \Delta C_p dT$$

or

$$\Delta H_T = \Delta H_0 + \int_{T_0}^T \Delta C_p dT \tag{5.85}$$

where

ΔH_T = heat of reaction at temperature T

ΔH_0 = heat of reaction at T_0, usually 25°C (reference temperature)

Note that the C_p of a given component must be multiplied by the number of moles of that component in order to have ΔH in calories or Btu.

Example 5.14 Hess's law and thermochemical equations

Determine the enthalpy change at 25°C for the reaction

$$C_{(s)} + 1/2\,O_{2(g)} \rightarrow CO_{(g)} \tag{A}$$

Given at 25°C, we have

$$C_{(s)} + O_{2(g)} \rightarrow CO_{2(g)} \qquad \Delta H = -94{,}050 \text{ cal/g-mole} \qquad \textbf{(B)}$$

$$CO_{(g)} + 1/2\, O_{2(g)} \rightarrow CO_{2(g)} \qquad \Delta H = -67{,}600 \text{ cal/g-mole} \qquad \textbf{(C)}$$

Solution

Reaction C written in reverse order is

$$CO_{2(g)} \rightarrow CO_{(g)} + 1/2\, O_{2(g)} \qquad \Delta H = 67{,}600 \text{ cal/g-mole}$$

Add this to reaction B:

$$C_{(s)} + O_{2(g)} \rightarrow CO_{2(g)} \qquad \Delta H = -94{,}050 \text{ cal/g-mole}$$

We get

$$CO_{2(g)} + C_{(s)} + O_{2(g)} \rightarrow CO_{(g)} + 1/2\, O_{2(g)} + CO_{2(g)} + 67{,}600 - 94{,}050$$

or

$$C_{(s)} + 1/2\, O_{2(g)} \rightarrow CO_{(g)} \qquad \Delta H = -26{,}450 \text{ cal/g-mole} \quad \triangleleft$$

Example 5.15 Standard heat of reaction

Find ΔH^0 for the reaction

$$NO + 1/2\, O_2 \rightarrow NO_2$$

Given:

Substance	ΔH^0_f (Btu/lb-mole)
$NO_{(g)}$	+38,800
$O_{2(g)}$	0
$NO_{2(g)}$	+14,564

Solution

$$\Delta H^0 = \Delta H^0_{products} - \Delta H^0_{reactants}$$
$$= (1 \times 14{,}564) - (1 \times 38{,}800 + 1/2 \times 0)$$
$$= -24{,}236 \text{ Btu/lb-mole} \quad \triangleleft$$

This is an exothermic reaction (heat is given off and ΔH^0 is negative).

Example 5.16   Standard heat of formation from a combustion reaction

The combustion of propane gives

$$C_3H_{8(g)} + 5O_{2(g)} \rightarrow 3CO_{2(g)} + 4H_2O_{(l)} \qquad \Delta H^0 = -530,600 \text{ cal/g-mole}$$

Find ΔH_f^0 for $C_3H_{8(g)}$.

Solution

$$\Delta H^0 = \text{heat of combustion} - \Delta H_{f \text{ products}}^0 - \Delta H_{f \text{ reactants}}^0$$

or

$$-530,600 = [3(-94,050) + 4(-68,302)]$$
$$-[\Delta H_f^0 \; C_3H_{8(g)} + 5 \times 0]$$
$$\Delta H_f^0 \; C_3H_{8(g)} = -24,830 \text{ cal/mole}$$

Checking this value against that obtained from the elements, we find

$$3C_{(s)} + 4H_{2(g)} \rightarrow C_3H_{8(g)} \qquad \Delta H^0 = -24,830 \text{ cal/mole} \quad \triangleleft$$

which is the same as above.

**Example 5.17   Change of heat of reaction with temperature
for the catalytic oxidation of ammonia**

What is the heat of reaction at $1800°F$ for

$$4NH_{3(g)} + 5O_{2(g)} \rightarrow 4NO_{(g)} + 6H_2O_{(g)}$$

Given:

$$\Delta H^0 = -389,208 \text{ Btu/4 lb-moles NH}_3$$

Component (all gaseous)	Average heat capacity between 77°F and 1800°F (Btu/lb-mole-°F)
NH_3	11.7
O_2	7.9
NO	7.8
H_2O	9.2

Solution

Let the base temperature be $77°F$ ($25°C$) and let us use the equation

$$\Delta H_{1800°F} = \Delta H_{77°F} + \int_{77°F}^{1800°F} \Delta C_p dT$$

$$= -389{,}208 + [4(7.8)(1800-77) + 6(9.2)(1800-77)]$$

$$-[4(11.7)(1800-77) + 5(7.9)(1800-77)]$$

$$= -389{,}200 + 172.3$$

and

$$\Delta H_{1800°F} = -389{,}035.7 \text{ Btu/4 lb-moles NH}_3$$

In this case the change, $+172.3$, is insignificant.

Example 5.18   Heat of reaction

CO_2 is reduced to CO according to the reaction

$$CO_2 + C \rightarrow 2CO$$

How much heat (Btu/lb-mole of CO product) is evolved when this reaction is carried out isothermally at $825°C$? The average heat capacities for CO_2, C, and CO are 12.0, 4.8, and 7.6 Btu/lb-mole-$°F$, respectively.

Solution

Using the heat of formation we get

$$CO_2 \rightarrow C + O_2 \qquad \Delta H = +94{,}050$$

$$2C + O_2 \rightarrow 2CO \qquad \Delta H = 2(-26{,}450)$$

$$= -52{,}900$$

$$CO_2 + C \rightarrow 2CO \qquad \Delta H = +41.15 \frac{\text{kcal}}{\text{g-mole of CO}_2}$$

$$\Delta H_{825°C} = \Delta H_{25°C} + \int_{25°C}^{825°C} (\Delta C_p)\, dT$$

$$C_p, \text{[Btu/lb-mole-}^\circ\text{F]} = C_p, \text{[cal/g-mole-}^\circ\text{C]}$$

$$\Delta H_{825^\circ C} = 41{,}150 + 2(7.6)(825 - 25) - 4.8(825 - 25)$$
$$-(12.0)(825 - 25)$$

$$= 41{,}150 + 12{,}160 - 13{,}440 = 39{,}870 \frac{\text{cal}}{2 \text{ g-moles CO}}$$

$$39{,}870 \frac{\text{cal}}{\text{g-mole}} \frac{\text{Btu}}{252 \text{ cal}} \frac{454 \text{ g}}{\text{lb}_m} = 39{,}870 \times 1.8 \frac{\text{cal}}{2 \text{ lb-moles CO}}$$

$$\frac{39{,}870 \times 1.8}{2} = 35{,}883 \text{ Btu/lb-moles CO} \quad \triangleleft$$

Example 5.19 Change of heat of reaction with temperature for HCl formation

Find the heat of reaction at 1000°K for this reaction:

$$1/2 \, H_{2(g)} + 1/2 \, Cl_{2(g)} \rightarrow HCl_{(g)}$$

Given:

$$\Delta H_{298^\circ K} = -22{,}060 \text{ cal}$$

Component (all gaseous)	Average heat capacity between 298°K and 1000°K (cal/g-mole-°K)
H_2	6.8
Cl_2	7.7
HCl	6.8

Solution

$$\Delta H_{1000^\circ K} = \Delta H_0 + \int_{298}^{1000} \Delta C_p dT$$

$$= -22{,}060 + [1(6.8)(1000 - 298)]$$
$$-[1/2(6.8)(1000 - 298) + 1/2(7.7)(1000 - 298)]$$
$$= 22{,}376 \text{ cal} \quad \triangleleft$$

**Example 5.20 Change of heat of reaction with temperature
in the formation of ammonia**

Given the reaction

$$\frac{1}{2} N_{2(g)} + \frac{3}{2} H_{2(g)} \rightarrow NH_{3(g)}$$

$$\Delta H_{298°K} = -11,040 \text{ cal}$$

and

Component (all gaseous)	C_p (cal/g-mole-$°K$)
N_2	$6.8 + 0.6 \times 10^{-3}T + 1.3 \times 10^{-7}T^2$
H_2	$6.6 + 0.8 \times 10^{-3}T$
NH_3	$6.2 + 7.9 \times 10^{-3}T - 7.3 \times 10^{-7}T^2$

Find the heat of reaction at $1000°K$.

Solution

$$\Delta H_{1000°K} = \Delta H_{298°K} + \int_{298°K}^{1000°K} \Delta C_p dT$$

$$= -11,040 + \int_{298}^{1000} (1)(6.2 + 7.9 \times 10^{-3}T - 7.3 \times 10^{-7}T^2)$$

$$- [(1/2(6.8 + 0.6 \times 10^{-3}T + 1.3 \times 10^{-7}T^2)$$

$$+ \frac{3}{2}(6.6 + 0.8 \times 10^{-3}T)] \, dT$$

or

$$\Delta H_{1000°K} = -11,040 + \int_{298}^{1000} [-7.1 + 6.4 \times 10^{-3}T - 7.9 \times 10^{-7}T^2] dT$$

$$= -11,040 + \left[-7.1T + 6.4 \times 10^{-3}\frac{T^2}{2} - \frac{7.9 \times 10^{-7}T^3}{3} \right]_{298}^{1000}$$

and finally,

$$\Delta H_{1000°K} = -13,390 \text{ calories} \quad \lhd$$

5.13   THEORETICAL FLAME TEMPERATURE (TFT)

The heat generated in burning fuels, along with any sensible heat of the fuels and the air, all cause a temperature rise in the gaseous product of combustion. If there is no heat loss to the surroundings, the maximum temperature reached in the complete combustion is called the theoretical flame temperature (see Figure 5.16). This temperature sets an upper limit for a given reaction, and it is useful in selecting the type of material to be used in the design of a reactor. The actual measured temperature is considerably lower than the adiabatic flame temperature due to both heat loss to the surroundings and dissociation of the combustion products.

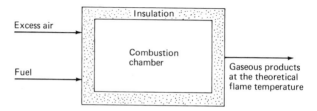

Figure 5.16. Theoretical flame temperature (TFT)

TFT computations require a heat balance and a choice of base temperature. For the steady state in Figure 5.16, we have

(Heat in, due to reaction) + (enthalpy of input material)

                                         = (enthalpy of product)   **(5.86)**

With a base temperature t_b, we have

$$n_f \Delta H_r + \int_{t_b}^{t_{air}} m_{air} C_{p_{air}} \, dt + \int_{t_b}^{t_f} m_{fuel} C_{p_{fuel}} \, dt$$

$$= m_{H_2O} C_{p(H_2O)}(100 - t_b) + m_{H_2O} \Delta H_{v(H_2O)} + \int_{100°C}^{TFT} m_{H_2O} C_{p[H_2O(g)]} \, dt$$

$$+ \int_{t_b}^{TFT} m_{CO_2} C_{p(CO_2)} \, dt + \int_{t_b}^{TFT} m_{N_2} C_{p(N_2)} \, dt + \int_{t_b}^{TFT} m_{O_2} C_{p(O_2)} \, dt$$

$$\tag{5.87}$$

where

$$n_f = \text{moles of fuel}$$

$$\Delta H_r = \text{heat of reaction (for this case it is taken at } t_b, \\ \text{with water in the liquid state)}$$

$$m = \text{mass or moles of various components}$$

$$\Delta H_v = \text{heat of vaporization of water at } 100°C$$

If the inlet temperature is the same as the base temperature and if ΔH_r at 25°C includes water in the vapor state, Equation 5.87 simplifies to

$$n_f \Delta H_r = \int_{t_b}^{TFT} m_i C_{p_i} dt \qquad (5.88)$$

where

$$m_i = \text{mass or moles of the } i^{\text{th}} \text{ component in the product}$$

$$C_{p_i} = \text{heat capacity of the } i^{\text{th}} \text{ component in the product}$$

If average heat capacities are given, Equation 5.88 becomes

$$n_f \Delta H_r = m_i C_{p_i} (TFT - t_b) \qquad (5.89)$$

However, due to the variation of C_p with temperature, integration is often used, and TFT computations usually lead to a quadratic or cubic equation that can be solved by trial and error.

Example 5.21   Adiabatic reaction temperature of ethyl alcohol

What is the adiabatic reaction temperature for the combustion of ethyl alcohol with 25% excess air? The alcohol and air are supplied at 25°C; water formed in the reaction is in the vapor state.

Solution

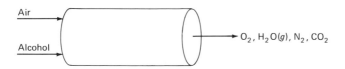

$$C_2H_5OH + 3O_2 \rightarrow 2CO_2 + 3H_2O$$

Basis: 1 mole of alcohol, base temperature = 25°C.

$$(3)(0.25) = 0.75 \text{ moles excess } O_2$$

or

$$3.0 + 0.75 = 3.75 \text{ moles (total } O_2)$$

$$\text{moles of } N_2 = (3.75)(79/21) = 14.1 \text{ moles}$$

Exit stream composition:

Component	Number of moles
O_2	0.75
H_2O	3.00
N_2	14.10
CO_2	2.00

Alcohol is liquid at 25°C and a pressure of 1 atm. The standard heat of combustion is $\Delta H_C = -326.70$ k-cal/mole. This quantity of energy must therefore be used to vaporize 3 moles of water at 25°C and then heat 2 moles of CO_2, 3 moles of H_2O vapor, 0.75 moles of O_2, and 14.1 moles of N_2 to the final temperature T. Hence

$$326{,}700 = (3)(10{,}520)^* + 2 \int_{298°K}^{T} (6.214 + 0.010396T - 3.45 \times 10^{-6}T^2) \, dT$$

$$+ 3 \int_{298°K}^{T} (7.256 + 0.00298T + 0.283 \times 10^{-6}T^2) \, dT$$

$$+ 0.75 \int_{298°K}^{T} (6.148 + 0.003102T - 0.923 \times 10^{-6}T^2) \, dT$$

$$+ 14.1 \int_{298°K}^{T} (6.524 + 0.00125T - 0.001 \times 10^{-6}T^2) \, dT$$

*The number 10,520 cal/g-mole is the latent heat of vaporization of water.

Combining the integrals, we get

$$295{,}140 = \int_{298°K}^{T} (130.8 + 0.0476T - 6.94 \times 10^{-6} T^2)\, dT$$

$$295{,}140 = 130.8\,(T - 298) + 0.0238\,[T^2 - (298)^2]$$

$$-2.31 \left[\left(\frac{T}{100}\right)^3 - (2.98)^3 \right]$$

Neglect second and third order terms for first trial; assume that $T = 2250°K$.

$$295{,}140 = 130.8\,(T - 298) + 0.0238\,[(2250)^2 - (298)^2]$$

$$-2.31\,[(25.5)^3 - (2.98)^3]$$

$$= 130.9\,(T - 298) + 152{,}500 - 38{,}200$$

$$T - 298 = 180{,}800/130.9 = 1380$$

$$T = 1680°K \quad (T \text{ assumed was too high})$$

By continued trial and error we get

$$\text{TFT} = T = 1990°K = 1717°C$$

Example 5.22   Theoretical flame temperature (TFT)

Certain natural gas has this composition:

Component	Mole %
CH_4	85
C_2H_4	3
C_6H_6	3
H_2	5
N_2	4
Total	100

Find the theoretical flame temperature for these two cases:

1. Natural gas and theoretical air enter the reactor at room temperature.

2. Natural gas is burned with 20% excess air. This air is humid, contains 1.5% water vapor, and is preheated to 600°C prior to entering the combustion chamber.

Given: From stoichiometry the gaseous products are

Component	Volume (m^3)
CO_2	1.09
H_2O	1.90
N_2	7.72

Solution

Basis: 1 m^3 of natural gas.

The combustion reactions are

$$CH_4 + 2O_2 \rightarrow CO_2 + 2H_2O$$
$$C_2H_4 + 3O_2 \rightarrow 2CO_2 + 2H_2O$$
$$C_6H_6 + 7\ 1/2\ O_2 \rightarrow 6CO_2 + 3H_2O$$
$$H_2 + 1/2\ O_2 \rightarrow H_2O$$

1. Let us use a base temperature of 25°C.

(Heat of combustion) + (sensible heat from fuel) + (sensible heat from air)

$$= [m\ C_p\ (\text{TFT} - t_{\text{base}})]_{\text{product}}$$

Data for the heat of combustion are given below:

Component	Calorific value (cal/m^3)
CH_4	0.85 X 8,560* = 7276
C_2H_4	0.03 X 14,480 = 434
C_6H_6	0.03 X 33,490 = 1005
H_2	0.05 X 2,582 = 129
Total	8844

*The number 8560 cal/m^3 is the calorific value of methane, CH_4.

Sensible heat from the fuel is expressed by

$$\Sigma m_i \, C_{p_i} (\text{inlet temperature} - \text{base temperature})$$

$$= \Sigma m_i \, C_{p_i} (25°C - 25°C) = 0$$

Sensible heat from the air is

$$(m \, C_p \Delta T)_{\text{air}} = m \, C_p (\text{inlet temperature} - \text{base temperature})$$

$$= m \, C_p (25°C - 25°C) = 0$$

Now let us find

$$[m \, C_p (\text{TFT} - t_{\text{base}})]_{\text{products}}$$

From the literature we find

Component	$C_{p(\text{avg})}$ (cal/m³-°C)
CO_2	$0.406 + 9 \times 10^{-5}t$
H_2O	$0.373 + 5 \times 10^{-5}t$
N_2	$0.302 + 2.2 \times 10^{-5}t$
O_2	$0.302 + 2.22 \times 10^{-5}t$

For the inlet, t is the temperature of the feed. For the outlet, t is the temperature of the gaseous product. For the products, let us represent TFT by t.

$$[m \, C_p{}^* (\text{TFT} - t_{\text{base}})]_{\text{products}} = [1.09 \, (0.406 + 9 \times 10^{-5}t)$$

$$+ 1.90 \, (0.373 + 5 \times 10^{-5}t) + 7.72 \, (0.302 + 2.2 \times 10^{-5}t)]$$

$$[t - 25°C] = 8844$$

after simplification,

$$8844 = 3.48t + 3.6 \times 10^{-4}t^2 - 87$$

or

$$3.6 \times 10^{-4}t^2 + 3.48t - 8757 = 0$$

Solve this quadratic equation by trial and error:

$*C_p$ is evaluated at the TFT.

t assumed	t found
2000	2100
2100	2090
2090	2090

Theoretical flame temperature $= \text{TFT} = t = 2090°C$

2. By stoichiometry, the theoretical amount of oxygen used is

$$1.70 + 0.09 + 0.225 + 0.025 = 2.040 \text{ m}^3$$

and the dry air theoretically required is

$$2.04 \times \frac{100}{21} = 9.72 \text{ m}^3$$

$$\text{Total dry air} = 9.72 + 9.72 \times \frac{20}{100} = 11.66 \text{ m}^3$$

Humid air contains 1.5% H_2O and 98.5% dry air, thus:

$$\text{Total humid air} = 11.66 \frac{100}{98.5} = 11.84 \text{ m}^3$$

$$H_2O \text{ in humid air} = 11.84 - 11.66 = 0.18 \text{ m}^3$$

$$\text{Total heat available} = 11.66 \, (0.302 + 2.2 \times 10^{-5} \times 600) \, (600 - 25)$$
$$+ \, 0.18 \, (0.373 + 5 \times 10^{-5} \times 600) \, (600 - 25)$$
$$+ \, 8,844 \approx 11,000 \text{ cal}$$

For this case, the products of combustion are increased by the excess air and the moisture in the air. Thus

Component in gaseous product	Volume (m^3)
CO_2	1.09
H_2O	$1.90 + 0.18 = 2.08$
N_2	$11.66 \times \frac{79}{100} = 9.21$
O_2	$1.94 \times \frac{21}{100} = 0.41$

Therefore

$$11,000 = [1.09\,(0.406 + 9 \times 10^{-5})$$
$$+\ 2.08\,(0.373 + 5 \times 10^{-5}t)$$
$$+\ 9.21\,(0.302 + 2.2 \times 10^{-5}t)$$
$$+\ 0.41\,(0.302 + 2.22 \times 10^{-5}t)]\qquad [t - 25]$$

or

$$11,000 = 4.136t + 4.0 \times 10^{-4}t^2$$
$$\text{TFT} = t \approx 2200°\text{C}$$

Part III: Material and Energy Interaction in Pollution Control*

Energy is the backbone of the industrial revolution; its production and use typify vivid examples in material and energy balances. The processes in between contribute very heavily to the pollution of our environment. The control of serious pollution is a must! The associated processes, especially in air pollution control, constitute ideal cases where material and energy balances are best applied. Prior to describing such processes, groundwork should cover pollution and air pollution abatement.

5.14 WHAT IS POLLUTION?

Pollution is the impairment of the purity of the atmosphere, water, and land by various noxious chemicals and refuse materials. To pollute is to render unclean and cause harm in varying degrees, depending on the concentration and type of pollutant. We speak of air pollution, water pollution, thermal pollution, and noise pollution. The air we breathe may contain harmful concentrations of sulfur dioxide, carbon monoxide, or hydrocarbons. Many lakes and rivers that were a beautiful sight refreshing to the eyes, brain and body have become badly polluted by industrial waste; even a swim in these bodies of water would be out of the question, let alone the survival of marine organisms. Various industries may discharge hot waste into rivers and lakes, rendering these thermally polluted and thus killing fish and other marine life. Can you imagine how nerve-wracking noise

*Taken from E. I. Shaheen, 1974, *Environmental pollution, awareness and control*, with permission from Engineering Technology Inc, Mahomet, Illinois; see this reference for further readings covering the environmental spectrum.

could be in some factory, especially for workers who stay with it eight hours a day or more? Have you ever been disturbed by the screeching noise of a subway, or the honking of horns in a city?

While the pollution problem has existed for centuries, the present-day industrial boom and population explosion have made it a critical one. Throughout the entire world, there is a great awareness; and especially in the United States, action is being taken on many fronts. The environmentalists succeeded in blocking and delaying the construction of the Alaska oil pipeline. Directly or indirectly resulting from the wave of environmentalist power and international politics, the topic of the day became "the energy crisis." Is it real? Or is it a designed counterattack?

Pollution tax, which is a levy on sulfur oxide emissions from industrial smoke stacks, is being seriously considered; so also is legislation to regulate the dumping of wastes on land or in wells, and control of sediment runoffs from construction sites. There is even a movement to charge federal taxes on gasolines with lead additives and on fuels containing excessive concentrations of sulfur. In an environmental message to Congress, it was declared, "the time has come for man to make his peace with nature . . . it is literally now or never." The call in the sixties was to reach the moon. The mission for the seventies, or the environmental decade, is to solve our energy problems, clean our environment, and combat pollution.

5.15 WHAT IS AIR POLLUTION?

The American Medical Association defines air pollution as "the excessive concentration of foreign matter in the air which adversely affects the well-being of the individual or causes damage to property." When we speak of air pollution, many think of the products of combustion and the emissions from various industries. This type of pollution includes gases, fumes, and fine solids from power plants and oil operations; exhausts from aircraft, automobiles, buses, trucks, and locomotives; products of incinerators; and radioactive fallout. There are pollutants in the air caused by nature not man; among these are forest fires ignited by lightning, gaseous and dust emissions from volcanoes, decaying vegetation, pollens, sand, and dust stirred by storms, bacteria and viruses activated at given intervals of the year cycle.

Major air pollution episodes took place in various parts of the world, causing great loss to human life, animal life, and seriously damaging vegetation. These disasters occurred in: the Meuse Valley, Belgium, 1930; the city of Donora, Pennsylvania, U.S.A., 1948; London, 1952; New York, U.S.A., 1953 and 1963; Poza Rica, Mexico, 1950; and the city of Los Angeles, U.S.A.

Table 5.7   ESTIMATED EMISSIONS OF AIR POLLUTANTS BY WEIGHT FOR THE U.S., 1969 (MILLIONS OF TONS PER YEAR)

Source	CO	Particulates	SO_x	Hydrocarbons	NO_x	Total	Percent change 1968-1969*
Transportation	111.5	0.8	1.1	19.8	11.2	144.4	−1.0
Fuel combustion in stationary sources	1.8	7.2	24.4	.9	10.0	44.3	+2.5
Industrial processes	12.0	14.4	7.5	5.5	0.2	39.6	+7.3
Solid waste disposal	7.9	1.4	0.2	2.0	0.4	11.9	−1.0
Miscellaneous	18.2	11.4	0.2	9.2	2.0	41.0	+18.5
Total	151.4	35.2	33.4	37.4	23.8	281.2	+3.2
Percent change	+1.3	+10.7	+5.7	+1.1	+4.8	—	—

*Computed by the 1969 method from the difference between 1969 estimates and 1968 estimates. The new method results in higher values for 1968 than those computed by EPA for 1968.

Source: The Mitre Corp. MTR-6013. Based on Environmental Protection Agency data. Council on Environmental Quality Report, August 1971.

The huge amount of air pollutants emitted per year is best illustrated in Table 5.7, and the most frequently encountered ones are shown in Table 5.8. Stringent air pollution control regulations must be met; the National Ambient Air Quality Standards, given in Table 5.9, have been issued by the Environmental Protection Agency; they constitute the backbone of such regulations. These standards are the basic criteria for a successful abatement program.

Table 5.8   MOST FREQUENTLY ENCOUNTERED AIR CONTAMINANTS

General type	Specific examples
Halogens	HF, HCl
Nitrogen compounds	NO, NO_2, NH_3
Organic matter	Aldehydes, hydrocarbons
Oxygen compounds	Ozone, CO, CO_2
Radioactive substances	Radioactive gases, aerosols
Solids	Fly ash, ZnO, $PbCl_2$, Pb, Be, asbestos
Sulfur compounds	SO_2, SO_3, H_2SO_4 mist, H_2S, mercaptans

Table 5.9   NATIONAL AMBIENT AIR QUALITY STANDARDS

Type of pollutant	Primary standards, pollutant concentration; enforcement by summer 1975		Secondary standards, optimum pollutant concentration; no time limit on enforcement	
	$\mu g/m^3$	ppm	$\mu g/m^3$	ppm
Carbon monoxide				
maximum 8-hr concentration	10,000	9.00	10,000	9.00
maximum 1-hr concentration	40,000	35.00	40,000	35.00
Hydrocarbons				
maximum 3-hr concentration				
(6-9 A.M.)	160	0.24	160	0.24
Nitrogen oxides				
annual arithmetical average	100	0.05	100	0.05
Particulate solids				
geometric mean per year	75		60	
maximum 24-hr concentration	260		150	
Photochemical oxidants				
maximum 1-hr concentration	160	0.08	160	0.08
Sulfur oxides				
annual arithmetical average	80	0.03	60	0.02
maximum 24-hr concentration	365	0.14	260	0.10
maximum 3-hr concentration	–	–	1300	0.50

Any maximum concentration reported here should not occur more than once a year.

Air pollution control equipment is used to prevent these pollutants from being a health hazard and from causing damage to property, plants, and animal life. In this course the recovery of useful substances from waste will minimize any economic losses. Four basic units will be briefly described here.

5.16   TYPICAL UNITS USED IN AIR POLLUTION CONTROL

These are the fabric or bag filter, cyclone separator, electrostatic precipitator, and the spray tower or scrubber.

Fabric Filters

The most common among fabric filters is the bag filter, which is similar to a large vacuum cleaner. Bags of various shapes are made of porous fabrics which can withstand temperature, chemical action, and preserve their strength.

The dust-laden gases pass through the fabric, which filters out the dust and lets the cleaner air through.

Cyclone Separator

The cyclone separator is the most widely used type of dust collector. It consists basically of a cylindrical or conical chamber. The dust-laden air enters the chamber tangentially at the top; the particles separate and settle at the bottom, and the cleaner air exits from another opening at the top as shown in Figure 5.17. The centrifugal forces, resulting from the tangential velocity of the air, carry the particles toward the wall of the cyclone, where they are led to a bottom receiver due to gravity and the descending vortex of the gas stream. The cyclone is essentially a settling chamber where gravitational acceleration of the particles is replaced by centrifugal accleration.

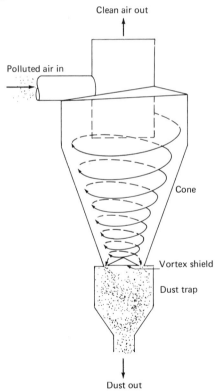

Figure 5.17.   Cyclone separator

Electrostatic Precipitators

These units are used for separating dust particles and mist from a polluted air stream. An electrostatic field imparts a charge on the particles, which are then attracted to a collecting electrode of an opposite charge. The polluted air passes over a high-voltage negative electrode whose voltage is of the order of 40,000 volts, or could be as high as 100,000 volts. An ionized atmosphere is created where the negative ions will engulf the dust and mist and give them a negative charge. Being negatively charged, these particles are carried through the gas at velocities of the order of 100 ft/sec and become attracted to the grounded or positively charged electrodes. The particles are then removed mechanically into a hopper for eventual disposal. This is clearly illustrated in Figure 5.18, where the collecting electrodes are parallel plates. These plates are generally 3 to 6 ft wide and 10 to 18 ft high.

Scrubbers

A scrubber is a "scrubbing" device which utilizes liquid, usually water, to assist in removing particulate matter, liquid or gaseous contaminants from a polluted air stream. Gas scrubbers, or wet scrubbers, are compact units requiring little maintenance and often giving the economic answer to air pollution abatement. The separation results from the direct collision of the dust particles with the water droplets. The larger particles, unable to maneuver and diverge around the droplets with the air because of their inertia, continue on a collision path and

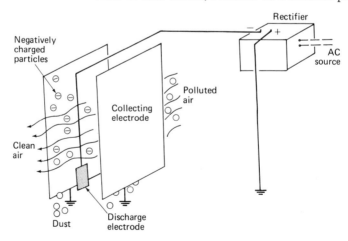

Figure 5.18.   Electrostatic precipitator (using parallel plates)

thus are carried with the down-flowing water. Separation also takes place due to gravitation and electrostatic effects. The example chosen is the spray tower, which is an absorber consisting of an empty cylinder, or tower, into which water is sprayed at the top through nozzles located at various points in the tower. The dirty air is introduced at the bottom and rises upward, making intimate contact with the sprayed water. The spraying of water, breaking it into droplets, increases the area of contact between the gas and the liquid, and thus promotes the separation as shown in Figure 5.19. A typical spray tower may have the dimensions: 36 in. diameter and 48 in. height.

These units and others make up the inherent components for typical processes in air pollution abatement.

5.17 STANDARD PROCESSES FOR REMOVING MAJOR POLLUTANTS

Processes for removing air pollutants are numerous, and describing them would require a complete volume. In this section we will cover the major processes for the removal of sulfur oxides, nitrogen oxides, and hydrogen sulfide.

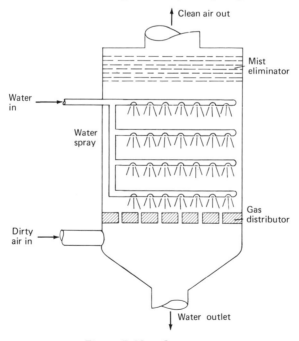

Figure 5.19.   Spray tower

Sulfur Oxides Removal

The leading processes for removing sulfur dioxide from flue gases are described below.

Limestone injection: Wet absorption. This is one of the most popular processes under development. Sulfur oxides, produced from burning oil and coal, react with the calcined products of limestone and dolomite to give some stable removable salts of calcium and sulfur. In this process, limestone and/or dolomite is pulverized along with coal in a mill; it is then fed to the high temperature zone of a furnace, where it is calcined to give CaO and MgO.

The air polluted with sulfur oxides enters a preheater and then goes to the furnace, where the temperature is above $1200°F$ (see Figure 5.20). The alkaline earth additives react with SO_2 and O_2 to give calcium sulfate, $CaSO_4$, called gypsum; some calcium sulfite, $CaSO_3$, is also produced. At this stage 20-30% of the sulfur oxides are removed. All the SO_3 is also removed. The sulfates, fly ash, and the unreacted lime pass through the air preheater on their way to the scrubber; here, water sprays create an intimate contact with the unreacted lime and the remaining SO_2. Sulfates and sulfites are formed, and removed along with particulate matter. The spent liquor from the scrubber and the sulfates, sulfites, and ash are allowed to settle in a settling tank. The scrubber liquor is recycled in order to reduce water requirements and minimize water pollution. The sulfates, sulfites, and ash are, most likely, used as landfill.

The cleaned gas passes through a mist eliminator to remove the remaining water. It is then reheated in a heat exchanger to improve its buoyancy. Part of the flue gas feeding the scrubber is used in the reheater and recycled back to the main stream.

This process was first researched in the U.S. by the Wisconsin Electric, Universal Oil Products, and Combustion Engineering. The removal efficiency of the Combustion Engineering process is guaranteed to be more than 80% for SO_2 and 98% for particulate matter. When the scrubber is replaced by high efficiency precipitators, the process is called dry-limestone injection process.

Lurgi adsorption process. Nearly all adsorption processes use carbon as the adsorbing agent. The Lurgi method is simple, and it is chosen here to illustrate the general approach to the adsorption of SO_2 (see Figure 5.21). Stack gas from a power plant is admitted to a dust collection unit for particulate removal. The gas then proceeds to a cooler and then to the adsorption tower, which is packed with carbon. The carbon adsorbs SO_2, and water is sprayed intermittently to remove

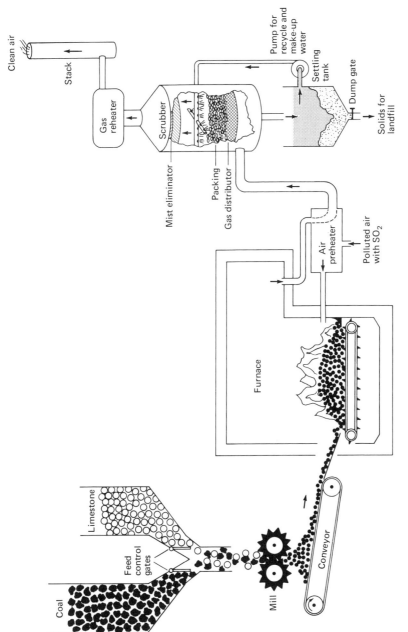

Figure 5.20. Limestone injection: Wet absorption

326

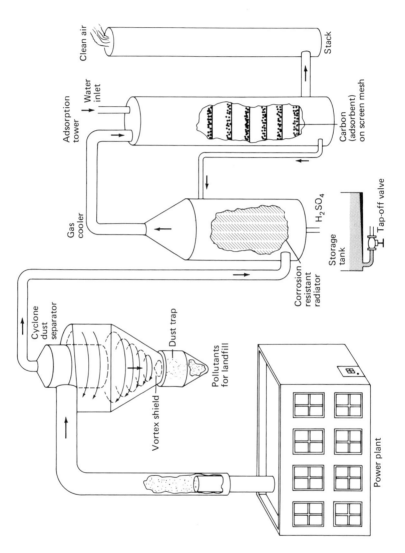

Figure 5.21. Lurgi adsorption process

the adsorbate as a weak acid. The weak acid thus removed from the adsorber is sprayed in a gas cooler, where it becomes slightly enriched due to the intimate contact with the oncoming polluted stream.

The clean gas leaves the adsorption tower to the stacks, and the by-product is the weak sulfuric acid.

Catalytic oxidation (Cat-Ox) process. This is an adaptation of a contact sulfuric acid plant modified to give high heat economy and small pressure drops. Monsanto developed Cat-Ox into the most advanced of the SO_2 removal processes. A fixed-bed catalytic converter is used to oxidize SO_2 to SO_3, so that it may be removed as a salable by-product of sulfuric acid (see Figure 5.22).

Hot flue gas at about $900°F$ coming from a power plant boiler is passed through a cyclone separator and an electrostatic precipitator to trap more than 99.5% of the particulate matter. This high efficiency of solids removal must be achieved so that the catalyst bed will not get plugged. The hot gas at about $880°F$ passes on to a fixed-bed catalytic converter of vanadium pentoxide (V_2O_5). The residence time is of the order of 0.3 sec. More than 90% of the SO_2 is converted to SO_3.

Flue gas from the converter is cooled in an economizer, which is a finned tube exchanger used to heat boiler feedwater. This flue gas, further, preheats the air which goes to the boiler; these steps appreciably improve the heat economy. Both the economizer and the air preheater are operated above $400°F$, since at this temperature sulfuric acid will not condense and cause corrosion.

The flue gas and its sulfuric acid content pass to a packed-bed absorption tower operating in conjunction with an external acid cooler. The cooled sulfuric acid is recycled into the tower, where it will intimately contact the flue gas. The exit gas leaves the top of the absorption tower at about $225°F$. Since this gas contains some acid mist, an electrostatic precipitator is finally used to remove this mist prior to discharging the flue gas to the stack. The acid is removed from the bottom and cooled in the acid cooler. A portion is recycled, while the remainder is stored and marketed.

In this process, essentially all the ash has been removed, and 90% of the SO_2 has been converted to sulfuric acid. The sale of this by-product acid will help in offsetting the operating costs.

To summarize, the basic processes in removing sulfur dioxide and sulfur trioxide from stack gases are essentially those of dry absorption, wet absorption, carbon adsorption, and catalytic oxidation.

Other processes. Although a few processes have been chosen to illustrate the basic approaches in sulfur oxides removal, quite a few other processes are in the

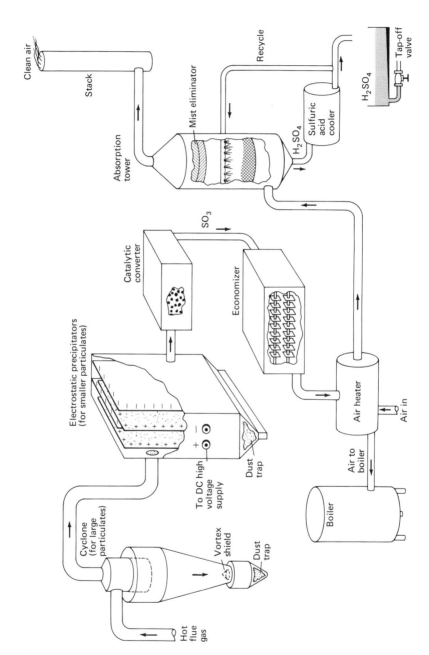

Figure 5.22. Catalytic oxidation (Cat-Ox) process for sulfur oxides removal

developing stage; among these is the *Alkalized Alumina* process, which was developed by the U.S. Bureau of Mines. It is a dry process whereby the absorption agent is sodium aluminate ($Na_2O \cdot Al_2O_3$) at $625°F$. The final product in this process is hydrogen sulfide, H_2S, which is transferred to a Claus unit for reclaiming sulfur.

The *DAP-Mn* process was developed by Mitsubishi Heavy Industries of Japan. This process uses manganese dioxide, MnO_2, as the absorption agent, and the final product is ammonium sulfate. The company claims that 90% of the sulfur dioxide may be removed in this process.

The *Marino* process is an ammonia scrubbing process. This technique has been used for a long time, whereby ammonia scrubbing removes SO_2 from the flue gases. However, recently some development was made by a Mexican company, and thus the name Marino after the brothers who developed it. The final product is ammonium sulfate, which is used as a fertilizer in Mexico, but it does not have a good market in the U.S.

The *Willman-Lord* process uses potassium sulfite, K_2SO_3, as the scrubbing agent. Potassium sulfite absorbs the sulfur dioxide to give potassium bisulfite, $KHSO_3$. Spent liquor is then cooled for the purpose of converting the bisulfite to pyrosulfite, $K_2S_2O_5$, and then steam stripping will give the sulfur dioxide. The final product is sulfur dioxide, which is fed into a sulfuric acid plant. Pilot studies at the Tempa Electric Company indicate that 90% of the sulfur dioxide may be removed in the process.

Reinluft process is an adsorption process where the adsorbent is a slowly moving bed of carbon, formed from semicoke carbonized under high vacuum at $1100°F$. Sulfur dioxide in the polluted stream is oxidized to sulfur trioxide and adsorbed with water on the carbon to form sulfuric acid. The activated carbon along with its adsorbate of sulfuric acid moves then to a regenerating section where the temperature is about $700°F$. The sulfuric acid dissociates into SO_3 and H_2O, and the SO_3 reacts with the carbon to give CO_2 and SO_2. The product gas, sulfur dioxide, is withdrawn from the lower section of the unit to a sulfuric acid plant for further use. This process was developed in Germany and it is under investigation there and in Great Britian.

Kiyoura process is a catalytic process for the recovery of sulfur. The high temperature flue gas goes through a particulate removing unit such as an electrostatic precipitator and then passes on to a catalytic converter consisting of vanadium pentoxide, V_2O_5. Ammonia is then injected into the gas. The ammonia, NH_3, reacts with the SO_3 formed in the catalytic reactor and also with the available water to give a solid substance, namely ammonium sulfate $(NH_4)_2SO_4$. This is a Japanese process which calls for the sale of the by-product; however, the market for ammonium sulfate is limited in the U.S.

Nitrogen Oxides Removal

Two important nitrogen oxides which exist in the atmosphere are nitric oxide, NO, and nitrogen dioxide, NO_2. There are five more oxides of nitrogen which are also known. These are N_2O, N_2O_3, N_2O_4, N_2O_5, and NO_3; N_2O_4 and NO_3 are rather unstable under atmospheric conditions. The oxides of nitrogen are usually represented by the symbol NO_x. In reality the symbol NO_x represents NO_2 and NO, which are the major pollutants we are concerned with when we speak of nitrogen oxide pollutants.

When gas, coal, or fuel oils are burned with air, the nitrogen in the air combines with some of the oxygen according to the reversible reaction:

$$N_2 + O_2 \rightleftharpoons 2NO$$

Whenever NO is formed, the rate of its decomposition becomes very slow under reaction conditions. It is usually formed at high temperatures, and an equilibrium concentration of approximately 2% in air is obtained at $3800°F$.

In the previous section we discussed the limestone wet-scrubbing process for the removal of sulfur dioxide. The same process removes also some nitrogen oxides from the polluted air. Of course, the polluted air in general may contain a combination of SO_2, NO_2 along with a series of other pollutants, depending on the circumstances at hand. Anyway, the wet-scrubbing process removes something like 20% of the nitrogen oxides. Let us now survey some of the basic processes for removing nitrogen oxides.

Reduction with natural gas. This is one of the simplest processes, whereby the natural gas combines with the nitrogen oxides and reduces them to harmless nitrogen and water. It is actually a combustion process, and variations of burners have been designed. One of these is shown in Figure 5.23. The polluted air containing nitrogen oxides in noxious concentrations is fed into a conduit. The reducing gas, such as natural gas, is fed into another conduit. The two streams enter a cylindrical portion, and the resulting mixture passes on to an inverted cone section. This mixture is ignited; the ignition process converts the nitrogen oxides to harmless nitrogen and water which may be discharged safely into the atmosphere. Polluted air must contain sufficient oxygen or another stream of oxygen must be fed in to support the combustion process. The amount of fuel which is necessary for supporting the combustion is very strongly influenced by the velocity at which the gaseous mixture enters into the burner. It has been found that if the combustible mixture enters at 120 ft/sec, the fuel ratio is high, but on the other hand, if the velocity is too low, the quantity of nitrogen oxides which escape unreduced also increases. Velocities above 20 ft/sec are usually used in order to help create some turbulent mixing and thus lessen the possibility of nitrogen oxides escaping the process without combustion. While this process is simple, the economics must be proven, simply because of the cost of energy supporting the combustion. Of course, a catalysis may be added to the process, and this may reduce the cost to some degree. However, since there is no by-product in such a process, it may be useful for small operations. Whenever dealing with power plants, where volumes of stack gas are essentially huge, other processes must be studied for their suitability, keeping in mind a salable by-product recovery which will help offset the expenses of pollution abatement.

Catalytic reduction. This process is usually used to treat the tail gas from nitric acid plants, which has been a nuisance problem for many years, especially because of the offensive reddish-brown plume which is usually associated with nitric acid plants. The catalytic treatment usually uses platinum, palladium, or rhodium as catalysts for speeding the reaction of the nitrogen oxides with the reducing agent, which is normally methane or natural gas. (See Figure 5.24.) The reactions involved are

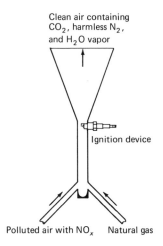

Figure 5.23. NO_x reduction with natural gas

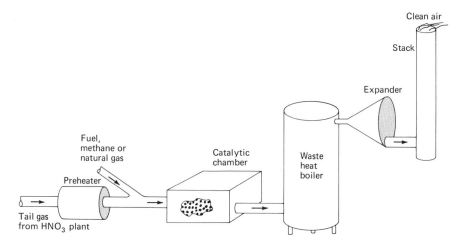

Figure 5.24. Catalytic reduction of NO_x in tail gas

$$CH_4 + 4NO_2 \rightarrow 4NO + CO_2 + 2H_2O \quad \text{(decolorization)}$$

$$CH_4 + 4NO \rightarrow CO_2 + 2H_2O + 2N_2 \quad \text{(abatement)}$$

$$CH_4 + 2O_2 \rightarrow CO_2 + 2H_2O \quad \text{(combustion)} \tag{5.90}$$

The tail gas from a nitric acid plant enters into a preheater. Fuel is then added and the product stream is fed to a catalytic chamber where the reduction takes place. The exit gas passes through a waste heat boiler, and then through an expander to be discharged into the atmosphere. This is, of course, a single stage operation, or single stage reactor. This setup may be repeated more than once, and by repeating this sequence, you could have a two-stage unit rather than one, for better efficiency. The catalyst temperature is usually about 800°C, or 1470°F. Units using palladium catalyst of the Honeycomb type have approximately a one-year life. Catalysts are expensive, and this process does not have any by-product to help in offsetting the cost of pollution abatement equipment.

Tyco process. This process has been developed by Tyco Laboratories, Inc. through their research contract from the National Air Pollution Control Administration. The basic chemistry of the chamber sulfuric acid process is applied for the purpose of removing both sulfur oxides and nitrogen oxides from a polluted air stream.

This process is depicted in Figure 5.25. Concentrated sulfuric acid is used to scrub both the sulfuric acid mist and the nitrogen oxides. This process gives a clean air stream free from nitrogen oxides and sulfur dioxide, and it gives two

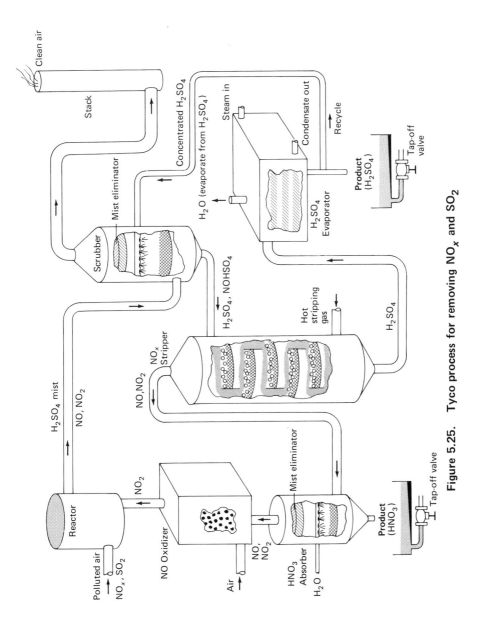

Figure 5.25. Tyco process for removing NO$_x$ and SO$_2$

by-products, namely, nitric acid, HNO_3, and sulfuric acid, H_2SO_4. Both of these products help in improving the economic potential of such a process by rendering the pollution abatement more promising.

Polluted air containing sulfur dioxide and nitrogen oxides enter into a reactor. The stream leaving this reactor consists essentially of sulfuric acid mist, NO, and NO_2, and it enters into a scrubber. The scrubbing agent is concentrated sulfuric acid which scrubs the entering stream from the acid mist and the nitrogen oxides. The exit gas is clean and harmless. The stream leaving the bottom of the scrubber consists of sulfuric acid and nitrogen thiosulfate, $NOHSO_4$. It enters into a nitrogen oxide stripper, whereby the hot stripping gas enters the unit and NO and NO_2 leave the top of the stripper to enter into a nitric acid absorber. Here the water entering the absorber will react with some of the NO and NO_2 to give a product, HNO_3, leaving the bottom of the absorber. At the top of the absorber, the stream consists of nitrogen oxides, again NO and NO_2, which enter into an oxidizer. The oxidizer also receives a stream of air or oxygen and transforms NO to NO_2, which enters the original first reactor, whereby it reacts again with the entering polluted stream.

Sulfuric acid leaving the stripper is concentrated in an evaporator. A certain portion of the acid is taken from the bottom of the evaporator as a product sulfuric acid for sale, and another portion is recycled for use as a scrubbing agent in the scrubber, whereby the nitrogen oxides and acid mist are removed. This process is still in the developing stage; some thought has been given to combining the NO oxidizer and the NO_x stripper. Such combination should help in reducing the equipment cost. The scrubber must have a very high efficiency, in the order of 99%, so that the NO_x balance could be kept in check, especially since a large sum of the NO_x is recycled. Almost ten times as much NO_x is recycled as in the original flue gas. Such precautions may give an overall process efficiency for NO_x removal of 90%.

Magnesium hydroxide scrubbing. In dealing with power plants large sums of nitrogen oxides are released into the atmosphere. Tremendous volumes of flue gas must be dealt with in the cleaning process. For example, a 750 MW gas-fired plant releases almost 5 tons of nitrogen oxides per hour, and the flue gas volume is about 70 million standard cubic feet per hour. This presents tremendous engineering problems and will be very expensive because of the needed equipment and the costly operations.

The magnesium hydroxide scrubbing process is an alkaline process developed by Esso Research & Engineering Co. under contract to the National Air Pollution Control Administration. Based on 1000 MW coal-fired power plant, where the coal contains 3% sulfur, the operating cost of the power plant complex may actually be reduced two cents per kilowatt-hour because of by-product recovery.

The key element in economical pollution abatement is to have a feasible process which will give an air stream free from pollutants and will give a useful, salable by-product.

In this process, the effluent from a power plant containing nitrogen oxides and, of course, some sulfur dioxide, along with other pollutants and particulate matter, enters into a spray tower whereby the particulate matter is removed from the bottom and taken to a settling pond (see Figure 5.26). The water is recycled to the spray tower. The exit gas from this unit enters into a scrubber, whereby the magnesium hydroxide solution enters at the top and the clean air leaves the scrubber at the top. The bottom stream is fed to a settler, where the magnesium sulfite is taken from the bottom to a unit for decomposing $MgSO_3$. Sulfur dioxide is given off and taken to a sulfuric acid plant to give sulfuric acid as a by-product for sale. Magnesium nitrite, $Mg(NO_2)_2$, leaves the settler into a nitrite decomposer, where decomposition takes place, and the magnesium hydroxide enters into a reactor which receives a stream of ammonia and some recycled nitric acid. The product is ammonium nitrate, NH_4NO_3. It is stored for later sale.

The magnesium nitrite decomposer will give a stream leaving at the top and containing nitrogen oxides. This stream will combine with an air stream so that both will be fed into an oxidizer, from which some recycled nitric acid is taken to the ammonia reactor, and from the top, a recycled nitrogen oxide is taken to be fed into the original scrubber. Lime water may be used in place of magnesium hydroxide. However, magnesium hydroxide scrubbing has the potential advantage in the ease of regenerating oxides from the sulfites, and nitrites of magnesium.

Another process must be mentioned here, and that is the selective reaction with *ammonia*, which is capable of reducing NO selectively in an oxygen environment. This is usually done using a platinum catalyst. The product is harmless nitrogen and water:

$$8NH_3 + 6NO_2 \rightarrow 7N_2 + 12H_2O$$
$$4NH_3 + 6NO \rightarrow 5N_2 + 6H_2O$$
$$NH_3 + 3O_2 \rightarrow 2N_2 + 6H_2O \tag{5.91}$$

This process has been used very little in nitric acid plants due to its limited success. However, the potential attraction for using such a process or for doing further work on it is that ammonia serves dual purpose by reducing the nitrogen oxides and by controlling sulfur oxide emissions, both in a single process. In general, this process is only feasible when relatively inexpensive ammonia is available on-site. Other reducing agents may be H_2S and H_2.

Aside from basic processes for NO_x removal, extensive work has been done on combustion modification techniques, which are essentially aimed at preventing nitrogen oxide formations. The results are summarized as follows.

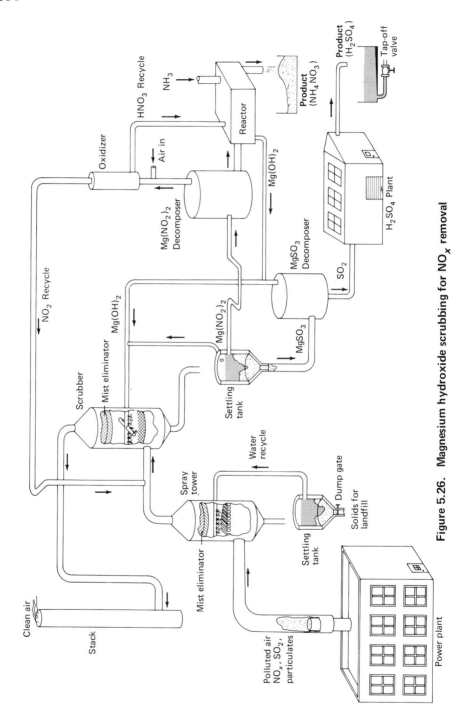

Figure 5.26. Magnesium hydroxide scrubbing for NO$_x$ removal

During combustion, NO_x emissions decrease with a decrease in the excess air, or a decrease in the preheat temperature, or a decrease in the heat release rate, or an increase in backmixing. However, NO_x emissions increase whenever the heat removal rate decreases and whenever the fuel nitrogen content decreases. Fuel gas combustions emit less NO_x than oil or coal, and fuel oil emits less NO_x than coal under similar conditions.

Hydrogen Sulfide Removal

Hydrogen sulfide is not as abundant in the air as nitrogen oxide and sulfur dioxide. If we were to give a detailed process for its removal, it would have to be similar to the processes used for purifying natural gas. Natural gas may contain from 2 to 4% hydrogen sulfide, which is very offensive to the smell, and on top of that, it is an acid which is harmful to the health of humans, animals, and plants, and it causes its share of destruction to solids, whether as H_2S or as SO_2 after combustion. Anyway, at this stage it seems to be satisfactory to present the basic reactions involved in some of the more known processes of hydrogen sulfide removal. These are summarized as follows.

Process or reagent	Reaction	Regeneration
Girbotol	$2RNH_2 + H_2S \rightleftharpoons (RNH_3)_2S$	Steam stripping
Phosphate	$K_3PO_4 + H_2S \rightleftharpoons KHS + K_2HPO_4$	Steam stripping
Seaboard	$Na_2CO_3 + H_2S \rightleftharpoons NaHCO_3 + NaHS$	Air blowing
Caustic soda	$2NaOH + H_2S \rightarrow Na_2S + 2H_2O$	None
Lime	$Ca(OH)_2 + H_2S \rightarrow CaS + 2H_2O$	None

The Girbotol or Ethanolamene process is the popular one used in the U.S. for natural gas purification. Di-Ethanolamene or Mono-Ethanolamene solutions are used to react with hydrogen sulfide. The product is stripped in a steam stripping tower. Finally, pure H_2S is obtained. Pure hydrogen sulfide may be taken through another process for making pure sulfur.

Finally, it should be mentioned here that the single biggest problem in air pollution comes from the use of *automotives*. Extensive research is being done to remove pollutants in the exhaust fumes coming from the internal combustion engine. Some serious thought is being given to replacing this classical engine by a new type of power plant powered by a battery or a fuel cell. The exhaust fumes contain nitrogen oxides, some particulate matter, lead, hydrocarbons, and carbon monoxide. All of these give varying degrees of harm to health. Both catalytic and noncatalytic burners have been proposed, and large sums of money have been spent on research and development toward finding a device which will render car exhaust free from pollution. The problems are numerous, but nevertheless the Air Quality Standards must be met and action is being taken on many fronts.

The exhaust gas contains a small amount of combustible matter and it must be heated to a rather high temperature, approximately 750°C, before it could support combustion. However, driving conditions change from slow speed, to medium, to high, and along with this, the exhaust gas temperature changes. These changes affect the operation of any after-burner device. After-burners have not been proven to be entirely satisfactory.

However, catalytic burners have been used to maintain combustion at normal exhaust temperatures, but catalysts have been poisoned by lead compounds. The catalyst life becomes short, and the device must be replaced. This becomes a burden economically. Lead in the exhaust comes from tetraethyl lead, which is used as an antiknock additive in gasolines. Once the lead poisoning problem is solved, catalytic oxidation would become effective in promoting complete combustion of automotive exhaust. Certainly some thought has been given to develop a device that will remove lead prior to admitting the exhaust gas into the catalyst unit, and pressures are mounting for the development of a lead substitute in gasoline.

NOMENCLATURE

Symbol	Meaning
A	Helmholtz free energy, Btu/lb$_m$, or available area for heat transfer, ft^2
a	Constant in equation of state and Example 5.7
a, b, c	Constants for heat capacity as a function of temperature
B	Bottoms stream, lb$_m$/hr
C_1, C_2	Constants
C_p	Heat capacity at constant pressure, Btu/lb$_m$-°R
C_v	Heat capacity at constant volume, Btu/lb$_m$-°R
D	Tube diameter, ft, or distillate or overhead, lb$_m$/hr
F	Feed, lb$_m$/hr
f	Friction factor, dimensionless

Symbol	Meaning
G	Gibbs free energy, Btu/lb$_m$
g	Gravitational acceleration, ft/sec^2
g_c	$32.2 \dfrac{\text{lb}_m}{\text{lb}_f} \dfrac{\text{ft}}{\text{sec}^2}$
H	Enthalpy, Btu/lb$_m$, subscript indicates stream
h_C	Enthalpy of condensate, Btu/lb$_m$
h_F	Enthalpy of feed, subscript indicates stream, Btu/lb$_m$
h_L	Enthalpy of thick liquor, Btu/lb$_m$
K.E.	Kinetic energy, ft-lb$_f$/lb$_m$
L	Thick liquor, lb$_m$/hr
m	Mass or moles of various components
MW	Molecular weight
N	Number of g-atoms
n	Number of moles in ideal gas law
P	Pressure, mm Hg or psi
P. E.	Potential energy, ft-lb$_f$/lb$_m$
Q	Heat, Btu
Q_c	Heat removed in the condenser, Btu/lb$_m$
Q_r	Heat added in the still or reboiler, Btu/lb$_m$
Q_{rev}	Reversible heat, Btu
R	Gas constant, or reflux, lb$_m$/hr
Re	Reynolds number, dimensionless
S	Entropy, Btu/°R, or stream flow rate, lb$_m$/hr
T	Temperature, °K or °R
T_b	Normal boiling point temperature, °K or °R
T_f	Melting point, °K or °R
t	Temperature, °C or °F
t_1	Inlet temperature of cooling medium, °F
t_2	Outlet temperature, °F

Symbol	Meaning
U	Internal energy, Btu/lb_m, or overall heat transfer coefficient, Btu/hr-ft^2-°F
V	Volume, ft^3, or vapor stream, lb_m/hr
V_1	Top vapor stream, lb_m/hr
v	Average velocity, ft/sec
W	Work, Btu or ft-lb_f/lb_m
W_f'	Shaft work, Btu or ft-lb_f/lb_m
x_F, x_L, x_D	Mass fraction of solute or a component in a liquid stream; the subscript indicates the stream, dimensionless
y	Mass fraction of solute or a component in the vapor, dimensionless
Z	Elevation from datum plane, ft

Greek letters	Meaning
α	Correction factor for Equation 5.6
ΔH_r	Heat of reaction, Btu/lb_m
ΔH_r^0	Standard heat of reaction, Btu/lb_m
ΔH_f^0	Standard heat of formation, Btu/lb_m
ΔH_v	Heat of vaporization, Btu/lb_m
Δt	Temperature gradient = (stream temperature) − (boiling point of solution)
μ	Fluid viscosity, lb_m/ft-sec
ρ	Density, lb_m/ft^3
ΣF	Total friction loss in energy equation, ft-lb_f/lb_m
ΣL	Total length of pipe, ft

REFERENCES

1. Foust, A. S., et al. 1964. *Principles of unit operations.* New York: John Wiley.

2. Gainer, H. G. 1963. Steady state heat and material balances. *Chemical Engineering* 20(2):116.

3. Henley, E. J., and Rosen, E. M. 1969. *Material and energy balance computations.* New York: John Wiley.

4. Hougen, O. A., Watson, K. M., and Ragatz, R. A. 1954, *Chemical process principles: Part I, Material and energy balances.* New York: John Wiley.

5. Johnson, H. F., Professor and Chairman, Department of Chemical Engineering, University of Tennessee, Knoxville, private communication.

6. Maron, S. H., and Prutton, C. F. 1959. *Principles of physical chemistry.* New York: Macmillan.

7. Peck, R. E., Professor of Chemical Engineering, Illinois Institute of Technology, Chicago, private communication.

8. Ranz, W. E. 1970. *Describing chemical engineering systems.* New York: McGraw-Hill.

9. Ravicz, A. E., and Norman, R. L. 1962. Heat and mass balancing on a digital computer. *Chemical Engineering Progress* 60(5):71.

10. Rosen, E. M. 1962. A machine computation method for performing material balances. *Chemical Engineering Progress* 58(10):69.

11. Schmidt, A. X., and List, H. L. 1962. *Material and energy balances.* Englewood Cliffs, N.J.: Prentice-Hall.

Air Pollution Control References

12. American Industrial Hygiene Association. 1968. *Air pollution manual.*

13. Bartok, W., Crawford, A. R., and Skopp, A. 1971. Control of NO_x emissions from stationary sources. *Chemical Engineering Progress* 67(2), 64-72.

14. Chemical Engineering. 1970. Environmental engineering. Deskbook Issue, *Chemical Engineering* 77(9), April 27.

15. Danielson, J. A. 1967. *Air pollution engineering manual.* Washington, D.C.: U.S. Government Printing Office.

16. Detwyler, T. R. 1971. *Man's impact on the environment.* New York: McGraw-Hill.

17. Environmental Science & Technology. 1971. National air quality standards finalized. *Environmental Science & Technology* 5(6):503.

18. Hall, H. J., and Bartok, W. 1971. NO_x control from stationary sources. *Environmental Science & Technology* 5(4):320-326.

19. Manufacturing Chemists' Association, Inc. 1952. *Air pollution abatement manual.* Washington, D.C.

20. Shaheen, E. I. 1974. *Environmental pollution, awareness and control.* Mahomet, Illinois: Engineering Technology Inc.

21. Shaheen, E. I., The energy crisis: Is it fabrication or miscalculation? *Environmental Science & Technology,* April 1974.

22. Squires, A. M. 1967. Air pollution: The control of SO_2 from power stacks, Part II—The removal of SO_2 from stack gases. *Chemical Engineering* 74(24), 133-140 (Nov. 20).

23. World Health Organization. 1961. *Air pollution.* New York: Columbia University Press.

PROBLEMS

5.1 Definitions

Define

1. Property of a system	7. Isothermal process
2. Extensive property	8. Adiabatic process
3. Process of state	9. Reversible process
4. Degrees of freedom	10. Critical point
5. Open system	11. Triple point
6. Quasistatic system	

5.2 First Partials from an Equation of State

A gas follows the equation of state:

$$P = \frac{nRT}{V} + \left(a + \frac{b}{T}\right)\left(\frac{n}{V}\right)^2$$

Find

1.
$$\left(\frac{\partial P}{\partial V}\right)_{n,\,T}$$

2.
$$\left(\frac{\partial T}{\partial V}\right)_{P,\,n}$$

5.3 Second Partial Derivatives for a Gas

For a gas whose equation of state is

1. $PV = zRT$

2. Van der Waals equation:

$$P = \frac{RT}{V - b} - \frac{a}{V^2}$$

3.
$$P = RT\left(\frac{1}{V} + \frac{a}{V^2}\right)$$

Find the second partial derivatives:

$$\left(\frac{\partial^2 P}{\partial T^2}\right)_V \quad \text{and} \quad \left(\frac{\partial^2 P}{\partial V^2}\right)_T$$

5.4   Equation of State Obtained from a Differential

Given the total differential

$$dV = \frac{R}{P}\,dT + \left(C - \frac{RT}{P^2}\right)dP$$

1. Is this an exact differential?
2. What is the equation of state for this gas?

5.5   Obtaining a Function from a Given Differential

A total differential for a gas is represented by:

$$dP = \left(\frac{R}{V - b}\right)dT + \left(\frac{2a}{V^3} - \frac{RT}{(V - b)^2}\right)dV$$

1. Is this an exact differential?
2. What is the function $P = P(T, V)$?

5.6 $(dU/dV)_T$ for a van der Waals Gas

What is the expression for $(dU/dV)_T$ for a van der Waals gas?

5.7 Expression for dU

Prove that

$$dU = C_v dT + \left[T\left(\frac{\partial P}{\partial T}\right)_V - P \right] dV$$

5.8 Maxwell Relations

Derive the Maxwell relations.

5.9 $C_p - C_v$

Prove that

$$C_p - C_v = -T\left(\frac{\partial V}{\partial T}\right)_P^2 \left(\frac{\partial P}{\partial V}\right)_T$$

5.10 ΔH and ΔU for a Gas

The equation of state for one mole of gas is

$$PV = RT + \frac{b}{V}$$

1. Give an expression for ΔH.
2. Give an expression for ΔU.

5.11 Change in Enthalpy Associated with Isothermal Compression

A gas follows the equation of state:

$$V = \frac{RT}{P} - c + aP$$

where
$$c = 38 \text{ ft}^3/\text{lb-mole}$$
$$a = 0.38 \text{ ft}^3/(\text{lb-mole})(\text{atm})$$

Calculate the change in enthalpy in Btu/lb-mole associated with the *isothermal compression* of this gas from 1 atm to 50 atm at 75°F.

5.12   Change of Enthalpy in Isothermal Expansion

A certain gas is expanded isothermally from 400°F and 50 atm to 1 atm. Calculate the change in enthalpy (Btu/lb-mole) if the equation of state is

$$P = \frac{T}{V-b} - \frac{a}{TV^2}$$

where

$$a = 7.7 \times 10^5 \; \frac{(\text{atm})\,(\text{ft}^6)\,(°\text{R})}{(\text{lb-mole})^2}$$

$$b = 0.69 \text{ ft}^3/\text{lb-mole}$$

5.13 Q as a Function of Path

An ideal gas has:

$$C_p = 4.0 + 3.0 \times 10^{-3} T \text{ cal/g-mole-}°\text{K}$$

$$C_v = 2.0 + 3.0 \times 10^{-3} T \text{ cal/g-mole-}°\text{K}$$

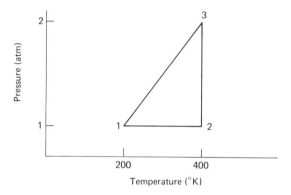

Figure P5.13.

In going from state 2 to state 3 along the indicated path, $Q = -1500$ cal/2 g-moles gas. See Figure P5.13.

Calculate Q in taking 2 moles of gas from state 1 to state 3 over each of the following paths.

1. From state 1 to state 2 along the horizontal line, and from state 2 to state 3 along the vertical line.

2. From state 1 to state 3 along the diagonal line (this line corresponds to a constant volume process).

5.14   Liquefaction of SO_2

Determine the energy required to liquefy 1 lb of 100% SO_2 by compression at 68°F. Given:

1.
$$dQ = dW + dU$$

2.
$$\left(\frac{\partial U}{\partial V}\right)_T = T\left(\frac{\partial P}{\partial T}\right)_V - P$$

3. SO_2 follows the van der Waals equation of state.

5.15   Isothermal and Quasistatic Compression of an Ideal Gas

One pound-mole of air at an initial temperature of 250°F and an initial volume of 5.0 ft^3 is isothermally and quasistatically compressed to half its volume. Assuming that air is an ideal gas, find

1. W

2. Change in internal energy

3. Q

5.16   Thermodynamics of an Isolated System

One pound-mole of an ideal gas is placed in one side of a container which is divided into two compartments of equal volume. The gas is at 50 psia and 100°F; the other compartment is a perfect vacuum. The system is completely isolated from the surroundings and perfectly insulated. The partition separating the two compartments is suddenly removed. Determine the final temperature and pressure of the gas, the work done, and heat transferred in this process.

$$C_p = 7 \text{ Btu/lb-mole-}°R$$
$$C_v = 5 \text{ Btu/lb-mole-}°R$$

5.17   Changes in W, ΔU, and C_p

The volume of hydrogen in a cylinder is $V_1 = 100$ ft^3 at 15 psia and 70°F. This hydrogen is compressed to $P_2 = 50$ psia according to $PV^{1.1} = $ constant. This hydrogen is now expanded at constant volume to $P_3 = 15$ psia, and further expansion is applied at constant pressure until the gas reaches the original state. Determine W, ΔU, and C_p for the overall process.

5.18 Steam Velocity upon Expansion through a Nozzle

Steam expands through a nozzle from a pressure of 200 psia to a final pressure of 2 psia. The initial and final enthalpy values of the steam are 1290 and 955 Btu/lb$_m$ respectively. Neglecting the initial velocity and heat losses, compute the final steam velocity (ft/sec).

5.19 Free Energy Change

A gas mixture containing 16.6% N_2, 16.6% Ar, and 66.67% H_2 by volume is passed over a suitable catalyst at 700°K and 600 atm. It is to be assumed that for such an original mixture, equilibrium is attained when the gases leaving the converter contain 34% ammonia by volume. Assuming that the ideal gas law applies, compute the free energy change at 427°C for the reaction

$$N_2 + 3H_2 \rightleftharpoons 2NH_3$$

5.20 Enthalpy of Steam

Calculate the enthalpy of steam at 312°F and 1 atm pressure relative to water at 112°F.

5.21 Enthalpy of Water from Steam Tables

Determine the enthalpy relative to 32°F of liquid water at 100 psia and 400°F.

5.22 Vacuum Gauge Reading for Boiling Water at 105° F

The vapor pressure of water at 105°F is 1.1 psia; at 212°F the vapor pressure is 14.7 psia. What will be the reading of a vacuum gauge for water boiling at 105°F?

5.23 Heat Capacity and Temperature

How does the heat capacity of a gas vary with temperature in the ordinary temperature range (40-400°F)?

5.24 Heat Capacity as a Function of Temperature

Heat capacity is given by

$$C_p = a + bT^{1/2} - c \cos T$$

Derive an expression for the mean heat capacity between temperature T_1 and T_2, where a, b, and c are constants.

5.25 Heat Capacity and Temperature

A heat capacity is given as

$$C_p = a + bT^{1/2} - cT^3$$

Derive an expression for the mean heat capacity between temperatures T_1 and T_2, where a, b, and c are constants.

5.26 Heat Capacity and Pressure

How does the heat capacity of a gas vary with pressure in the ordinary pressure range (1-4 atm)?

5.27 Mean Heat Capacity in a Hypothetical Reaction

Given the reaction

$$A + B = C$$

The product C undergoes a phase transformation at temperature T_2. The following thermodynamic data are available $(T_1 < T_2 < T_3)$:

> ΔH for the reaction at T_1 and T_3
>
> $\overline{C_p}$ for A and B in the temperature range T_1 to T_3
>
> $\overline{C_p}$ for C in the temperature range T_1 to T_2
>
> ΔH for the phase transformation in C at T_2

Derive an expression for the mean heat capacity of product C in the temperature range T_2 to T_3.

5.28 Why Does R Appear in Certain Relationships?

What is the gas constant R? Explain briefly why it appears in the:

1. Equation relating specific heats at constant pressure and constant volume of an ideal gas

2. Clausius-Clapeyron equation

5.29   Clausius-Clapeyron Equation and the Melting of Ice at 300 Atm

Ice melts at $0°C$ and 1 atm. What is the melting point of ice at 300 atm? Given:

$$\Delta H \text{ at normal melting point} = 80 \text{ cal/g}$$

$$\rho_{ice} = 0.92 \text{ g/cm}^3$$

$$\rho_{H_2O} = 1.00 \text{ g/cm}^3$$

5.30   Melting Point of Ethyl Ether

The normal melting point of ethyl ether, $C_4H_{10}O$, is $-116.3°C$, and the heat of fusion is 23.54 cal/g. What is the melting point of ethyl ether under 10 atm?

5.31   Heat Absorbed in the Isobaric Vaporization of Water at 150°C

The heat of vaporization of water at 1 atm and $100°C$ is 540 cal/g. Assume that the specific heat of liquid water is 1 cal/g-$°K$ and that the molal heat capacity of water vapor is $8.6 + 0.003T$ cal/g-mole-$°K$, where T is in $°K$.

Calculate the heat absorbed when 1 g-mole of water is vaporized isobarically at $150°C$.

5.32   Heat of Vaporization of Benzene

Below its boiling point at 1 atm the variation of the vapor pressure of benzene with temperature is given by

$$\log_{10} P = 7.26 - \frac{1402.5}{T} - \frac{51,387}{T^2} \qquad P, \text{ mm Hg}; T, °K$$

from which the normal boiling point at 1 atm is found to be $80.20°C$. The specific volume of saturated benzene vapor at its boiling point at 1 atm is 356 cm^3/g, and that of liquid benzene is 1.2 cm^3/g. Calculate the heat of vaporization (Btu/lb$_m$) at the boiling temperature.

5.33 Pressure as a Function of Altitude

Find an expression for pressure as a function of altitude. Assume constant temperature and ideal gas behavior.

5.34 Variation of Pressure with Elevation

Find an equation for the variation of pressure with elevation in an ideal gas when the temperature decreases linearly with increasing height (at height Z_0, $P = P_0$, and $T = T_0$).

5.35 Direction of Flow, Friction, and the Energy Equation

Water flows through a horizontal pipe consisting of a section of 6-in. I.D. joined to a section of 12-in. I.D. A pressure gauge at a point in the 6-in. section reads 10 psig, and a similar gauge at a point in the 12-in. section reads 20 psig. Find the direction of flow and the frictional energy loss between the two points when the pipe carries 6 ft^3/sec. (Density of $H_2O = 62.4$ lb$_m$/ft^3.)

5.36 The Energy Equation and Pressure at a Nozzle

A water tank 2/3 full has a constant pressure of 15 psig. A 3/4-in. I.D. hose discharges 75 gal/min of water. With the nozzle located 15 ft below water surface, and energy loss due to friction is 1.2 ft-lb$_f$/lb$_m$, find the pressure at the nozzle.

5.37 Exit Temperature in Heating Air

Air is being heated in a 1-in. standard steel pipe. The flow rate at the entrance section is 4500 ft^3/hr, the temperature is 70°F, and the pressure is 1 atm absolute. The heating element is 750 watts, and the exit pressure is 0.2 atm. Find the exit temperature of the air.

5.38 Outlet Temperature in a Compressor

Air is compressed in a well-insulated 1 HP compressor at the input rate of 133.5 ft^3/sec. The intake air is atmospheric air at 70°F and the outlet pressure is 3 atm. The outlet point is 10 ft lower than the inlet; both lines are large enough so that the velocities are negligible. The specific heat (C_p) is 0.24 Btu/lb$_m$-°F. What is the outlet temperature? (*Note:* Some of the data given are not needed.)

5.39 Heat Balance in the Concentration of CuSO₄ Solution

A 10% $CuSO_4$ solution at 75°F is concentrated to 33 1/3% in an evaporator. The pressure in the evaporator is such that the solution boils at 150°F. Saturated steam is available at 250°F. Condensate leaves at condensing temperature. Latent heat at 150°F = 1008; at 250°F = 945 Btu/lb$_m$. Write a heat balance equation with 150°F as the datum plane to show the steam consumption per 1000 lb$_m$ of feed. The specific heat of $CuSO_4$ solutions may be assumed to be 0.9 Btu/lb$_m$·°F.

5.40 Pumping of Crude Oil

Crude oil with a viscosity of 2900 centipoises and a specific gravity of 0.86 is being pumped at a flow rate of 80 bbl/hr. The pipeline used is 1 mi long and has 3.07-in. I.D.

1. Determine the horsepower required if the pump efficiency is 40%.

2. A "bright" engineer thought of lowering the viscosity to 500 cps by heating the oil to 110°F, and thus he decreased pumping requirements. Assuming isothermal flow, determine if this approach is economical. Given:

$$C_{p\,oil} = 0.5 \text{ Btu/lb}_m\text{-°F}$$

The cost of electricity for pumping is 0.7 cents/kWh. The cost of steam for heating is 35.0 cents/10⁶ Btu.

5.41 Water Siphon

Water is to be siphoned from a tank 5 ft in diameter and 6 ft in height. The height of the water is 5 ft and the inlet of the 1/2-in. I.D. siphon is 3.5 ft below the water surface. How far below the water surface should the siphon outlet be placed to give a flow rate of 0.75 gal/min? (See Figure P5.41.)

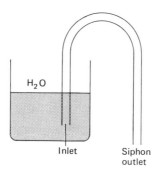

Figure P5.41.

  1. Assume friction is negligible.

  2. Assume friction is 4.0 ft-lb$_f$/lb$_m$.

5.42   Definitions

Define

  1. Reynolds number (give mathematical expression)

  2. Total energy equation

  3. C_p (give mathematical expression)

  4. Limiting reactant

  5. Raoult's law

5.43   Standard Heat of Formation of AgCl

What is the standard heat of formation of AgCl? Given:

$$\Delta H^0 \text{(cal)}$$

	ΔH^0(cal)
$Ag_2O_{(s)} + 2HCl_{(g)} \rightarrow 2AgCl_{(s)} + H_2O_{(l)}$	$-77{,}610$
$2Ag_{(s)} + \frac{1}{2}O_{2(g)} \rightarrow Ag_2O_{(s)}$	$-7{,}310$
$\frac{1}{2}H_{2(g)} + \frac{1}{2}Cl_{2(g)} \rightarrow HCl_{(g)}$	$-22{,}060$
$H_{2(g)} + \frac{1}{2}O_{2(g)} \rightarrow H_2O_{(l)}$	$-68{,}320$

5.44   Heat of Formation of Ammonia

Ammonia gas is made by the reaction

$$\frac{1}{2}N_{2(g)} + \frac{3}{2}H_{2(g)} \rightarrow NH_{3(g)} \qquad \Delta H_f^0 = -11 \text{ kcal/g-mole}$$

  1. Find an expression for the heat of formation of NH_3 as a function of temperature.

  2. What is ΔH_f at 300°C?

5.45   Free Energy of Formation of $N_2O_{4(g)}$

Find the free energy of formation of $N_2O_{4(g)}$ at 25°C. Given:

$$\Delta G^0_{25°C}(\text{cal})$$

$$\frac{1}{2} N_{2(g)} + \frac{1}{2} O_{2(g)} \rightarrow NO_{(g)} \qquad 20,720$$

$$2NO_{2(g)} \rightarrow N_2O_{4(g)} \qquad -1,380$$

$$NO_{(g)} + \frac{1}{2} O_{2(g)} \rightarrow NO_{2(g)} \qquad -8,330$$

5.46   Heat Loss from a Combustion Chamber

Liquid octane fuel at 75°F is fed with 300% excess air at 275°F to a combustion chamber. What is the heat loss per lb-mole of fuel if the gaseous product leaves at 1000°F?

5.47   Heat Taken from Gases in a Regenerator

The flue gases from a calcining furnace contain 11.1% CO_2, 5.7% O_2, 0.8% CO, 6.3% H_2O, and the rest N_2. These gases go to the regenerator at 1725°C, entering the regenerator at the rate of 22,000 ft³/min. In the regenerator they are cooled to 200°C. From the following formulas for the molal heat capacities of the components, compute the amount of heat which is taken from these gases in the regenerator.

Component	C_p (Btu/lb-mole-°K)
N_2, O_2, CO	$6.50 + 0.0010\ T$
H_2O	$8.81 - 0.0019\ T$
CO_2	$7.0\ \ + 0.0071\ T$

5.48   Heat Loss in a Boiler Fired with Coal

A boiler is fired with a coal containing 69% C, 5% S, 2% N, and 11% ash under such conditions that elimination of combustible matter from the ash is complete. The flue gas is sampled through a tube filled with dry PbO_2 to absorb SO_2. Its analysis shows 11.6% CO_2, 0.9% CO, and 7.8% O_2. The air enters the furnace 50% saturated at 75°F, at which temperature the vapor pressure of water is 22.2 mm Hg. The stack temperature is 760°F. The barometer is 740 mm Hg. On the assumption that the sulfur all goes into the gas as SO_2, compute

1. Percent excess air used in the furnace

2. The Btu loss up the stack per pound of fuel fired due to (a) unburnt CO, (b) latent heat of water, (c) sensible heat

5.49 Thermal Efficiency in the Combustion of Coal

A coal contains 9% ash and has a gross heating value (based on burning all carbon) of 12,000 Btu/lb$_m$. After the coal was burned in a furnace, the clinker was found to contain 10% carbon. If the heat of combustion of carbon is 14,500 Btu/lb$_m$, what is the thermal efficiency of the combustion?

5.50 Heating Value of CH_4-C_4H_6 Mixture

A gas consists of 10% methane, 90% ethane. What is the heating value of this gas (Btu/lb-mole)?

5.51 Heat of Reaction and ΔH as a Function of Temperature

1. Given: The following reactions and thermal data at 25°C.

$$2Fe_{(s)} + \tfrac{3}{2} O_{2(g)} \rightarrow Fe_2O_{3(s)} \qquad \Delta H = -198{,}500 \text{ cal}$$

$$2FeO_{(s)} + \tfrac{1}{2} O_{2(g)} \rightarrow Fe_2O_{3(s)} \qquad \Delta H = -69{,}900 \text{ cal}$$

$$Fe_{(s)} + 2H^+ \rightarrow Fe^{2+} + H_{2(g)} \qquad \Delta H = -20{,}600 \text{ cal}$$

$$\tfrac{1}{2} H_{2(g)} \rightarrow H^+ \qquad \Delta H = 0 \text{ cal}$$

$$H_{2(g)} + \tfrac{1}{2} O_{2(g)} \rightarrow H_2O_{(l)} \qquad \Delta H = -68{,}400 \text{ cal}$$

Calculate the heat of the reaction for

$$FeO_{(s)} + 2H^+ \rightarrow H_2O_{(l)} + Fe^{2+}$$

2. Derive an equation for ΔH as a function of temperature for the reaction

$$N_{2(g)} + O_{2(g)} \rightarrow 2NO_{(g)} \qquad \Delta H_{293°K} = 43{,}300 \text{ cal}$$

Heat capacity data are

$$N_2 \qquad C_p = 6.76 + 0.606 \times 10^{-3} T$$

$$O_2 \qquad C_p = 6.76 + 0.606 \times 10^{-3} T$$

$$NO \qquad C_p = 8.05 + 0.233 \times 10^{-3} T$$

where C_p = heat capacity at constant pressure, cal/g-mole-°K

T = absolute temperature, °K

5.52   Heat of Reaction at 1100°C

Given: The reaction

$$2CO_{(g)} + O_{2(g)} \rightarrow 2CO_{2(g)} \qquad \Delta H^0 = -135,800 \text{ cal}$$

Find the heat of reaction at 1100°C.

5.53   Density of a Gas Mixture and Partial Pressure of Constituents

When 1.74 g of Cl_2 and 1.57 g of SO_2 are introduced into a 750 cm³ bulb at 190°C, partial reaction into SO_2Cl_2 takes place and the pressure becomes 2 atm at equilibrium. Calculate

1. The density of the mixture
2. Partial pressure of each constituent at equilibrium

5.54   Fraction of Ammonia Dissociated at 400°C

At 400°C, the $K_p = 78.1$ atm for the reaction

$$NH_{3(g)} = \frac{1}{2} N_{2(g)} + \frac{3}{2} H_{2(g)}$$

Find an equation for the equilibrium fraction of ammonia dissociated at 400°C as a function of the total pressure in atmospheres. Assume ideal gas law behavior.

5.55   Quantity of Heat Needed to Cause a Given Change in Temperature

A gaseous mixture contains

Component	Mole %
CO	35
CO_2	20
N_2	45

What is the amount of heat necessary to raise the temperature of 1 lb-mole of this mixture from 25°C to 250°C?

5.56 Liquefaction of SO_2 in a Gas Mixture

A mixture of 88% SO_2 and 12% N_2 at 68°F is to be cooled to −28°F by means of refrigerated brine in order to recover the SO_2 by liquefaction. Determine the heat requirements for the process

$$\Delta H_f^0 [SO_{2(g)}] = -70.9 \text{ kcal/mole} \qquad \Delta H_f^0(SO_{2(l)}) = -103.03 \text{ kcal/mole}$$

The boiling point of SO_2 is −10.0°C.

5.57 Theoretical Flame Temperature in the Combustion of Carbon

Twelve pounds of pure carbon are burned with pure oxygen. What is the maximum theoretical flame temperature? The mean molal heat capacity of CO_2 may be taken as 13.0 and that of O_2 as 8.5 Btu/lb-mole-°F. Carbon and O_2 are at 75°F at start.

5.58 Adiabatic Flame Temperature in the Combustion of Carbon

Find the adiabatic flame temperature for the combustion of carbon with 100% excess air.

5.59 Theoretical Flame Temperature of a Certain Fuel

The combustion of a certain fuel gives 5 moles flue gas/1 mole fuel burned. Fuel and air enter at 140°F. Find the theoretical flame temperature. Given:

Net heat of combustion of fuel at 140°F = 3.6×10^5 Btu/lb-mole

Heat capacity of flue gases = C_p = $10 + 0.004 \, T$ Btu/lb-mole-°R

(T is in degrees Rankine.)

5.60 Adiabatic Gas Temperature in a Converter Producing $SO_{3(g)}$

A sulfuric acid plant burns pure sulfur with excess air to produce sulfur dioxide. The burner gases (SO_2, O_2, N_2) are first sent to a waste heat boiler where the gas temperature is reduced to 400°C, and then to a catalytic converter where sulfur dioxide is oxidized to sulfur trioxide. For a plant using 500 SCFM of air per pound of sulfur burned, calculate the adiabatic gas temperature in the converter as a function of the fraction y of SO_2 converted to SO_3. The average molal heat capacities of the gases and the heat of reaction at the converter temperatures are

Component	Average molal heat capacity (cal/g-mole-°C)
SO_2	11.7
SO_3	17.0
O_2	7.8
N_2	7.3

Heat of reaction for

$$SO_{2(g)} + \frac{1}{2} O_{2(g)} \rightarrow SO_{3(g)}$$

at 1 atm, $400°C = 23,000$ cal/g-mole

5.61   Stack Gas at Theoretical Flame Temperature

The product from a coke oven analyzes

Component	Mole %
CO_2	2.1
C_2H_4	1.0
O_2	0.3
CO	6.2
H_2	57.4
CH_4	27.3
N_2	5.7
Total	100.0

1. What is the lower heating value of the above gas in Btu/ft^3 (68°F, 1 atm)?

2. How many moles of stack gas will be produced per 100 moles of coke oven gas, if 50% excess air is used?

3. Determine an average heat capacity for the stack gas.

4. To what temperature will the stack gas be heated (theoretical flame temperature, 50% excess air)?

5.62 Theoretical Flame Temperature

Calculate the theoretical flame temperature of a gas containing 25% CO and 75% N_2 when burned with 50% excess air and when both gas and air have been pre-heated to 400°F. Given:

$$H = \text{enthalpy of gas in cal/g-mole relative to } 18°C$$

$$= a(T - 291) + b[T^2 - (291)^2] + c[T^3 - (291)^3]$$

$$T = \text{degrees Kelvin}$$

Gas	a	Coefficients	
		$b \times 10^2$	$c \times 10^6$
CO_2	6.85	0.4266	−0.825
CO	6.25	0.1046	−0.153
O_2	6.13	0.1495	−0.269
N_2	6.30	0.0910	−0.115

$$CO + \tfrac{1}{2} O_2 \rightarrow CO_2 + 67,410 \text{ cal}$$

5.63 Mass and Energy Balances in a Cyclohexane Process

In a cyclohexane process we have

Component	Enthalpy (Btu/lb_m) at 300°F	Enthalpy (Btu/lb_m) at 450°F
H_2	816	1335
CH_4	212	314
C_6H_6	258	317
C_6H_{12}	259	334

In each reactor 66.1 lb-moles/hr of benzene react completely; the temperature in all reactors must be maintained between 300 and 400°F. The first reactor R_1 is critical; its temperature is controlled by dilution with liquid recycle from the separator. (See the flow diagram, Figure P5.63, based on one hour's operation.)

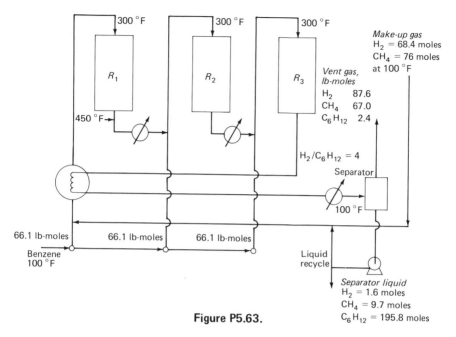

Figure P5.63.

Find

1. Amount of liquid recycle required by 100, 150, and 200 lb-moles/hr of total feed (C_6H_6 and H_2).

2. With correct liquid recycle, determine composition of each stream.

5.64 Gas Reaction Conducted in Metal Tubes Packed with Catalyst

A gas reaction conducted in metal tubes packed with catalyst absorbs 25×10^6 Btu/hr. The tubes are heated by direct contact with combustion gases, the product of burning CO with 80% of the theoretical air. Owing to the metallurgical characteristics of the tubes, the temperature of the heating gases in contact with them must not exceed 1200°F. Under normal operating conditions, the heating gases are withdrawn from the reactor at 1000°F, and a portion of these gases is recycled and mixed with the gases leaving the steam generator in order to reduce the temperature of the gases entering the reactor to 1200°F.

The CO entering the combustion chamber at 60°F, is burned with preheated air, and then passed into a steam generator producing saturated steam at 450 psig from boiler feed water at 60°F. The combustion gases leave the steam generator at 3000°F. The combustion gases contain a negligible amount of free oxygen.

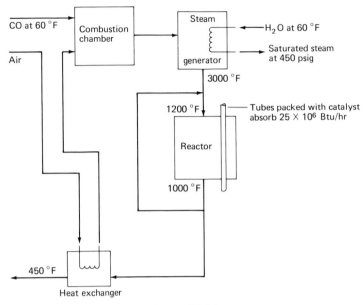

Figure P5.64.

Part of the sensible heat of the combustion gases leaving the reactor is re-covered by heat exchange with the combustion air in a countercurrent heat ex-changer. The exhaust gases leave the heat exchanger at 450°F. Calculate:

1. Composition of the exhaust gas leaving the heat exchanger
2. Moles of CO fired per hour
3. Moles of recycle gas per hour
4. Moles of air used per hour
5. Temperature of preheated air
6. Pounds of steam generated per hour

Component	Mean molal heat capacity (Btu/lb-mole-°F)			
	60-450°F	60-1000°F	60-1200°F	60-3000°F
O_2	7.20	7.55	7.65	8.26
N_2	7.00	7.17	7.26	7.85
CO_2	9.80	10.86	11.14	12.75
CO	7.03	7.24	7.31	7.92

Heat of combustion of CO at $77°F = 67,636$ cal/g-mole; enthalpy of saturated steam at 450 psig is 1204.6 Btu/lb$_m$. Data are given in the table.

A diagram of the process is shown in Figure P5.64.

PROBLEMS IN AIR POLLUTION CONTROL*

5.65 Control of Particulates

An electric power plant puts out a large quantity of particulate matter from its smokestacks. What type of pollution control equipment would you recommend for this power plant to control its particulate output? Why?

5.66 Cyclone Separator

What are the two most important factors that must be taken into consideration, from an engineering viewpoint, when designing a cyclone-separator?

5.67 Wet Scrubbers

Explain how a wet scrubber really works. Document your statements by using the available literature.

5.68 SO$_2$ Removal

Describe a new process for the removal of SO$_2$; you should present your material clearly and in detail.

5.69 NO$_x$ Abatement

What is a promising process for nitrogen oxides removal? Give a simple flow diagram.

5.70 Catalytic Reduction

Where is catalytic reduction used in air pollution? Give a chemical reaction and simple flow diagram for removing the undesired pollutant.

---

* Problems 5.65 to 5.76 are taken from E.I. Shaheen, 1974. *Environmental Pollution, awareness and control*, with permission from Engineering Technology Inc., Mahomet, Illinois.

5.71 Your Job Is to Meet Air Quality Standards

Suppose you are hired by a chemical plant for work on air pollution control in meeting new air quality standards. The plant is found to be emitting acid mists and has been ordered to come up with an abatement schedule. You are then assigned the job of determining the most efficient and economical method for removing the acid mist. What general method and equipment would you choose? Will there be any special materials needed in the process? Will large amounts of water or power be needed? Can there be any profitable by-product recovery?

5.72 Vicious Circle of Environmental Pollution

When does air pollution abatement become water pollution? How serious is the problem, and what do you know about the vicious circle of polluting the environment? What are the conflicts with energy demand and the energy crisis?

5.73 Particles Carried in a Stack Gas

When a solid sphere is allowed to fall from rest in a fluid, it will accelerate until it reaches a constant velocity called terminal velocity. This is found by *Stokes' law:*

$$U_t = \frac{gD_p^2(\rho_s - \rho_0)}{18\,\mu_0} \tag{3.1}$$

where

U_t = Stokes' law, particle terminal velocity, ft/sec

g = gravitational acceleration, ft/sec^2

ρ_s = density of solids, lb_m/ft^3

ρ_0 = density of the fluid medium, lb_m/ft^3

μ_0 = viscosity of the fluid medium, air, lb_m/ft-sec

This equation is valid only when the particle Reynolds number is less than 0.1, namely,

$$Re = \frac{D_p U_t \rho_s}{\mu_0} < 0.1 \tag{3.2}$$

where *Re* is the particle Reynolds number, which is dimensionless.

With this background, consider a stack gas containing fine particles exiting at a vertical velocity of 1.1 ft/sec.

1. What is the maximum diameter, in microns ($1\,\mu = 10^{-6}$ meter), of particles carried through the chimney?

2. Does Stokes' law apply?

Given:

$$\rho_{\,gas} = 0.044\ \text{lb}_m/\text{ft}^3$$

$$\mu_{\,gas} = 0.025\ \text{centipoise}$$

$$\rho_{\,particles} = 68.6\ \text{lb}_m/\text{ft}^3$$

5.74 Cooling, and Particulate Removal in a Stack Gas

A gaseous effluent at $1900°F$ is discharged from a furnace at the rate of 14,000 ft^3/min at a pressure of 1.2 atm. The particulate content of this gas is $500\,\mu g/m^3$. A spray scrubber is used to both cool the effluent to $220°F$ and remove particulate matter. See Figure P5.74. Find

1. Mass of water needed for cooling if the inlet water temperature is $70°F$

2. Mass of particulates that must be removed to comply with a standard permitting a maximum of $140\,\mu g/m^3$ of particles in the air

3. The minimum amount of water needed to remove solids as indicated in part 2

4. Volume of the stack gas

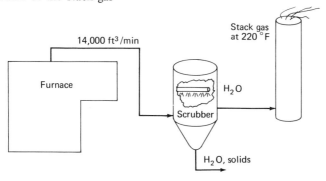

Figure P5.74.

5.75 Designing for Air Pollution Abatement

A power plant supplies electricity for a community of 150,000 population with relatively moderate industry. The power plant uses coal as a source of energy. Your job is to ultimately equip this plant with the latest equipment in air pollution abatement. Your target is to remove as many particulates, SO_2, and NO_x as needed to comply with the Ambient Air Quality Standards. You can approach the problem as follows.

1. Obtain typical pertinent data from the literature and draw a neat flow diagram, properly labeled and containing the basic data
2. Design the necessary equipment

You should clearly identify the source of equations used and all other sources of information. You must be neat, clear, and certainly systematic.

5.76 Experiment in Air or Water Pollution Control

Choose and build a simple experiment for an interesting class demonstration depicting a successful air or water pollution technique. Visual observation of the actions involved would be desirable.

Mathematical Review

Before dealing with some of the most essential thermodynamic functions, the student may need a brief review of related mathematics.

A1.1 PARTIAL DERIVATIVES

Partial derivatives arise when differentiating a function with two or more independent variables. For the function

$$z = f(x,y)$$

the first partial derivative with respect to x is defined by

$$\frac{\partial z}{\partial x} = \underset{\Delta x \to 0}{\text{limit}} \frac{f(x + \Delta x, y) - f(x,y)}{\Delta x}$$

and the first partial derivative with respect to y is

$$\frac{\partial z}{\partial y} = \underset{\Delta y \to 0}{\text{limit}} \frac{f(x, y + \Delta y) - f(x,y)}{\Delta y}$$

The second partial derivative is obtained from the first:

$$\frac{\partial^2 z}{\partial x^2} = \frac{\partial}{\partial x}\left[\frac{\partial z}{\partial x}\right]$$

and

$$\frac{\partial^2 z}{\partial y^2} = \frac{\partial}{\partial y}\left[\frac{\partial z}{\partial y}\right]$$

Example A1.1

Given the function

$$z = x^2 - 2xy + 3y^2$$

find

1. $\partial z/\partial y$ 2. $\partial^2 z/\partial x^2$ 3. $\partial z/\partial y$ 4. $\partial^2 z/\partial y^2$

Solution

1. To obtain $\partial z/\partial x$ we treat y as a constant. Thus

$$\frac{\partial z}{\partial x} = 2x - 2y$$

This is sometimes written as $(\partial z/\partial x)_y$ to indicate that y is held constant.

2.

$$\frac{\partial^2 z}{\partial x^2} = \frac{\partial}{\partial x}\left(\frac{\partial z}{\partial x}\right)$$

$$= \frac{\partial}{\partial x}(2x - 2y)$$

$$= 2$$

3. To find $\partial z/\partial y$ we treat x as a constant. Thus

$$\frac{\partial z}{\partial y} = -2x + 6y$$

4.

$$\frac{\partial^2 z}{\partial y^2} = \frac{\partial}{\partial y}\left(\frac{\partial z}{\partial y}\right)$$

$$= \frac{\partial}{\partial y}(-2x + 6y)$$

$$= 6$$

Example A1.2

Let

$$z = \frac{x^2}{y} + \frac{y^2}{x}$$

Find

1. $\partial z/\partial x$ and $\partial^2 z/\partial x^2$

2. $\partial z/\partial y$ and $\partial^2 z/\partial y^2$

Solution

1. Again, treat y as a constant and get

$$\frac{\partial z}{\partial x} = \frac{2x}{y} - \frac{y^2}{x^2}$$

and

$$\frac{\partial^2 z}{\partial x^2} = \frac{\partial}{\partial x}\left(\frac{\partial z}{\partial x}\right) = \frac{2}{y} + \frac{2y^2}{x^3}$$

2. Now treat x as a constant and differentiate to get

$$\frac{\partial z}{\partial y} = -\frac{x^2}{y^2} + \frac{2y}{x}$$

and

$$\frac{\partial^2 z}{\partial y^2} = \frac{\partial}{\partial y}\left(\frac{\partial z}{\partial y}\right) = \frac{2x^2}{y^3} + \frac{2}{x}$$

Example A1.3

We are given the function

$$u = 3x^3 z + 5xy^2 - ay^3 z$$

Find

    1. $(\partial u/\partial x)_{y,z}$ 2. $(\partial u/\partial y)_{x,z}$ 3. $(\partial u/\partial z)_{x,y}$

Solution

1. Holding y and z constant we get, upon differentiation,

$$\left(\frac{\partial u}{\partial x}\right)_{y,z} = 9x^2 z + 5y^2$$

2. $$(\partial u/\partial y)_{x,z} = 10xy - 3azy^2$$

3. $$(\partial u/\partial z)_{x,y} = 3x^3 - ay^3$$

A1.2 IMPLICIT DIFFERENTIATION

The function,

$$y = 2x^2 + 3z$$

is an *explicit* function of y, since it separates y and expresses it as a function of other variables. The function

$$y - 2x^2 - 3z = 0$$

is an *implicit* function, since it implies that we can solve for y; but y has not been separated to one side of the equation. It is sometimes difficult to solve explicitly for a certain variable, such as y, in this equation:

$$x^5 + 4xy^3 - 3y^5 = 5$$

To determine the derivative dy/dx we do not need to solve for y and then differentiate; instead we can exercise the method of *implicit differentiation*. This is simply done by differentiating all terms with respect to x and solving for dy/dx. Let us illustrate.

Example A1.4

Given the function

$$x^5 + 4xy^3 - 3y^5 = 5$$

find dy/dx.

Solution

Use implicit differentiation and differentiate both sides of the equation with respect to x. Thus

$$\frac{d}{dx}(x^5) + \frac{d}{dx}(4xy^3) - \frac{d}{dx}(3y^5) = \frac{d}{dx}(5) \qquad \text{(A1.1)}$$

Let us take each term separately:

$$\frac{d}{dx}(x^5) = 5x^4$$

In $d/dx\,(4xy^3)$, we have the product of two variables, and we know that $d(uv) = u'v + v'u$, where u' is a derivative of u. Therefore

$$\frac{d}{dx}(4xy^3) = 4\frac{d}{dx}(xy^3)$$

$$= 4\left[\frac{dx}{dx}(y^3) + x\frac{d}{dx}(y^3)\right]$$

$$= 4y^3 + 12xy^2\frac{dy}{dx}$$

Following this approach, Equation A1.1 becomes

$$5x^4 + 4y^3 + 12xy^2\frac{dy}{dx} - 15y^4\frac{dy}{dx} = 0$$

Solve this equation for dy/dx:

$$5x^4 + 4y^3 = (15y^4 - 12xy^2)\frac{dy}{dx}$$

Thus

$$\frac{dy}{dx} = \frac{5x^4 + 4y^3}{15y^4 - 12xy^2}$$

Remember, from calculus,

$$\frac{d}{dx}(u^n) = nu^{n-1}\frac{du}{dx}$$

Here we have y^5, and we treat it similarly:

$$\frac{d}{dx}(3y^5) = 15y^4\frac{dy}{dx}$$

Example A1.5

Given

$$8x^3 + 10y^2 = 20$$

find dy/dx.

Solution

Use implicit differentiation:

$$\frac{d}{dx}(8x^3) + \frac{d}{dx}10y^2 = \frac{d}{dx}(20)$$

or

$$24x^2 + 20y\frac{dy}{dx} = 0$$

$$\frac{dy}{dx} = -\frac{24x^2}{20y}$$

Example A1.6

Given the equation

$$x^2y - xy^2 + x^2 + y^2 = 7$$

find dy/dx.

Solution

$$\frac{d}{dx}(x^2y) - \frac{d}{dx}(xy^2) + \frac{d}{dx}(x^2) + \frac{d}{dx}(y^2) = \frac{d}{dx}(7)$$

or

$$x^2\frac{dy}{dx} + 2xy - 2xy\frac{dy}{dx} - y^2 + 2x + 2y\frac{dy}{dx} = 0$$

and

$$\frac{dy}{dx} = \frac{y^2 - 2x - 2xy}{x^2 + 2y - 2xy}$$

Example A1.7

Consider the van der Waals equation of state:

$$\left(P + \frac{n^2 a}{V^2}\right)(V - nb) = nRT$$

Determine

$$1. \left(\frac{\partial V}{\partial T}\right)_{P,n} \qquad 2. \left(\frac{\partial V}{\partial P}\right)_{T,n}$$

Solution

1. Let us hold P and n constant as indicated in the question; then differentiate the equation with respect to V. We get

$$\left(P + \frac{n^2 a}{V^2}\right)\left(\frac{\partial V}{\partial T}\right)_{P,n} + (V - nb)\left(-\frac{2n^2 a}{V^3}\right)\left(\frac{\partial V}{\partial T}\right)_{P,n} = nR$$

Factor out $(\partial V/\partial T)_{P,n}$:

$$\left[\left(P + \frac{n^2 a}{V^2}\right) - \left(2\frac{n^2 a}{V^3}\right)(V - nb)\right]\left(\frac{\partial V}{\partial T}\right)_{P,n} = nR$$

and

$$\left(\frac{\partial V}{\partial T}\right)_{P,n} = \frac{nR}{P + \dfrac{n^2 a}{V^2} - \dfrac{2n^2 a}{V^2} + \dfrac{2n^3 ab}{V^3}}$$

$$\left(\frac{\partial V}{\partial T}\right)_{P,n} = \frac{nR}{P - \dfrac{n^2 a}{V^2} + \dfrac{2n^3 ab}{V^3}}$$

2. Hold T and n constant and differentiate the equation with respect to P:

$$\left(P + \frac{n^2 a}{V^3}\right)\left(\frac{\partial V}{\partial P}\right)_{T,n} + (V - nb)\left(\frac{\partial P}{\partial P}\right)_{T,n} + (V - nb)\left(-\frac{2n^2 a}{V^3}\right)\left(\frac{\partial V}{\partial P}\right)_{T,n} = 0$$

or

$$\left[\left(P + \frac{n^2 a}{V^2}\right) - \frac{2n^2 a}{V^3}(V - nb)\right]\left(\frac{\partial V}{\partial P}\right)_{T,n} + (V - nb) = 0$$

and

$$\left(\frac{\partial V}{\partial P}\right)_{T,n} = -\frac{(V-nb)}{P - \dfrac{n^2 a}{V^2} + \dfrac{2n^3 ab}{V^3}}$$

Example A1.8

When three resistances are connected in parallel, one has the relationship

$$\frac{1}{R} = \frac{1}{R_1} + \frac{1}{R_2} + \frac{1}{R_3}$$

What is $\partial R/\partial R_2$?

Solution

Differentiate, implicitly, both sides of the equation with respect to R_2. Thus

$$-\frac{\partial R}{\partial R_2}\left(\frac{1}{R^2}\right) = -\frac{1}{R_2^2}$$

and

$$\frac{\partial R}{\partial R_2} = \left(\frac{R}{R_2}\right)^2$$

A1.3 TOTAL DIFFERENTIALS

The total differential of a function

$$u = u(x,y,z,t)$$

(this means u is a function of x, y, z and t) is defined by

$$du = \frac{\partial u}{\partial x}\,dx + \frac{\partial u}{\partial y}\,dy + \frac{\partial u}{\partial z}\,dz + \frac{\partial u}{\partial t}\,dt$$

We can divide by ds to get du/ds in case x, y, z, and t are differentiable functions of s. Let us illustrate.

Example A1.9

What is the total differential of

$$u = x^2 y + x^3 y^2 + xyz$$

Solution

$$du = \left(\frac{\partial u}{\partial x}\right) dx + \frac{\partial u}{\partial y} dy + \frac{\partial u}{\partial z} dz$$

$$\frac{\partial u}{\partial x} = 2xy + 3x^2 y^2 + yz$$

$$\frac{\partial u}{\partial y} = x^2 + 2x^3 y + xz$$

$$\frac{\partial u}{\partial z} = xy$$

Therefore

$$du = (2xy + 3x^2 y^2 + yz)\, dx + (x^2 + 2x^3 y + xz)\, dy + (xy)\, dz$$

Let us write the total differential:

$$du = \left(\frac{\partial u}{\partial x}\right)_y dx + \left(\frac{\partial u}{\partial y}\right)_x dy$$

Divide through by dy and hold u constant:

$$\left(\frac{du}{dy}\right)_u = \left(\frac{\partial u}{\partial x}\right)_y \left(\frac{dx}{dy}\right)_u + \left(\frac{\partial u}{\partial y}\right)_x \left(\frac{dy}{dy}\right)_u$$

Our problem is already solved, and all we need is a small algebraic manipulation. This last equation becomes

$$0 = \left(\frac{\partial u}{\partial x}\right)_y \left(\frac{\partial x}{\partial y}\right)_u + \left(\frac{\partial u}{\partial y}\right)_x$$

Now divide by $(\partial u/\partial y)_x$ to get

$$\left(\frac{\partial u}{\partial x}\right)_y \left(\frac{\partial x}{\partial y}\right)_u \left(\frac{\partial y}{\partial u}\right)_x = -1$$

This desired relationship may easily be remembered if you follow the sequence indicated by the arrows:

It is often necessary to establish relationships between partial derivatives. Here is a quick and simple manipulation: Given a function

$$u = u(x,y)$$

prove that

$$\left(\frac{\partial u}{\partial x}\right)_{y} \left(\frac{\partial x}{\partial y}\right)_{u} \left(\frac{\partial y}{\partial u}\right)_{x} = -1$$

A1.4 CHANGE OF VARIABLES

Assume that we are dealing with continuous functions and let

$$u = u(x,y)$$

with the continuous partial derivatives $\partial u/\partial x$ and $\partial u/\partial y$. Now let x and y be functions of other variables such as

$$x = x(r,s)$$

and

$$y = y(r,s)$$

The function u may be expressed in terms of r and s as follows:

$$\frac{\partial u}{\partial r} = \frac{\partial u}{\partial x} \frac{\partial x}{\partial r} + \frac{\partial u}{\partial y} \frac{\partial y}{\partial r}$$

and

$$\frac{\partial u}{\partial s} = \frac{\partial u}{\partial x} \frac{\partial x}{\partial s} + \frac{\partial u}{\partial y} \frac{\partial y}{\partial s}$$

This approach may be extended to any number of variables.

Example A1.10

Given:

$$u = x^2 + xy + y^2$$

$$x = 2r + s$$

$$y = r - 2s$$

Find

1. $\partial u / \partial r$ 2. $\partial u / \partial s$

Solution

1.

$$\frac{\partial u}{\partial r} = \frac{\partial u}{\partial x}\frac{\partial x}{\partial r} + \frac{\partial u}{\partial y}\frac{\partial y}{\partial r}$$

$$= (2x + y)(2) + (x + 2y)(1)$$

$$= 4x + 2y + x + 2y$$

$$= 5x + 4y$$

2.

$$\frac{\partial u}{\partial s} = \frac{\partial u}{\partial x}\frac{\partial x}{\partial s} + \frac{\partial u}{\partial y}\frac{\partial y}{\partial s}$$

$$= (2x + y)(1) + (x + 2y)(-2)$$

$$= 2x + y - 2x - 4y$$

$$= -3y$$

A1.5 EXACT DIFFERENTIALS

Consider the functions $M(x,y)$ and $N(x,y)$ to be continuous functions with continuous partial derivatives.

The necessary and sufficient condition for the exactness of

$$M(x,y)\, dx + N(x,y)\, dy = 0$$

is that

$$\frac{\partial M}{\partial y} = \frac{\partial N}{\partial x}$$

Variables that are *independent of path* are called *point functions* or *exact differentials*. This is illustrated in Figure A1.1.

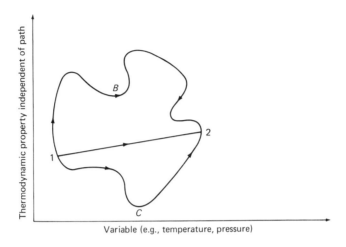

Figure A1.1 **Independence of the Path**

We can go from state 1 to state 2 via at least three routes, namely $1\rightarrow2$, $1\rightarrow B\rightarrow2$, $1\rightarrow C\rightarrow2$, and other routes. Every time we get the same value for the property, since such a property is independent of the path.

Example A1.11

Given the equation:

$$(x^2 + y^2)\, dx + 2xy\ dy = 0$$

Is this an exact differential?

Solution

$$(x^2 + y^2)\, dx + 2xy\ dy = 0$$

$$M\, dx + N\, dy = 0$$

$$\frac{\partial M}{\partial y} = 2y$$

$$\frac{\partial N}{\partial x} = 2y$$

Thus

$$\frac{\partial M}{\partial y} = \frac{\partial N}{\partial x} = 2y$$

and we have an exact differential.

Example A1.12

A certain gas follows this equation of state:

$$P = \frac{RT}{V} + \frac{a + bT}{V^2}$$

Is dP an exact differential?

Solution

$$P = P(T, V) = \text{pressure is a function of } T \text{ and } V$$

$$dP = \left(\frac{\partial P}{\partial T}\right)_V dT + \left(\frac{\partial P}{\partial V}\right)_T dV$$

Let

$$dP = M\,dT + N\,dV$$

Let us find out if the condition for exactness is satisfied. That is,

$$\left(\frac{\partial M}{\partial V}\right)_T = \left(\frac{\partial N}{\partial T}\right)_V$$

$$\left(\frac{\partial P}{\partial T}\right)_V = \frac{R}{V} + \frac{b}{V^2} = M$$

$$\left(\frac{\partial P}{\partial V}\right)_T = -\frac{RT}{V^2} - \frac{2(a + bT)}{V^3} = N$$

and

$$\left(\frac{\partial M}{\partial V}\right)_T = \left[\frac{\partial}{\partial V}\right]_T \left[\frac{R}{V} + \frac{b}{V^2}\right]$$

$$= -\frac{R}{V^2} - \frac{2b}{V^3} = -\left(\frac{R}{V^2} + \frac{2b}{V^3}\right)$$

$$\left(\frac{\partial N}{\partial T}\right)_V = \left[\frac{\partial}{\partial T}\right]_V \left[-\frac{RT}{V^2} - \frac{2(a + bT)}{V^3}\right]$$

$$= -\frac{R}{V^2} - \frac{2b}{V^3} = -\left(\frac{R}{V^2} + \frac{2b}{V^3}\right)$$

Therefore

$$\left(\frac{\partial M}{\partial V}\right)_T = \left(\frac{\partial N}{\partial T}\right)_V = -\left(\frac{R}{V^2} + \frac{2b}{V^3}\right)$$

and dP is an exact differential.

Now let us find the function $u(x,y)$ whose differential is exact:

$$du = M(x,y)\ dx + N(x,y)\ dy$$

Since u is a function of x and y, we can write

$$du = \left(\frac{\partial u}{\partial x}\right) dx + \frac{\partial u}{\partial y}\ dy \qquad \text{(A1.2)}$$

Compare this with

$$du = M\ dx + N\ dy$$

Then

$$\frac{\partial u}{\partial x} = M$$

$$\frac{\partial u}{\partial y} = N$$

Integrate $\partial u/\partial x = M$ and hold y constant:

$$du = \int_x u\ dx$$

$$u(x,y) = \int M(x,y)\ dx + f(y) \qquad \text{(A1.3)}$$

where $f(y)$ is a certain function of y, which is essentially a constant of integration. The function $u(x,y)$ satisfies the condition

$$\frac{\partial u}{\partial x} = u(x,y)$$

for any choice of $f(y)$. Let us see how it will satisfy the condition

$$\frac{\partial u}{\partial y} = N(x,y)$$

To do this we differentiate Equation A1.3 with respect to y holding x constant:

$$\frac{\partial u(x,y)}{\partial y} = \frac{\partial}{\partial y} \int M(x,y) \; dx + \frac{\partial f(y)}{\partial y} \tag{A1.4}$$

For Equation A1.2 we have

$$N(x,y) = \frac{\partial u}{\partial y}$$

and, by substitution, Equation A1.4 becomes

$$N(x,y) = \frac{\partial}{\partial y} \int M(x,y) \; dx + \frac{\partial f(y)}{\partial y} \tag{A1.5}$$

The function $f(y)$ is found by the equation

$$\frac{\partial f(y)}{\partial y} = N(x,y) - \frac{\partial}{\partial y} \int M(x,y) \; dx \tag{A1.6}$$

This method for finding a function is best understood by using some examples.

Example A1.13

Find the function $u(x,y)$ whose differential is

$$du = (x^2 + y^2) \ dx + 2xy \ dy$$
$$= M \ dx + N \ dy$$

$$\frac{\partial M}{\partial y} = \frac{\partial}{\partial y} (x^2 + y^2) = 2y$$

$$\frac{\partial N}{\partial x} = \frac{\partial}{\partial x} (2xy) = 2y$$

Thus the condition for exactness is satisfied, and

$$u = \int u \ dx + f(y)$$

$$u = \int (x^2 + y^2) \ dx + f(y)$$

$$= \frac{x^3}{3} + y^2 x + f(y)$$

Since

$$\frac{\partial u}{\partial y} = N(x,y)$$

we get

$$\frac{\partial u}{\partial y} = \frac{\partial}{\partial y} \left[\frac{x^3}{3} + y^2 x + f(y) \right] = N(x,y)$$

$$\frac{\partial u}{\partial y} = 2xy + \frac{\partial f(y)}{\partial y} = 2xy$$

and

$$\frac{\partial f(y)}{\partial y} = 2xy - 2xy$$

$$= 0$$

Thus $f(y) = $ constant $= C$. (We can write $df(y)$ instead of $\partial f(y)$ if we wish, since f is the function of y alone.)

$$u = \frac{x^3}{3} + y^2 x + C$$

Example A1.14

Given the differential

$$du = (2x^3 + 3y) \ dx + (3x + y - 1) \ dy$$

find the function u.

Solution

$$\frac{\partial M}{\partial y} = \frac{\partial}{\partial y}(2x^3 + 3y) = 3$$

$$\frac{\partial N}{\partial x} = \frac{\partial}{\partial x}(3x + y - 1) = 3$$

The condition of exactness is satisfied, since

$$\frac{\partial M}{\partial y} = \frac{\partial N}{\partial x} = 3$$

and

$$u = \int M \ dx + f(y)$$

$$= \int (2x^3 + 3y) \ dx + f(y)$$

$$= \frac{2x^4}{4} + 3yx + f(y)$$

$$= \frac{x^4}{2} + 3xy + f(y) \tag{A1.7}$$

Since

$$\frac{\partial u}{\partial y} = N(x,y) = (3x + y - 1)$$

Let us equate this to the result obtained when Equation A1.7 is differentiated with respect to y, and holding x constant, we get

$$\frac{\partial u}{\partial y} = \frac{\partial}{\partial y}\left[\frac{x^4}{2} + 3xy + f(y)\right] = 3x + y - 1$$

$$= 3x + \frac{\partial f(y)}{\partial y} = 3x + y - 1$$

and

$$\frac{\partial f(y)}{\partial y} = 3x + y - 1 - 3x = y - 1$$

Upon integration one obtains

$$f(y) = \int (y - 1) \ dy = \frac{y^2}{2} - y + \text{constant}$$

and the required function is

$$u = \frac{x^4}{2} + 3xy + \frac{y^2}{2} - y + C$$

A1.6 DIFFERENTIATION AND INTEGRATION FORMULAS

Differentiation

1.
$$\frac{d}{dx}(au) = a\frac{du}{dx}$$

2.
$$\frac{d}{dx}(u+v) = \frac{du}{dx} + \frac{dv}{dx} = u' + v'$$

3.
$$\frac{d}{dx}(uv) = u\frac{dv}{dx} + v\frac{du}{dx} = u'v + v'u$$

4.
$$\frac{d}{dx}\left(\frac{u}{v}\right) = \frac{1}{v^2}\left(v\frac{du}{dx} - u\frac{dv}{dx}\right) = \frac{u'v - v'u}{v^2}$$

5.
$$\frac{d}{dx}f(u) = \frac{d}{du}f(u)\frac{du}{dx}$$

6.
$$\frac{d}{dx}u^n = nu^{n-1}\frac{du}{dx}$$

7.
$$\frac{d}{dx}x^n = nx^{n-1}$$

8.
$$\frac{d}{dx}e^u = e^u\frac{du}{dx}$$

9.
$$\frac{d}{dx}e^{au} = ae^{au}\frac{du}{dx}$$

10.
$$\frac{d}{dx}a^u = a^u \ln a \frac{du}{dx}$$

11.
$$\frac{d}{dx}x^n = x^x(1 + \ln x)$$

12.
$$\frac{d}{dx}\log_a x = \frac{1}{x\ln a} = \frac{\log a^e}{x}$$

13.
$$\frac{\partial}{\partial x}f(x,y) = \lim_{\Delta x \to 0}\frac{f(x + \Delta x, y) - f(x,y)}{\Delta x}$$

14.
$$\frac{\partial}{\partial y}f(x,y) = \lim_{\Delta y \to 0}\frac{f(x, y + \Delta y) - f(x,y)}{\Delta y}$$

15.
$$\frac{\partial}{\partial x}\left(\frac{\partial f}{\partial y}\right) = \frac{\partial^2 f}{\partial x\, \partial y}$$

16.
$$\frac{\partial}{\partial x}\left(\frac{\partial f}{\partial x}\right) = \frac{\partial^2 f}{\partial x^2}$$

17.
$$\frac{\partial}{\partial y}\left(\frac{\partial f}{\partial y}\right) = \frac{\partial^2 f}{\partial y^2}$$

18.
$$u = u(x,y,z,t)$$

$$du = \frac{\partial u}{\partial x}\ dx + \frac{\partial u}{\partial y}\ dy + \frac{\partial u}{\partial z}\ dz + \frac{\partial u}{\partial t}\ dt$$

19.
$$u = u(x,y)$$

$$x = x(r,s); y = y(r,s)$$

$$\frac{\partial u}{\partial r} = \frac{\partial u}{\partial x}\ \frac{\partial x}{\partial r} + \frac{\partial u}{\partial y}\ \frac{\partial y}{\partial r}$$

$$\frac{\partial u}{\partial s} = \frac{\partial u}{\partial x}\ \frac{\partial x}{\partial s} + \frac{\partial u}{\partial y}\ \frac{\partial y}{\partial s}$$

Integration

1.
$$\int a\,du = au + c$$

2.
$$\int af(x)\ dx = a \int f(x)\ dx$$

3.
$$\int \frac{1}{u}\,du = \ln\ u + c$$

4.
$$\int u^n\ du = \frac{u^{n+1}}{n+1} + c$$

5.
$$\int e^u\ du = e^u + c$$

6.
$$\int u^{au}\ du = \frac{e^{au}}{a} + c$$

7.
$$\int ue^{au}\ du = \frac{e^{au}}{a^2}(au - 1) + c$$

8.
$$\int a^u\ du = \frac{a^u}{\ln a} + c$$

9.
$$\int u\, dv = uv - \int v\, du$$

10.
$$\int u\, \frac{dv}{dx}\, dx = uv - \int v\, \frac{du}{dx}\, dx$$

11.
$$\int \frac{f(x)}{f(x)}\, dx = \log f(x) + c$$

12.
$$\int a^u \log a\, du = a^u + c$$

13.
$$\int \log u\, du = u \log u - u + c$$

14.
$$\int u \log u\, du = \frac{u^2}{2} \log u + \frac{u^2}{4} + c$$

2. APPENDIX

Numerical Methods for Solving Simultaneous Linear Equations

Among the many methods available for solving systems of linear equations, the following are among the simplest. As such, they are the most suitable for the type of equations usually encountered in this course.

A2.1 CRAMER'S METHOD (DETERMINANTS)

In a system of n linear equations in n unknowns, the value of each unknown is equal to the ratio of two determinants. The denominator of each of these ratios is the determinant of the coefficients, D.

$$
\begin{aligned}
A_1 W + B_1 X + C_1 Y + D_1 Z &= E_1 \\
A_2 W + B_2 X + C_2 Y + D_2 Z &= E_2 \\
A_3 W + B_3 X + C_3 Y + D_3 Z &= E_3 \\
A_4 W + B_4 X + C_4 Y + D_4 Z &= E_4
\end{aligned}
\qquad
D =
\begin{vmatrix}
A_1 & B_1 & C_1 & D_1 \\
A_2 & B_2 & C_2 & D_2 \\
A_3 & B_3 & C_3 & D_3 \\
A_4 & B_4 & C_4 & D_4
\end{vmatrix}
$$

The numerator is the determinant obtained by replacing the coefficients of the desired unknown by the constant terms in the appropriate column. For example,

$$
X = \frac{
\begin{vmatrix}
A_1 & E_1 & C_1 & D_1 \\
A_2 & E_2 & C_2 & D_2 \\
A_3 & E_3 & C_3 & D_3 \\
A_4 & E_4 & C_4 & D_4
\end{vmatrix}
}{D}
\qquad
Y = \frac{
\begin{vmatrix}
A_1 & B_1 & E_1 & D_1 \\
A_2 & B_2 & E_2 & D_2 \\
A_3 & B_3 & E_3 & D_3 \\
A_4 & B_4 & E_4 & D_4
\end{vmatrix}
}{D}
$$

For any system in which $D = 0$, no unique solution exists. That is, the equations are not linearly independent; one or more additional independent equations are required to obtain a unique solution.

Determinants of order 2 or 3 (that is, 2 X 2 or 3 X 3) may be evaluated by using the method of diagonals. Determinants of order 4 or greater *must* be evaluated by using "expansion by minors" until the determinant is reduced to an expression involving determinants of order 3 or lower. These can then be evaluated by the method of diagonals. Thus, the method of diagonals is *not* valid for orders higher than 3.

Method of Diagonals

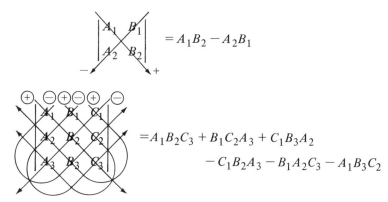

Method of Minors

In this method, a row or column of the determinant is chosen, and each element of this row or column is multiplied by its *cofactor*. The cofactor is a determinant of order one less than the original determinant. For example,

$$\begin{vmatrix} A_1 & B_1 & C_1 & D_1 \\ A_2 & B_2 & C_2 & D_2 \\ A_3 & B_3 & C_3 & D_3 \\ A_4 & B_4 & C_4 & D_4 \end{vmatrix} = +C_1 \begin{vmatrix} A_2 & B_2 & D_2 \\ A_3 & B_3 & D_3 \\ A_4 & B_4 & D_4 \end{vmatrix} - C_2 \begin{vmatrix} A_1 & B_1 & D_1 \\ A_3 & B_3 & D_3 \\ A_4 & B_4 & D_4 \end{vmatrix}$$

$$+C_3 \begin{vmatrix} A_1 & B_1 & D_1 \\ A_2 & B_2 & D_2 \\ A_4 & B_4 & D_4 \end{vmatrix} - C_4 \begin{vmatrix} A_1 & B_1 & D_1 \\ A_2 & B_2 & D_2 \\ A_3 & B_3 & D_3 \end{vmatrix}$$

Each term in the resulting expression is determined as follows.

$$\begin{vmatrix} A_1 & B_1 & C_1 & D_1 \\ A_2 & B_2 & C_2 & D_2 \\ A_3 & B_3 & C_3 & D_3 \\ A_4 & B_4 & C_4 & D_4 \end{vmatrix} \Rightarrow (-1)^{r+c} \times C_2 \times (\text{cofactor}) = (-1)^{2+3} \; C_2 \begin{vmatrix} A_1 & B_1 & D_1 \\ A_3 & B_3 & D_3 \\ A_4 & B_4 & D_4 \end{vmatrix}$$

It is usually convenient to choose the row or column containing the most zeros, since doing so will minimize the number of terms to be evaluated in the resulting expression.

For determinants of order greater than 4, the cofactors must also be evaluated by this method. Successive expansions of all resulting determinants must be performed until none of order greater than 3 remain.

For determinants above order 4, evaluation by Cramer's method becomes extremely cumbersome. In addition to the large number of terms (20 terms for order 5, 120 terms for order 6, and so on), the possibility of making errors in sign or of transposing elements is high. Therefore, use of this method should be restricted to systems of order 3 and lower (unless there is a sufficient number of zero elements to warrant its use).

A2.2 MATRIX METHODS

Two of the most commonly used methods are the Gauss elemination technique (which involves triangularizing the system matrix) and the Gauss-Jordan method. Both of these methods have certain advantages over Cramer's method for solving systems of more than three equations (unless enough coefficients are zero). For paper-and-pencil computations, there is less chance of making sign errors or of transposing terms, because the size of the expressions being treated at any one time is relatively small. In addition, while Cramer's method is never used in digital computer computations because of the extremely large number of operations involved (additions, multiplications, and so on), these matrix methods are widely used because the number of operations is greatly reduced.*

---

*A full discussion of the computer use of these methods is beyond the scope of this course. However, it must be noted that it is extremely desirable to minimize the number of operations required to effect a solution because each additional computation introduces additional error. In fact, there are solution procedures that are mathematically correct and feasible but in which the number of operations is so large that the error introduced is of a magnitude comparable to that of the solution itself. Such methods have little use in computer applications.

The system matrix is formed as follows for a four-equation system.

$$
\begin{aligned}
A_1 W + B_1 X + C_1 Y + D_1 Z &= E_1 \\
A_2 W + B_2 X + C_2 Y + D_2 Z &= E_2 \\
A_3 W + B_3 X + C_3 Y + D_3 Z &= E_3 \\
A_4 W + B_4 X + C_4 Y + D_4 Z &= E_4
\end{aligned}
\Rightarrow
\begin{bmatrix}
A_1 & B_1 & C_1 & D_1 & E_1 \\
A_2 & B_2 & C_2 & D_2 & E_2 \\
A_3 & B_3 & C_3 & D_3 & E_3 \\
A_4 & A_4 & C_4 & D_4 & E_4
\end{bmatrix}
$$

The following two rules govern the computations involved in solving the system.

1. Multiplying each element in a row (*not* a column) by a constant different from zero yields a matrix representing an equivalent system (that is, one having the same solutions for the unknowns).

$$
\begin{bmatrix}
A_1 & B_1 & C_1 & D_1 & E_1 \\
A_2 & B_2 & C_2 & D_2 & E_2 \\
A_3 & B_3 & C_3 & D_3 & E_3 \\
A_4 & B_4 & C_4 & D_4 & E_4
\end{bmatrix}
=
\begin{bmatrix}
A_1 & B_1 & C_1 & D_1 & E_1 \\
tA_2 & tB_2 & tC_2 & tD_2 & tE_2 \\
A_3 & B_3 & C_3 & D_3 & E_3 \\
A_4 & B_4 & C_4 & D_4 & E_4
\end{bmatrix}
$$

2. Replacing each element of a row by the sum of that element and a certain multiple (the same nonzero multiple for each element) of the corresponding element in another chosen row yields a matrix representing an equivalent system.

$$
\begin{bmatrix}
A_1 & B_1 & C_1 & D_1 & E_1 \\
A_2 & B_2 & C_2 & D_2 & E_2 \\
A_3 & B_3 & C_3 & D_3 & E_3 \\
A_4 & B_4 & C_4 & D_4 & E_4
\end{bmatrix}
=
$$

$$
\begin{bmatrix}
(mA_4 + A_1) & (mB_4 + B_1) & (mC_4 + C_1) & (mD_4 + D_1) & (mE_4 + E_1) \\
A_2 & B_2 & C_2 & D_2 & E_2 \\
A_3 & B_3 & C_3 & D_3 & E_3 \\
A_4 & B_4 & C_4 & D_4 & E_4
\end{bmatrix}
$$

Gauss Elimination Technique

The goal of this method is to use the above rules to form a triangularized equivalent matrix. For example,

$$
\begin{bmatrix}
1 & S_1 & T_1 & U_1 & P_1 \\
0 & 1 & T_2 & U_2 & P_2 \\
0 & 0 & 1 & U_3 & P_3 \\
0 & 0 & 0 & 1 & P_4
\end{bmatrix}
\Rightarrow
\begin{array}{rl}
W + S_1 X + T_1 Y + U_1 Z = P_1 & \text{(A2.1)} \\
X + T_2 Y + U_2 Z = P_2 & \text{(A2.2)} \\
Y + U_3 Z = P_3 & \text{(A2.3)} \\
Z = P_4 & \text{(A2.4)}
\end{array}
$$

Then, by a process of back-substitution, the values of W, X, and Y can be determined. That is, substitute Equation A2.4 into Equation A2.3 to find Y, then substitute Z and Y into Equation A2.2 to find X, and so on.

Gauss-Jordan Method

The goal of this method is to use the two rules to form an equivalent matrix that will give the solutions directly. For example,

$$
\begin{bmatrix}
0 & 1 & 0 & 0 & P_1 \\
0 & 0 & 0 & 1 & P_2 \\
1 & 0 & 0 & 0 & P_3 \\
0 & 0 & 1 & 0 & P_4
\end{bmatrix}
\Rightarrow
\begin{array}{l}
X = P_1 \\
Z = P_2 \\
W = P_3 \\
Y = P_4
\end{array}
$$

If the equations of the system are not all linearly independent, the Gauss-Jordan method should yield one row containing all zeros (or two or more rows having corresponding elements directly proportional by a single constant) at some point during the computations. However, due to slide rule inaccuracy and rounding of numbers in actual practice, this may not occur. It is therefore very important that the solutions obtained be substituted into the original equations to check their accuracy.

If the solutions do not check when substituted into the original equations, it is because either a mistake was made in computation or because one or more of the equations was not independent. In the latter case, it is possible to obtain a different set of solutions each time the computations are performed, due to small differences in rounding, and so on. Therefore, if this occurs, or if one suspects that the system may not be independent, the determinant of the coefficients should be computed as described for Cramer's method. If the determinant is nonzero, it may be advisable to use the algebraic method (or possibly Cramer's method) to attempt a solution.

SOLUTION OF EXAMPLE 4.13 BY MATRICES

Gauss Elimination Method

Using the Gauss elimination method, the system matrix is

$$
\begin{bmatrix}
0.80 & 0.0 & 0.3 & 0.10 & 800 \\
0.00 & 0.8 & 0.1 & 0.10 & 540 \\
0.16 & 0.2 & 0.6 & 0.72 & 620 \\
0.04 & 0.0 & 0.0 & 0.08 & 40
\end{bmatrix}
$$

1. Divide row 1 elements by 0.8, then
2. Multiply the row 1 elements by −0.16 (row 1 unchanged) and add the products to the corresponding elements of row 3, then
3. Multiply the row 1 elements by −0.04 (row 1 unchanged) and add the products to the corresponding elements of row 3.

$$
\begin{bmatrix}
1 & 0.0 & 0.375 & 0.125 & 1000 \\
0 & 0.8 & 0.100 & 0.100 & 540 \\
0 & 0.2 & 0.540 & 0.700 & 460 \\
0 & 0.0 & -0.015 & 0.075 & 0
\end{bmatrix}
$$

4. Divide row 2 elements by 0.8, then
5. Multiply the row 2 elements by −0.2 and add the products to row 3.

$$
\begin{bmatrix}
1 & 0 & 0.375 & 0.125 & 1000 \\
0 & 1 & 0.125 & 0.125 & 675 \\
0 & 0 & 0.515 & 0.675 & 325 \\
0 & 0 & -0.015 & 0.075 & 0
\end{bmatrix}
$$

6. Divide row 3 elements by 0.515, then

7. Multiply the row 3 elements by 0.015 and add the products to row 4.

$$\begin{bmatrix} 1 & 0 & 0.375 & 0.12500 & 1000.000 \\ 0 & 1 & 0.125 & 0.12500 & 675.000 \\ 0 & 0 & 1.000 & 1.31000 & 631.000 \\ 0 & 0 & 0.000 & 0.09465 & 9.465 \end{bmatrix}$$

8. Divide row 4 elements by 0.09465.

$$\begin{bmatrix} 1 & 0 & 0.375 & 0.125 & 1000 \\ 0 & 1 & 0.125 & 0.125 & 675 \\ 0 & 0 & 1.000 & 1.310 & 631 \\ 0 & 0 & 0.000 & 1.000 & 100 \end{bmatrix}$$

The corresponding system of equations is therefore

$$W + 0.0X + 0.375Y + 0.125Z = 1000$$
$$X + 0.125Y + 0.125Z = 675$$
$$Y + 1.310Z = 631$$
$$Z = 100$$

and, by the process of back-substitution, the solutions are

$$Z = 100 \text{ lb/hr}$$
$$Y + 1.310(100) = 631 \Rightarrow Y = 500 \text{ lb/hr}$$
$$X + 0.125(500) + 0.125(100) = 675 \Rightarrow X = 600 \text{ lb/hr}$$
$$W + 0.0(600) + 0.375(500) + 0.125(100) = 1000 \Rightarrow W = 800 \text{ lb/hr}$$

Gauss-Jordan Method

Using the Gauss-Jordan method, the system matrix is

$$\begin{bmatrix} 0.80 & 0.0 & 0.3 & 0.10 & 800 \\ 0.00 & 0.8 & 0.1 & 0.10 & 540 \\ 0.16 & 0.2 & 0.6 & 0.72 & 620 \\ 0.04 & 0.0 & 0.0 & 0.08 & 40 \end{bmatrix}$$

1. Divide the row 1 elements by 0.8, then

2. Multiply the row 1 elements by -0.16 (row 1 unchanged) and add the products to the corresponding elements of row 3, then

3. Multiply the row 1 elements by -0.04 (row 1 unchanged) and add the products to the corresponding elements of row 4.

$$\begin{bmatrix} 1 & 0.0 & 0.375 & 0.125 & 1000 \\ 0 & 0.8 & 0.100 & 0.100 & 540 \\ 0 & 0.2 & 0.540 & 0.700 & 460 \\ 0 & 0.0 & -0.015 & 0.075 & 0 \end{bmatrix}$$

4. Divide the row 2 elements by 0.8, then

5. Multiply the row 2 elements by -0.2 and add the products to row 3.

$$\begin{bmatrix} 1 & 0 & 0.375 & 0.125 & 1000 \\ 0 & 1 & 0.125 & 0.125 & 675 \\ 0 & 0 & 0.515 & 0.675 & 325 \\ 0 & 0 & -0.015 & 0.075 & 0 \end{bmatrix}$$

6. Divide the row 3 elements by 0.515, then

7. Multiply the row 3 elements by -0.375 and add the products to row 1, then

8. Multiply the row 3 elements by -0.125 and add the products to row 2, then

9. Multiply the row 3 elements by $+0.015$ and add the products to row 4.

$$\begin{bmatrix} 1 & 0 & 0 & -0.36625 & 763.375 \\ 0 & 1 & 0 & -0.03875 & 596.125 \\ 0 & 0 & 1 & 1.31000 & 631.000 \\ 0 & 0 & 0 & 0.09465 & 9.465 \end{bmatrix}$$

10. Divide the row 4 elements by 0.09465, then

11. Multiply the row 4 elements by −1.310 and add the products to row 3, then

12. Multiply the row 4 elements by +0.03875 and add the products to row 2, then

13. Multiply the row 4 elements by +0.36625 and add the products to row 1.

$$\begin{bmatrix} 1 & 0 & 0 & 0 & 800 \\ 0 & 1 & 0 & 0 & 600 \\ 0 & 0 & 1 & 0 & 500 \\ 0 & 0 & 0 & 1 & 100 \end{bmatrix}$$

The corresponding system of equations is therefore

$$W = 800 \text{ lb/hr}$$

$$X = 600 \text{ lb/hr}$$

$$Y = 500 \text{ lb/hr}$$

$$Z = 100 \text{ lb/hr}$$

APPENDIX **3.**

Macroscopic Mechanical Energy and Momentum Balances

A3.1 MECHANICAL ENERGY BALANCE

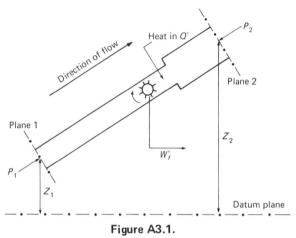

Figure A3.1.

Consider the flow system shown in the figure in which a fluid is flowing under isothermal conditions. Assume steady-state flow. By "steady-state" one means that the conditions at each point in the stream do not change with time; that is, mass rates of flow into and from the system are constant, and the rates of additions of heat and production of work are constant. The system is bounded by plane 1 and plane 2, and, in accordance with the principle of conservation of energy, *the total energy leaving the system is equal to the total energy entering the system.* The energies under consideration in this system are those carried by the fluid and those transferred between the fluid and its surroundings.

The energies carried by the fluid include internal energy, kinetic energy, potential energy, and *PV* energy. The *PV* energy is the product of the force exerted

395

by the fluid immediately behind the entrance point times the distance through which it acts. Let

X_1 = distance through which the force acts

P_1 = pressure at plane 1

S_1 = cross-sectional area at plane 1

F_1 = force exerted by the fluid behind the entrance point, on the neighboring fluid to the right of the entrance point

Thus

$$F_1 X_1 = P_1(S_1 X_1) = P_1 V_1 \qquad \text{(A3.1)}$$

The energies transferred between the system and its surroundings include: (1) The heat Q' absorbed by the flowing material from the surroundings, and (2) the work W'_f done on the surroundings by the flowing fluid.

The balance of all the energies involved in the flow system may be written as

$$wU_1 + w(\text{K.E.})_1 + wz_1 \frac{g}{g_c} + wP_1 V_1 + wQ'$$

$$= wU_2 + w(\text{K.E.})_2 + wz_2 \frac{g}{g_c} + wP_2 V_2 + wW'_f \qquad \text{(A3.2)}$$

where

U = internal energy (Btu/lb$_m$)

w = mass flow rate (lb$_m$/hr)

K.E. = kinetic energy/lb$_m$

z = height from reference plane (ft)

P = pressure (psia)

V = specific volume (lb$_m$/ft^3)

Subscript 1 refers to plane 1; subscript 2 refers to plane 2

Divide both sides of Equation A3.2 by w and express it in a difference form:

$$\Delta U + \Delta(\text{K.E.}) + \frac{g}{g_c} \Delta z + \Delta(PV) = Q' - W'_f \qquad \text{(A3.3)}$$

As a result of flow, fluid friction occurs wherever there is a stress on the fluid. This friction converts mechanical energy into heat. Thus

$$Q = Q' + \Sigma F \qquad \text{(A3.4)}$$

and

$$W'_f = W - \Sigma F \qquad \text{(A3.5)}$$

where

Q = heat absorbed by the fluid

Q' = heat transferred from the surroundings

W = total work done by the fluid

W'_f = work transferred to the surroundings (shaft work)

ΣF = total fluid friction

Therefore

$$Q' = Q - \Sigma F$$

which, substituted in Equation A3.3, yields

$$\Delta U + \Delta(\text{K.E.}) + \frac{g}{g_c} \Delta z + \Delta(PV) = Q - \Sigma F - W'_f \qquad \text{(A3.6)}$$

Since

$$dU = T\,dS - P\,dV \quad \text{or} \quad \int dU = \int T\,dS - \int P\,dV \qquad \text{(A3.7)}$$

we know that

$$\Delta U = T\Delta S - \int P\,dV \quad \text{or} \quad \Delta U = Q - \int P\,dV$$

Substituting Equation A3.6, we get

$$Q - \int_{V_1}^{V_2} P\,dV + \Delta(\text{K.E.}) + \frac{g}{g_c} \Delta z + \Delta(PV) + \Sigma F - Q + W'_f = 0$$

$$\Delta(PV) = \int_{V_1}^{V_2} P\,dV + \int_{P_1}^{P_2} V\,dP - \int_{V_1}^{V_2} P\,dV + \Delta(\text{K.E.}) + \frac{g}{g_c} \Delta z$$

$$+ \int_{V_1}^{V_2} P\,dV + \int_{P_1}^{P_2} V\,dP + \Sigma F + W'_f = 0$$

Thus

$$\Delta(\text{K.E.}) + \frac{g}{g_c}\,\Delta z + \int_{P_1}^{P_2} \frac{1}{\mathscr{P}}\,dP + W'_f + \Sigma F = 0 \qquad \text{(A3.8)}$$

We use the script $\mathscr{P}$ because V = specific volume. In general,

$$\Delta(\text{K.E.}) = \Delta\left(\frac{v^2}{2g_c\alpha}\right)$$

where

$$v = \text{average velocity}$$

$$\alpha = \text{correction factor, to account for the effect of}$$
velocity distribution in the flow channel on
the average kinetic energy

Finally, the energy equation becomes

$$\Delta\left(\frac{v^2}{2g_c\alpha}\right) + \frac{g}{g_c}\,\Delta z + \int_{P_1}^{P_2} \frac{1}{\mathscr{P}}\,dP + W'_f + \Sigma F = 0 \qquad \text{(A3.9)}$$

Keep in mind that each term in Equation A3.9 has a unit of ft-lb$_f$/lb$_m$.

Although any one of the energy terms might be calculated from the energy balance, often we need to determine the power requirements for moving a fluid at a specified rate through a piping system.

A3.2 MOMENTUM (FORCE BALANCE)

It should be pointed out that *the rate of momentum is a force*. From the definition of momentum, one can write

$$\text{Momentum} = mv = (\text{mass})\,(\text{velocity})$$

$$\text{Rate of momentum} = mv/\text{time} \quad \left(\frac{\text{lb}_m\,(\text{ft/sec})}{\text{sec}} = \frac{\text{lb}_m\text{-ft}}{\text{sec}^2}\right)$$

From Newton's second law of motion, we have

$$\text{Force} = ma \quad \left(\frac{\text{lb}_m\text{-ft}}{\text{sec}^2}\right)$$

Rate of momentum = force

Thus the momentum balance is simply a force balance. For the system shown in Figure A3.1, the momentum balance is

$$(\text{Rate of momentum in}) - (\text{rate of momentum out}) + \begin{pmatrix} \text{sum of forces} \\ \text{acting on system} \end{pmatrix} = 0$$

For an incompressible fluid (constant density, $\mathcal{P}$), the following equation may be written:

$$\{(\mathcal{P}v_1 S_1)\langle v_1\rangle - (\mathcal{P}v_2 S_2)\langle v_2\rangle\} + \{P_1 S_1 - P_2 S_2\} - \{F\} + m_{tot}g = 0 \qquad \textbf{(A3.10)}$$

Average   Pressure
velocity   forces

The first two terms in the above equation represent the rate of momentum influx and efflux by virtue of the bulk-fluid motion. (F) is the force of the fluid on the solid. The expression $(m_{tot}g)$ refers to the force of gravity on the total mass of fluid.

Equation A3.10, the momentum balance equation, is very useful for computing the forces acting on surfaces of pieces of equipment, such as pipe bends.

4. APPENDIX

Atomic Numbers and Weights of the Elements

Table A4.1 Atomic Numbers and Weights of the Elements (1)

(Table reflects caution on accuracy; based on the assigned relative mass of $^{12}C = 12$.)

The following values apply to elements as they exist in materials of terrestrial origin and to certain artificial elements. When used with the footnotes, they are reliable to ± 1 in the last digit, or ± 3 if that digit is in small type.

Element	Symbol	Atomic number	Atomic weight
Actinium	Ac	89	
Aluminum	Al	13	26.9815[a]
Americium	Am	95	
Antimony	Sb	51	121.7s
Argon	Ar	18	39.948[b,c,d,g]
Arsenic	As	33	74.9216[a]
Astatine	At	85	
Barium	Ba	56	137.34
Berkelium	Bk	97	
Beryllium	Be	4	9.01218[a]
Bismuth	Bi	83	208.9806[a]
Boron	B	5	10.81[c,d,e]
Bromine	Br	35	79.904[c]
Cadmium	Cd	48	112.40
Calcium	Ca	20	40.08
Californium	Cf	98	
Carbon	C	6	12.011[b,d]
Cerium	Ce	58	140.12
Cesium	Cs	55	132.9055[a]
Chlorine	Cl	17	35.453[c]
Chromium	Cr	24	51.996[c]
Cobalt	Co	27	58.9332[a]
Copper	Cu	29	63.546[c,d]

Table A4.1 Atomic Numbers and Weights of the Elements (*cont.*)

Element	Symbol	Atomic number	Atomic weight
Curium	Cm	96	
Dysprosium	Dy	66	162.5o
Einsteinium	Es	99	
Erbium	Er	68	167.26
Europium	Eu	63	151.96
Fermium	Fm	100	
Fluorine	F	9	18.9984[a]
Francium	Fr	87	
Gadolinium	Gd	64	157.25
Gallium	Ga	31	69.72
Germanium	Ge	32	72.59
Gold	Au	79	196.9665[a]
Hafnium	Hf	72	178.49
Helium	He	2	4.00260[b,c]
Holmium	Ho	67	164.9303[a]
Hydrogen	H	1	1.0080[b,d]
Indium	In	49	114.82
Iodine	I	53	126.9045[a]
Iridium	Ir	77	192.22
Iron	Fe	26	55.847
Krypton	Kr	36	83.80
Lanthanium	La	57	138.9055[b]
Lawrencium	Lr	103	
Lead	Pb	82	207.2[d,g]
Lithium	Li	3	6.941[c,d,e]
Lutetium	Lu	71	174.97
Magnesium	Mg	12	24.305[c]
Manganese	Mn	25	54.9380[a]
Mendelevium	Md	101	
Mercury	Hg	80	200.59
Molybdenum	Mo	42	95.94
Neodymium	Nd	60	144.24
Neon	Ne	10	20.179[c]
Neptunium	Np	93	237.0482[b]
Nickel	Ni	28	58.71
Niobium	Nb	41	92.9064[a]
Nitrogen	N	7	14.0067[b,c]
Nobelium	No	102	
Osmium	Os	76	190.2
Oxygen	O	8	15.9994[b,c,d]
Palladium	Pd	46	106.4
Phosphorus	P	15	30.9738[a]
Platinum	Pt	78	195.09
Plutonium	Pu	94	
Polonium	Po	84	
Potassium	K	19	39.102

Table A4.1 Atomic Numbers and Weights of the Elements (*cont.*)

Element	Symbol	Atomic number	Atomic weight
Praseodymium	Pr	59	140.9077[a]
Promethium	Pm	61	
Protactinium	Pa	91	231.0359[a]
Radium	Ra	88	226.0254[a,f,g]
Radon	Rn	86	
Rhenium	Re	75	186.2
Rhodium	Rh	45	102.9055[a]
Rubidium	Rb	37	85.4678[c]
Ruthenium	Ru	44	101.07
Samarium	Sm	62	150.4
Scandium	Sc	21	44.9559[a]
Selenium	Se	34	78.96
Silicon	Si	14	28.086[d]
Silver	Ag	47	107.868[e]
Sodium	Na	11	22.9898[a]
Strontium	Sr	38	87.62[g]
Sulfur	S	16	32.06[d]
Tantalum	Ta	73	180.9479[b]
Technetium	Tc	43	98.9062[f]
Tellurium	Te	52	127.60
Terbium	Tb	65	158.9254[a]
Thallium	Tl	81	204.37
Thorium	Th	90	232.0381[a]
Thulium	Tm	69	168.9342[a]
Tin	Sn	50	118.69
Titanium	Ti	22	47.90
Tungsten	W	74	183.85
Uranium	U	92	238.029[b,c,e]
Vanadium	V	23	50.9414[b,c]
Wolfram	W	74	183.85
Xenon	Xe	54	131.30
Ytterbium	Yb	70	173.04
Yttrium	Y	39	88.9059[a]
Zinc	Zn	30	65.37
Zirconium	Zr	40	91.22

[a] Mononuclidic element.
[b] Element with one predominant isotope (about 99 to 100% abundance).
[c] Element for which the atomic weight is based on calibrated measurements.
[d] Element for which variation in isotopic abundance in terrestrial samples limits the precision of the atomic weight given.
[e] Element for which users are cautioned against the possibility of large variations in atomic weight due to inadvertent or undisclosed artificial isotopic separation in commercially available materials.
[f] Most commonly available long-lived isotope; see "Table of Selected Radioactive Isotopes."
[g] In some geological specimens this element has a highly anomalous isotopic composition, corresponding to an atomic weight significantly different from that given.

Conversions and Physical Constants

Air, dry composition, volume %	78.09 N_2, 20.95 O_2, 0.93 Ar, 0.03 others
Area	1 acre = 43,560 ft^2 = 4074 m^2 = 0.001563 mi^2
Density	62.4 lb/ft^3 = 8.33 lb/gal, water at 68°F
	1 g/ml, water at 4°C
	1.29 g/liter, air at 0°C
	0.0808 lb/ft^3, air at 0°C
	13.6 g/cm^3, mercury at room temperature
	7.8 g/cm^3, steel at room temperature
Energy	252 cal/Btu, 778 ft-lb_f/Btu
	4.186 joules/cal
	550 ft-lb_f/sec/hp, 0.75 kw/hp
Gravitational acceleration	32.2 ft/sec^2, 980 cm/sec^2
	$g_c = 32.2\ (lb_m/lb_f)(ft/sec^2)$ = gravitational constant
Ideal gas law constant, R	1.987 Btu/lb-mole-°R, 1.987 cal/g-mole-°K
	82.0 cm^3-atm/g-mole-°K
	0.73 ft^3-atm/lb-mole-°R
	1545 ft^3-lb_f/ft^2-lb-mole-°R
	10.73 ft^3-psia/lb-mole-°R
Length	2.54 cm/in., 30.48 cm/ft
	10^6 micron/m, 5280 ft/mi
	1000 microns/mm, 1.1516 mi/nautical mi
	10^4 angstroms/micron, 1.1516 mi/hr/knot

403

Mass	454 g/lb$_m$, 2.20 lb/kg, 28.4 g/oz, 7000 grains/lb
	2000 lb/ton
	2240 lb/long ton
	1000 kg/metric ton

Pressure

1 atm = 760 mm Hg = 14.7 lb$_f$/in.^{2} = 29.92 in. Hg
= 33.91 ft water at 39.1°F = 0.987 bar

P_{H_2O} at 25°C = 23.6 mm Hg

1 torr = 1 mm Hg

Specific volume
of gases

359 ft^3/lb-mole = 22.4 liters/g-mole at 32°F, 1 atm
= 385 ft^3/lb-mole at 68°F (20°C), 1 atm

Temperature

1.8Δ°F/Δ°C,   1.8Δ°R/Δ°K

°K = °C + 273

°R = °F + 460

°C = 5/9 (°F − 32)

°F = 1.8°C + 32

Velocity

1 mi/hr = 88 ft/min

Speed of sound = 1129 ft/sec = 344 m/sec
(at 20°C, 1 atm, air)

Velocity of light in vacuum = 3 × 10^8 m/sec

Viscosity

6.72 × 10^{-4} lb$_m$/ft-sec = 1 centipoise = 1 cp

100 cp/poise

1 poise = 1 g/cm-sec, $\nu = \mu/\rho$ = kinematic viscosity

1 stoke = 1 cm^2/sec

Viscosity for water at 20°C = 1.00 cp

Viscosity for air at 20°C = 0.018 cp

Viscosity for mercury at 20°C = 1.547 cp

Volume

7.48 gal/ft^3, 42.0 gal/bbl (petroleum), 29.6 ml/oz

3.78 liter/gal, 28.3 liter/ft^3, 2 pt/qt, 473 ml/pt

Useful constants

π = 3.1416

e = 2.718

ln = 2.303 log$_{10}$

Avogadro's number = 6.02 × 10^{23} molecules/g-mole

Stefan-Boltzmann constant = 0.171 × 10^8 Btu/ft^2-hr-°R^4

Boltzmann constant = 1.38 × 10^{-16} erg/°K

Faraday's number = 96,500 coulomb/equivalent

Mass of proton/mass of electron = 1836

ΔH_V (H$_2$O) at 212°F = 540 cal/g = 970 Btu/lb

ΔH_f (H$_2$O) at 0°C = 80 cal/g

Steam tables give the thermodynamic properties of steam and water. For example, consider the first saturated steam table in the following Table A6–1. If the temperature of the water-water vapor system placed in a given container is 110° F, the corresponding saturated vapor pressure is shown under the column of absolute pressure, and it is 1.2750 lb/in.² This means that water would boil at 110° F if the confining pressure is equal to the saturated vapor pressure at this temperature, namely 1.2750 lb_f/in.² This means you have to apply vacuum in order to reach this low pressure which will allow water to boil at 110° F. You have been used to the fact that water boils at 212° F; i.e., when the saturated vapor pressure is equal to the atmospheric pressure or confining pressure of 14.696 lb_f/in.² Again at 110° F, the specific volume of the saturated liquid is $V_f = 0.016165$ ft³/lb_m, and that of the saturated vapor is $V_g = 265.39$ ft³/lb_m. Going from liquid to vapor, the change in specific volume is

$$V_{fg} = V_g - V_f = 265.39 - 0.016165 = 265.37 \text{ ft}^3/lb_m$$

Similarly, the enthalpies of saturated liquid and saturated vapor at 110° F are, respectively: $h_f = 77.98$, and $h_g = 1109.3$ Btu/lb_m. The change in enthalpy or heat of vaporization is

$$h_{fg} = h_g - h_f = 1109.3 - 77.98 = 1031.4 \text{ Btu}/lb_m$$

This is the heat necessary to evaporate one lb_m of water at 110° F. Values for entropy are read in a similar manner. These are given in Btu/lb_m-°R.

Let us now consider Table A6–3 on superheated steam. For example, at an absolute pressure of 30 lb_f/in.², the corresponding saturated temperature is 250.34° F. However, the system may be heated to 400° F. This means we have superheated steam, and the degrees of superheat are

$$Sh = 400° \text{ F} - 250.34° \text{ F} = 149.66° \text{ F}$$

Under the 400 column, we can find the following:

Specific volume, $V = 16.892$ ft³/lb_m

Enthalpy, $h = 1237.8$ Btu/lb_m

Eutropy, $S = 1.7937$ Btu/lb_m-°R

405

Table A6.1 Saturated Steam, Temperature Table (2, 4)

Temp Fahr t	Abs Press. Lb per Sq In. p	Sat. Liquid v_f	Specific Volume Evap v_{fg}	Sat. Vapor v_g	Sat. Liquid h_f	Enthalpy Evap h_{fg}	Sat. Vapor h_g	Sat. Liquid s_f	Entropy Evap s_{fg}	Sat. Vapor s_g	Temp Fahr t
32.0	0.08859	0.016022	3304.7	3304.7	0.0179	1075.5	1075.5	0.0000	2.1873	2.1873	32.0
34.0	0.09600	0.016021	3061.9	3061.9	1.996	1074.4	1076.4	0.0041	2.1762	2.1802	34.0
36.0	0.10395	0.016020	2839.0	2839.0	4.008	1073.2	1077.2	0.0081	2.1651	2.1732	36.0
38.0	0.11249	0.016019	2634.1	2634.2	6.018	1072.1	1078.1	0.0122	2.1541	2.1663	38.0
40.0	1.12163	0.016019	2445.8	2445.8	8.027	1071.0	1079.0	0.0162	2.1432	2.1594	40.0
42.0	0.13143	0.016019	2272.4	2272.4	10.035	1069.8	1079.9	0.0202	2.1325	2.1527	42.0
44.0	0.14192	0.016019	2112.8	2112.8	12.041	1068.7	1080.7	0.0242	2.1217	2.1459	44.0
46.0	0.15314	0.016020	1965.7	1965.7	14.047	1067.6	1081.6	0.0282	2.1111	2.1393	46.0
48.0	0.16514	0.016021	1830.0	1830.0	16.051	1066.4	1082.5	0.0321	2.1006	2.1327	48.0
50.0	0.17796	0.016023	1704.8	1704.8	18.054	1065.3	1083.4	0.0361	2.0901	2.1262	50.0
52.0	0.19165	0.016024	1589.2	1589.2	20.057	1064.2	1084.2	0.0400	2.0798	2.1197	52.0
54.0	0.20625	0.016026	1482.4	1482.4	22.058	1063.1	1085.1	0.0439	2.0695	2.1134	54.0
56.0	0.22183	0.016028	1383.6	1383.6	24.059	1061.9	1086.0	0.0478	2.0593	2.1070	56.0
58.0	0.23843	0.016031	1292.2	1292.2	26.060	1060.8	1086.9	0.0516	2.0491	2.1008	58.0
60.0	0.25611	0.016033	1207.6	1207.6	28.060	1059.7	1087.7	0.0555	2.0391	2.0946	60.0
62.0	0.27494	0.016036	1129.2	1129.2	30.059	1058.5	1088.6	0.0593	2.0291	2.0885	62.0
64.0	0.29497	0.016039	1056.5	1056.5	32.058	1057.4	1089.5	0.0632	2.0192	2.0824	64.0
66.0	0.31626	0.016043	989.0	989.1	34.056	1056.3	1090.4	0.0670	2.0094	2.0764	66.0
68.0	0.33889	0.016046	926.5	926.5	36.054	1055.2	1091.2	0.0708	1.9996	2.0704	68.0
70.0	0.36292	0.016050	868.3	868.4	38.052	1054.0	1092.1	0.0745	1.9900	2.0645	70.0
72.0	0.38844	0.016054	814.3	814.3	40.049	1052.9	1093.0	0.0783	1.9804	2.0587	72.0
74.0	0.41550	0.016058	764.1	764.1	42.046	1051.8	1093.8	0.0821	1.9708	2.0529	74.0
76.3	0.44420	0.016063	717.4	717.4	44.043	1050.7	1094.7	0.0858	1.9614	2.0472	76.0
78.0	0.47461	0.016067	673.8	673.9	46.040	1049.5	1095.6	0.0895	1.9520	2.0415	78.0
80.0	0.50683	0.016072	633.3	633.3	48.037	1048.4	1096.4	0.0932	1.9426	2.0359	80.0
82.0	0.54093	0.016077	595.5	595.5	50.033	1047.3	1097.3	0.0969	1.9334	2.0303	82.0
84.0	0.57702	0.016082	560.3	560.3	52.029	1046.1	1098.2	0.1006	1.9242	2.0248	84.0
86.0	0.61518	0.016087	227.5	527.5	54.026	1045.0	1099.0	0.1043	1.9151	2.0193	86.0
88.0	0.65551	0.016093	496.8	496.8	56.022	1043.9	1099.9	0.1079	1.9060	2.0139	88.0
90.0	0.69813	0.016099	468.1	468.1	58.018	1042.7	1100.8	0.1115	1.8970	2.0086	90.0
92.0	0.74313	0.016105	441.3	441.3	60.014	1041.6	1101.6	0.1152	1.8881	2.0033	92.0
94.0	0.79062	0.016111	416.3	416.3	62.010	1040.5	1102.5	0.1188	1.8792	1.9980	94.0
96.0	0.84072	0.016117	392.8	392.9	64.006	1039.3	1103.3	0.1224	1.8704	1.9928	96.0
98.0	0.89356	0.016123	370.9	370.9	66.003	1038.2	1104.2	0.1260	1.8617	1.9876	98.0
100.0	0.94924	0.016130	350.4	350.4	67.999	1037.1	1105.1	0.1295	1.8530	1.9825	100.0
102.0	1.00789	0.016137	331.1	331.1	69.995	1035.9	1105.9	0.1331	1.8444	1.9775	102.0
104.0	1.06965	0.016144	313.1	313.1	71.992	1034.8	1106.8	0.1366	1.8358	1.9725	104.0
106.0	1.1347	0.016151	296.16	296.18	73.99	1033.6	1107.6	0.1402	1.8273	1.9675	106.0
108.0	1.2030	0.016158	280.28	280.30	75.98	1032.5	1108.5	0.1437	1.8188	1.9626	108.0
110.0	1.2750	0.016165	265.37	265.39	77.98	1031.4	1109.3	0.1472	1.8105	1.9577	110.0
112.0	1.3505	0.016173	251.37	251.38	79.98	1030.2	1110.2	0.1507	1.8021	1.9528	112.0
114.0	1.4299	0.016180	238.21	238.22	81.97	1029.1	1111.0	0.1542	1.7938	1.9480	114.0
116.0	1.5133	0.016188	225.84	225.85	83.97	1027.9	1111.9	0.1577	1.7856	1.9433	116.0
118.0	1.6009	0.016196	214.20	214.21	85.97	1026.8	1112.7	0.1611	1.7774	1.9386	118.0
120.0	1.6927	0.016204	203.25	203.26	87.97	1025.6	1113.6	0.1646	1.7693	1.9339	120.0
122.0	1.7891	0.016213	192.94	192.95	89.96	1024.5	1114.4	0.1680	1.7613	1.9293	122.0
124.0	1.8901	0.016221	183.23	183.24	91.96	1023.3	1115.3	0.1715	1.7533	1.9247	124.0
126.0	1.9959	0.016229	174.08	174.09	93.96	1022.2	1116.1	0.1749	1.7453	1.9202	126.0
128.0	2.1068	0.016238	165.45	165.47	95.96	1021.0	1117.0	0.1783	1.7374	1.9157	128.0
130.0	2.2230	0.016247	157.32	157.33	97.96	1019.8	1117.8	0.1817	1.7295	1.9112	130.0
132.0	2.3445	0.016256	149.64	149.66	99.95	1018.7	1118.6	0.1851	1.7217	1.9068	132.0
134.0	2.4717	0.016265	142.40	142.41	101.95	1017.5	1119.5	0.1884	1.7140	1.9024	134.0
136.0	2.6047	0.016274	135.55	135.57	103.95	1016.4	1120.3	0.1918	1.7063	1.8980	136.0
138.0	2.7438	0.016284	129.00	129.11	105.95	1015.2	1121.1	0.1951	1.6986	1.8937	138.0
140.0	2.8892	0.016293	122.98	123.00	107.95	1014.0	1122.0	0.1985	1.6910	1.8895	140.0
142.0	3.0411	0.016303	117.21	117.22	109.95	1012.9	1122.8	0.2018	1.6534	1.8852	142.0
144.0	3.1997	0.016312	111.74	111.76	111.95	1011.7	1123.6	0.2051	1.6759	1.8810	144.0
146.0	3.3653	0.016322	106.58	106.59	113.95	1010.5	1124.5	0.2084	1.6684	1.8769	146.0
148.0	3.5381	0.016332	101.68	101.70	115.95	1009.3	1125.3	0.2117	1.6610	1.8727	148.0
150.0	3.7184	0.016343	97.05	97.07	117.95	1008.2	1126.1	0.2150	1.6536	1.8686	150.0
152.0	3.9065	0.016353	92.66	92.68	119.95	1007.0	1126.9	0.2183	1.6463	1.8646	152.0
154.0	4.1025	0.016363	88.50	88.52	121.95	1005.8	1127.7	0.2216	1.6390	1.8606	154.0
156.0	4.3068	0.016374	84.56	84.57	123.95	1004.6	1128.6	0.2248	1.6318	1.8566	156.0
158.0	4.5197	0.016384	80.82	80.83	125.96	1003.4	1129.4	0.2281	1.6245	1.8526	158.0
160.0	4.7414	0.016395	77.27	77.29	127.96	1002.2	1130.2	0.2313	1.6174	1.8487	160.0
162.0	4.9722	0.016406	73.90	73.92	129.96	1001.0	1131.0	0.2345	1.6103	1.8448	162.0
164.0	5.2124	0.016417	70.70	70.72	131.96	999.8	1131.8	0.2377	1.6032	1.8409	164.0
166.0	5.4623	0.016428	67.67	67.68	133.97	998.6	1132.6	0.2409	1.5961	1.8371	166.0
168.0	5.7223	0.016440	64.78	64.80	135.97	997.4	1133.4	0.2441	1.5892	1.8333	168.0
170.0	5.9926	0.016451	62.04	62.06	137.97	996.2	1134.2	0.2473	1.5822	1.8295	170.0
172.0	6.2736	0.016463	59.43	59.45	139.98	995.0	1135.0	0.2505	1.5753	1.8258	172.0
174.0	6.5656	0.016474	56.95	56.97	141.98	993.8	1135.8	0.2537	1.5684	1.8221	174.0
176.0	6.8690	0.016486	54.59	54.61	143.99	992.6	1136.6	0.2568	1.5616	1.8184	176.0
178.0	7.1840	0.016498	52.35	52.36	145.99	991.4	1137.4	0.2600	1.5548	1.8147	178.0

Table A6.1   Saturated Steam, Temperature Table (*cont.*)

Temp Fahr t	Abs Press. Lb per Sq In. p	Specific Volume			Enthalpy			Entropy			Temp Fahr t
		Sat. Liquid v_f	Evap v_{fg}	Sat. Vapor v_g	Sat. Liquid h_f	Evap h_{fg}	Sat. Vapor h_g	Sat. Liquid s_f	Evap s_{fg}	Sat. Vapor s_g	
180.0	7.5110	0.016510	50.21	50.22	148.00	990.2	1138.2	0.2631	1.5480	1.8111	180.0
182.0	7.850	0.016522	48.172	18.189	150.01	989.0	1139.0	0.2662	1.5413	1.8075	182.0
184.0	8.203	0.016534	46.232	46.249	152.01	987.8	1139.8	0.2694	1.5346	1.8040	184.0
186.0	8.568	0.016547	44.383	44.400	154.02	986.5	1140.5	0.2725	1.5279	1.8004	186.0
188.0	8.947	0.016559	42.621	42.638	156.03	985.3	1141.3	0.2756	1.5213	1.7969	188.0
190.0	9.340	0.016572	40.941	40.957	158.04	984.1	1142.1	0.2787	1.5148	1.7934	190.0
192.0	9.747	0.016585	39.337	39.354	160.05	982.8	1142.9	0.2818	1.5082	1.7900	192.0
194.0	10.168	0.016598	37.808	37.824	162.05	981.6	1143.7	0.2848	1.5017	1.7865	194.0
196.0	10.605	0.016611	36.348	36.364	164.06	980.4	1144.4	0.2879	1.4952	1.7831	196.0
198.0	11.058	0.016624	34.954	34.970	166.08	979.1	1145.2	0.2910	1.4888	1.7798	198.0
200.0	11.526	0.016637	33.622	33.639	168.09	977.9	1146.0	0.2940	1.4824	1.7764	200.0
204.0	12.512	0.016664	31.135	31.151	172.11	975.4	1147.5	0.3001	1.4697	1.7698	204.0
208.0	13.568	0.016691	28.862	28.878	176.14	972.8	1149.0	0.3061	1.4571	1.7632	208.0
212.0	14.696	0.016719	26.782	26.799	180.17	970.3	1150.5	0.3121	1.4447	1.7568	212.0
216.0	15.901	0.016747	24.878	24.894	184.20	967.8	1152.0	0.3181	1.4323	1.7505	216.0
220.0	17.186	0.016775	23.131	23.148	188.23	965.2	1153.4	0.3241	1.4201	1.7442	220.0
224.0	18.556	0.016805	21.529	21.545	192.27	962.6	1154.9	0.3300	1.4081	1.7380	224.0
228.0	20.015	0.016834	20.056	20.073	196.31	960.0	1156.3	0.3359	1.3961	1.7320	228.0
232.0	21.567	0.016864	18.701	18.718	200.35	957.4	1157.8	0.3417	1.3842	1.7260	232.0
236.0	23.216	0.016895	17.454	17.471	204.40	954.8	1159.2	0.3476	1.3725	1.7201	236.0
240.0	24.968	0.016926	16.304	16.321	208.45	952.1	1160.6	0.3533	1.3609	1.7142	240.0
244.0	26.826	0.016958	15.243	15.260	212.50	949.5	1162.0	0.3591	1.3494	1.7085	244.0
248.0	28.796	0.016990	14.264	14.281	216.56	946.8	1163.4	0.3649	1.3379	1.7028	248.0
252.0	30.883	0.017022	13.358	13.375	220.62	944.1	1164.7	0.3706	1.3266	1.6972	252.0
256.0	33.091	0.017055	12.520	12.538	224.69	941.4	1166.1	0.3763	1.3154	1.6917	256.0
260.0	35.427	0.017089	11.745	11.762	228.76	938.6	1167.4	0.3819	1.3043	1.6862	260.0
264.0	37.894	0.017123	11.025	11.042	232.83	935.9	1168.7	0.3876	1.2933	1.6808	264.0
268.0	40.500	0.017157	10.358	10.375	236.91	933.1	1170.0	0.3932	1.2823	1.6755	268.0
272.0	43.249	0.017193	9.738	9.755	240.99	930.3	1171.3	0.3987	1.2715	1.6702	272.0
276.0	46.147	0.017228	9.162	9.180	245.08	927.5	1172.5	0.4043	1.2607	1.6650	276.0
280.0	49.200	0.017264	8.627	8.644	249.17	924.6	1173.8	0.4098	1.2501	1.6599	280.0
284.0	52.414	0.01730	8.1280	8.1453	253.3	921.7	1175.0	0.4154	1.2395	1.6548	284.0
288.0	55.795	0.01734	7.6634	7.6807	257.4	918.8	1176.2	0.4208	1.2290	1.6498	288.0
292.0	59.350	0.01738	7.2301	7.2475	261.5	915.9	1177.4	0.4263	1.2186	1.6449	292.0
296.0	63.084	0.01741	6.8259	6.8433	265.6	913.0	1178.6	0.4317	1.2082	1.6400	296.0
300.0	67.005	0.01745	6.4483	6.4658	269.7	910.0	1179.7	0.4372	1.1979	1.6351	300.0
304.0	71.119	0.01749	6.0955	6.1130	273.8	907.0	1180.9	0.4426	1.1877	1.6303	304.0
308.0	75.433	0.01753	5.7655	5.7830	278.0	904.0	1182.0	0.4479	1.1776	1.6256	308.0
312.0	79.953	0.01757	5.4566	5.4742	282.1	901.0	1183.1	0.4533	1.1676	1.6209	312.0
316.0	84.688	0.01761	5.1673	5.1849	286.3	897.9	1184.1	0.4586	1.1576	1.6162	316.0
320.0	89.643	0.01766	4.8961	4.9138	290.4	894.8	1185.2	0.4640	1.1477	1.6116	320.0
324.0	94.826	0.01770	4.6418	4.6595	294.6	891.6	1186.2	0.4692	1.1378	1.6071	324.0
328.0	100.245	0.01774	4.4030	4.4208	298.7	888.5	1187.2	0.4745	1.1280	1.6025	328.0
332.0	105.907	0.01779	4.1788	4.1966	302.9	885.3	1188.2	0.4798	1.1183	1.5981	332.0
336.0	111.820	0.01783	3.9681	3.9859	307.1	882.1	1189.1	0.4850	1.1086	1.5936	336.0
340.0	117.992	0.01787	3.7699	3.7878	311.3	878.8	1190.1	0.4902	1.0990	1.5892	340.0
344.0	124.430	0.01792	3.5834	3.6013	315.5	875.5	1191.0	0.4954	1.0894	1.5849	344.0
348.0	131.142	0.01797	3.4078	3.4258	319.7	872.2	1191.1	0.5006	1.0799	1.5806	348.0
352.0	138.138	0.01801	3.2423	3.2603	323.9	868.9	1192.7	0.5058	1.0705	1.5763	352.0
356.0	145.424	0.01806	3.0863	3.1044	328.1	865.5	1193.6	0.5110	1.0611	1.5721	356.0
360.0	153.010	0.01811	2.9392	2.9573	332.3	862.1	1194.4	0.5161	1.0517	1.5678	360.0
364.0	160.903	0.01816	2.8002	2.8184	336.5	858.6	1195.2	0.5212	1.0424	1.5637	364.0
368.0	169.113	0.01821	2.6691	2.6873	340.8	855.1	1195.9	0.5263	1.0332	1.5595	368.0
372.0	177.648	0.01826	2.5451	2.5633	345.0	851.6	1196.7	0.5314	1.0240	1.5554	372.0
376.0	186.517	0.01831	2.4279	2.4462	349.3	848.1	1197.4	0.5365	1.0148	1.5513	376.0
380.0	195.729	0.01836	2.3170	2.3353	353.6	844.5	1198.0	0.5416	1.0057	1.5473	380.0
384.0	205.294	0.01842	2.2120	2.2304	357.9	840.8	1198.7	0.5466	0.9966	1.5432	384.0
388.0	215.220	0.01847	2.1126	2.1311	362.2	837.2	1199.3	0.5516	0.9876	1.5392	388.0
392.0	225.516	0.01853	2.0184	2.0369	366.5	833.4	1199.9	0.5567	0.9786	1.5352	392.0
396.0	236.193	0.01858	1.9291	1.9477	370.8	829.7	1200.4	0.5617	0.9696	1.5313	396.0
400.0	247.259	0.01864	1.8444	1.8630	375.1	825.9	1201.0	0.5667	0.9607	1.5274	400.0
404.0	258.725	0.01870	1.7640	1.7827	379.4	822.0	1201.5	0.5717	0.9518	1.5234	404.0
408.0	270.600	0.01875	1.6877	1.7064	383.8	818.2	1201.9	0.5766	0.9429	1.5195	408.0
412.0	282.894	0.01881	1.6152	1.6340	388.1	814.2	1202.4	0.5816	0.9341	1.5157	412.0
416.0	295.617	0.01887	1.5463	1.5651	392.5	810.2	1202.8	0.5866	0.9253	1.5118	416.0
420.0	308.780	0.01894	1.4808	1.4997	396.9	806.2	1203.1	0.5915	0.9165	1.5080	420.0
424.0	322.391	0.01900	1.4184	1.4374	401.3	802.2	1203.5	0.5964	0.9077	1.5042	424.0
428.0	336.463	0.01906	1.3591	1.3782	405.7	798.0	1203.7	0.6014	0.8990	1.5004	428.0
432.0	351.00	0.01913	1.30266	1.32179	410.1	793.9	1204.0	0.6063	0.8903	1.4966	432.0
436.0	366.03	0.01919	1.24887	1.26806	414.6	789.7	1204.2	0.6112	0.8816	1.4928	436.0
440.0	381.54	0.01926	1.19761	1.21687	419.0	785.4	1204.4	0.6161	0.8729	1.4890	440.0
444.0	397.56	0.01933	1.14874	1.16806	423.5	781.1	1204.6	0.6210	0.8643	1.4853	444.0
448.0	414.09	0.01940	1.10212	1.12152	428.0	776.7	1204.7	0.6259	0.8557	1.4815	448.0
452.0	431.14	0.01947	1.05764	1.07711	432.5	772.3	1204.8	0.6308	0.8471	1.4778	452.0
456.0	448.73	0.01954	1.01518	1.03472	437.0	767.8	1204.8	0.6356	0.8385	1.4741	456.0

Table A6.1 Saturated Steam, Temperature Table (*cont.*)

Temp Fahr t	Abs Press. Lb per Sq In. p	Specific Volume Sat. Liquid v_f	Evap v_{fg}	Sat. Vapor v_g	Enthalpy Sat. Liquid h_f	Evap h_{fg}	Sat. Vapor h_g	Entropy Sat. Liquid s_f	Evap s_{fg}	Sat. Vapor s_g	Temp Fahr t
460.0	466.87	0.01961	0.97463	0.99424	441.5	763.2	1204.8	0.6405	0.8299	1.4704	460.0
464.0	485.56	0.01969	0.93588	0.95557	446.1	758.6	1204.7	0.6454	0.8213	1.4667	464.0
468.0	504.83	0.01976	0.89885	0.91862	450.7	754.0	1204.6	0.6502	0.8127	1.4629	468.0
472.0	524.67	0.01984	0.86345	0.88329	455.2	749.3	1204.5	0.6551	0.8042	1.4592	472.0
476.0	545.11	0.01992	0.82958	0.84950	459.9	744.5	1204.3	0.6599	0.7956	1.4555	476.0
480.0	566.15	0.02000	0.79716	0.81717	464.5	739.6	1204.1	0.6648	0.7871	1.4518	480.0
484.0	587.81	0.02009	0.76613	0.78622	469.1	734.7	1203.8	0.6696	0.7785	1.4481	484.0
488.0	610.10	0.02017	0.73641	0.75658	473.8	729.7	1203.5	0.6745	0.7700	1.4444	488.0
492.0	633.03	0.02026	0.70794	0.72820	478.5	724.6	1203.1	0.6793	0.7614	1.4407	492.0
496.0	656.61	0.02034	0.68065	0.70100	483.2	719.5	1202.7	0.6842	0.7528	1.4370	496.0
500.0	680.86	0.02043	0.65448	0.67492	487.9	714.3	1202.2	0.6890	0.7443	1.4333	500.0
504.0	705.78	0.02053	0.62938	0.64991	492.7	709.0	1201.7	0.6939	0.7357	1.4296	504.0
508.0	731.40	0.02062	0.60530	0.62592	497.5	703.7	1201.1	0.6987	0.7271	1.4258	508.0
512.0	757.72	0.02072	0.58218	0.60289	502.3	698.2	1200.5	0.7036	0.7185	1.4221	512.0
516.0	784.76	0.02081	0.55997	0.58079	507.1	692.7	1199.8	0.7085	0.7099	1.4183	516.0
520.0	812.53	0.02091	0.53864	0.55956	512.0	687.0	1199.0	0.7133	0.7013	1.4146	520.0
524.0	841.04	0.02102	0.51814	0.53916	516.9	681.3	1198.2	0.7182	0.6926	1.4108	524.0
528.0	870.31	0.02112	0.49843	0.51955	521.8	675.5	1197.3	0.7231	0.6839	1.4070	528.0
532.0	900.34	0.02123	0.47947	0.50070	526.8	669.6	1196.4	0.7280	0.6752	1.4032	532.0
536.0	931.17	0.02134	0.46123	0.48257	531.7	663.6	1195.4	0.7329	0.6665	1.3993	536.0
540.0	962.79	0.02146	0.44367	0.46513	536.8	657.5	1194.3	0.7378	0.6577	1.3954	540.0
544.0	995.22	0.02157	0.42677	0.44834	541.8	651.3	1193.1	0.7427	0.6489	1.3915	544.0
548.0	1028.49	0.02169	0.41048	0.43217	546.9	645.0	1191.9	0.7476	0.6400	1.3876	548.0
552.0	1062.59	0.02182	0.39479	0.41660	552.0	638.5	1190.6	0.7525	0.6311	1.3837	552.0
556.0	1097.55	0.02194	0.37966	0.40160	557.2	632.0	1189.2	0.7575	0.6222	1.3797	556.0
560.0	1133.38	0.02207	0.36507	0.38714	562.4	625.3	1187.7	0.7625	0.6132	1.3757	560.0
564.0	1170.10	0.02221	0.35099	0.37320	567.6	618.5	1186.1	0.7674	0.6041	1.3716	564.0
568.0	1207.72	0.02235	0.33741	0.35975	572.9	611.5	1184.5	0.7725	0.5950	1.3675	568.0
572.0	1246.26	0.02249	0.32429	0.34678	578.3	604.5	1182.7	0.7775	0.5859	1.3634	572.0
576.0	1285.74	0.02264	0.31162	0.33426	583.7	597.2	1180.9	0.7825	0.5766	1.3592	576.0
580.0	1326.17	0.02279	0.29937	0.32216	589.1	589.9	1179.0	0.7876	0.5673	1.3550	580.0
584.0	1367.7	0.02295	0.28753	0.31048	594.6	582.4	1176.9	0.7927	0.5580	1.3507	584.0
588.0	1410.0	0.02311	0.27608	0.29919	600.1	574.7	1174.8	0.7978	0.5485	1.3464	588.0
592.0	1453.3	0.02328	0.26499	0.28827	605.7	566.8	1172.6	0.8030	0.5390	1.3420	592.0
596.0	1497.8	0.02345	0.25425	0.27770	611.4	558.8	1170.2	0.8082	0.5293	1.3375	596.0
600.0	1543.2	0.02364	0.24384	0.26747	617.1	550.6	1167.7	0.8134	0.5196	1.3330	600.0
604.0	1589.7	0.02382	0.23374	0.25757	622.9	542.2	1165.1	0.8187	0.5097	1.3284	604.0
608.0	1637.3	0.02402	0.22394	0.24796	628.8	533.6	1162.4	0.8240	0.4997	1.3238	608.0
612.0	1686.1	0.02422	0.21442	0.23865	634.8	524.7	1159.5	0.8294	0.4896	1.3190	612.0
616.6	1735.9	0.02444	0.20516	0.22960	640.8	515.6	1156.4	0.8348	0.4794	1.3141	616.0
620.0	1786.9	0.02466	0.19615	0.22081	646.9	506.3	1153.2	0.8403	0.4689	1.3092	620.0
624.0	1839.0	0.02489	0.18737	0.21226	653.1	496.6	1149.8	0.8458	0.4583	1.3041	624.0
628.0	1892.4	0.02514	0.17880	0.20394	659.5	486.7	1146.1	0.8514	0.4474	1.2988	628.0
632.0	1947.0	0.02539	0.17044	0.19583	665.9	476.4	1142.2	0.8571	0.4364	1.2934	632.0
636.0	2002.8	0.02566	0.16226	0.18792	672.4	465.7	1138.1	0.8628	0.4251	1.2879	636.0
640.0	2059.9	0.02595	0.15427	0.18021	679.1	454.6	1133.7	0.8686	0.4134	1.2821	640.0
644.0	2118.3	0.02625	0.14644	0.17269	685.9	443.1	1129.0	0.8746	0.4015	1.2761	644.0
648.0	2178.1	0.02657	0.13876	0.16534	692.9	431.1	1124.0	0.8806	0.3893	1.2699	648.0
652.0	2239.2	0.02691	0.13124	0.15816	700.0	418.7	1118.7	0.8868	0.3767	1.2634	652.0
656.0	2301.7	0.02728	0.12387	0.15115	707.4	405.7	1113.1	0.8931	0.3637	1.2567	656.0
660.0	2365.7	0.02768	0.11663	0.14431	714.9	392.1	1107.0	0.8995	0.3502	1.2498	660.0
664.0	2431.1	0.02811	0.10946	0.13757	722.9	377.7	1100.6	0.9064	0.3361	1.2425	664.0
668.0	2498.1	0.02858	0.10229	0.13087	731.5	362.1	1093.5	0.9137	0.3210	1.2347	668.0
672.0	2566.6	0.02911	0.09514	0.12424	740.2	345.7	1085.9	0.9212	0.3054	1.2266	672.0
676.0	2636.8	0.02970	0.08799	0.11769	749.2	328.5	1077.6	0.9287	0.2892	1.2179	676.0
680.0	2708.6	0.03037	0.08080	0.11117	758.5	310.1	1068.5	0.9365	0.2720	1.2086	680.0
684.0	2782.1	0.03114	0.07349	0.10463	768.2	290.2	1058.4	0.9447	0.2537	1.1984	684.0
688.0	2857.4	0.03204	0.06595	0.09799	778.8	268.2	1047.0	0.9535	0.2337	1.1872	688.0
692.0	2934.5	0.03313	0.05797	0.09110	790.5	243.1	1033.6	0.9634	0.2110	1.1744	692.0
696.0	3013.4	0.03455	0.04916	0.08371	804.4	212.8	1017.2	0.9749	0.1841	1.1591	696.0
700.0	3094.3	0.03662	0.03857	0.07519	822.4	172.7	995.2	0.9901	0.1490	1.1390	700.0
702.0	3135.5	0.03824	0.03173	0.06997	835.0	144.7	979.7	1.0006	0.1246	1.1252	702.0
704.0	3177.2	0.04108	0.02192	0.06300	854.2	102.0	956.2	1.0169	0.0876	1.1046	704.0
705.0	3198.3	0.04427	0.01304	0.05730	873.0	61.4	934.4	1.0329	0.0527	1.0856	705.0
705.47*	3208.2	0.05078	0.00000	0.05078	906.0	0.0	906.0	1.0612	0.0000	1.0612	705.47*

*Critical temperature

Table A6.2   Saturated Steam, Pressure Table (2, 4)

Abs Press. Lb/Sq In. p	Temp Fahr t	Specific Volume Sat. Liquid v_f	Evap v_{fg}	Sat. Vapor v_g	Enthalpy Sat. Liquid h_f	Evap h_{fg}	Sat. Vapor h_g	Entropy Sat. Liquid s_f	Evap s_{fg}	Sat. Vapor s_g	Abs Press. Lb/Sq In. p
0.08865	32.018	0.016022	3302.4	3302.4	0.0003	1075.5	1075.5	0.0000	2.1872	2.1872	0.08865
0.25	59.323	0.016032	1235.5	1235.5	27.382	1060.1	1087.4	0.0542	2.0425	2.0967	0.25
0.50	79.586	0.016071	641.5	641.5	47.623	1048.6	1096.3	0.0925	1.9446	2.0370	0.50
1.0	101.74	0.016136	333.59	333.60	69.73	1036.1	1105.8	0.1326	1.8455	1.9781	1.0
5.0	162.24	0.016407	73.515	73.532	130.20	1000.9	1131.1	0.2349	1.6094	1.8443	5.0
10.0	193.21	0.016592	38.404	38.420	161.26	982.1	1143.3	0.2836	1.5043	1.7879	10.0
14.696	212.00	0.016719	26.782	26.799	180.17	970.3	1150.5	0.3121	1.4447	1.7568	14.696
15.0	213.03	0.016726	26.274	26.290	181.21	969.7	1150.9	0.3137	1.4415	1.7552	15.0
20.0	227.96	0.016834	20.070	20.087	196.27	960.1	1156.3	0.3358	1.3962	1.7320	20.0
30.0	250.34	0.017009	13.7266	13.7436	218.9	945.2	1164.1	0.3682	1.3313	1.6995	30.0
40.0	267.25	0.017151	10.4794	10.4965	236.1	933.6	1169.8	0.3921	1.2844	1.6765	40.0
50.0	281.02	0.017274	8.4967	8.5140	250.2	923.9	1174.1	0.4112	1.2474	1.6586	50.0
60.0	292.71	0.017383	7.1562	7.1736	262.2	915.4	1177.6	0.4273	1.2167	1.6440	60.0
70.0	302.93	0.017482	6.1875	6.2050	272.7	907.8	1180.6	0.4411	1.1905	1.6316	70.0
80.0	312.04	0.017573	5.4536	5.4711	282.1	900.9	1183.1	0.4534	1.1675	1.6208	80.0
90.0	320.28	0.017659	4.8779	4.8953	290.7	894.6	1185.3	0.4643	1.1470	1.6113	90.0
100.0	327.82	0.017740	4.4133	4.4310	298.5	888.6	1187.2	0.4743	1.1284	1.6027	100.0
110.0	334.79	0.01782	4.0306	4.0484	305.8	883.1	1188.9	0.4834	1.1115	1.5950	110.0
120.0	341.27	0.01789	3.7097	3.7275	312.6	877.8	1190.4	0.4919	1.0960	1.5879	120.0
130.0	347.33	0.01796	3.4364	3.4544	319.0	872.8	1191.7	0.4998	1.0815	1.5813	130.0
140.0	353.04	0.01803	3.2010	3.2190	325.0	868.0	1193.0	0.5071	1.0681	1.5752	140.0
150.0	358.43	0.01809	2.9958	3.0139	330.6	863.4	1194.1	0.5141	1.0554	1.5695	150.0
160.0	363.55	0.01815	2.8155	2.8336	336.1	859.0	1195.1	0.5206	1.0435	1.5641	160.0
170.0	368.42	0.01821	2.6556	2.6738	341.2	854.8	1196.0	0.5269	1.0322	1.5591	170.0
180.0	373.08	0.01827	2.5129	2.5312	346.2	850.7	1196.9	0.5328	1.0215	1.5543	180.0
190.0	377.53	0.01833	2.3847	2.4030	350.9	846.7	1197.6	0.5384	1.0113	1.5498	190.0
200.0	381.80	0.01839	2.2689	2.2873	355.5	842.8	1198.3	0.5438	1.0016	1.5454	200.0
210.0	385.91	0.01844	2.16373	2.18217	359.9	839.1	1199.0	0.5490	0.9923	1.5413	210.0
220.0	389.88	0.01850	2.06779	2.08629	364.2	835.4	1199.6	0.5540	0.9834	1.5374	220.0
230.0	393.70	0.01855	1.97991	1.99846	368.3	831.8	1200.1	0.5588	0.9748	1.5336	230.0
240.0	397.39	0.01860	1.89909	1.91769	372.3	828.4	1200.6	0.5634	0.9665	1.5299	240.0
250.0	400.97	0.01865	1.82452	1.84317	376.1	825.0	1201.1	0.5679	0.9585	1.5264	250.0
260.0	404.44	0.01870	1.75548	1.77418	379.9	821.6	1201.5	0.5722	0.9508	1.5230	260.0
270.0	407.80	0.01875	1.69137	1.71013	383.6	818.3	1201.9	0.5764	0.9433	1.5197	270.0
280.0	411.07	0.01880	1.63169	1.65049	387.1	815.1	1202.3	0.5805	0.9361	1.5166	280.0
290.0	414.25	0.01885	1.57597	1.59482	390.6	812.0	1202.6	0.5844	0.9291	1.5135	290.0
300.0	417.35	0.01889	1.52384	1.54274	394.0	808.9	1202.9	0.5882	0.9223	1.5105	300.0
350.0	431.73	0.01912	1.30642	1.32554	409.8	794.2	1204.0	0.6059	0.8909	1.4968	350.0
400.0	444.60	0.01934	1.14162	1.16095	424.2	780.4	1204.6	0.6217	0.8630	1.4847	400.0
450.0	456.28	0.01954	1.01224	1.03179	437.3	767.5	1204.8	0.6360	0.8378	1.4738	450.0
500.0	467.01	0.01975	0.90787	0.92762	449.5	755.1	1204.7	0.6490	0.8148	1.4639	500.0
550.0	476.94	0.01994	0.82183	0.84177	460.9	743.3	1204.3	0.6611	0.7936	1.4547	550.0
600.0	486.20	0.02013	0.74962	0.76975	471.7	732.0	1203.7	0.6723	0.7738	1.4461	600.0
650.0	494.89	0.02032	0.68811	0.70843	481.9	720.9	1202.8	0.6828	0.7552	1.4381	650.0
700.0	503.08	0.02050	0.63505	0.65556	491.6	710.2	1201.8	0.6928	0.7377	1.4304	700.0
750.0	510.84	0.02069	0.58880	0.60949	500.9	699.8	1200.7	0.7022	0.7210	1.4232	750.0
800.0	518.21	0.02087	0.54809	0.56896	509.8	689.6	1199.4	0.7111	0.7051	1.4163	800.0
850.0	525.24	0.02105	0.51197	0.53302	518.4	679.5	1198.0	0.7197	0.6899	1.4096	850.0
900.0	531.95	0.02123	0.47968	0.50091	526.7	669.7	1196.4	0.7279	0.6753	1.4032	900.0
950.0	538.39	0.02141	0.45064	0.47205	534.7	660.0	1194.7	0.7358	0.6612	1.3970	950.0
1000.0	544.58	0.02159	0.42436	0.44596	542.6	650.4	1192.9	0.7434	0.6476	1.3910	1000.0
1050.0	550.53	0.02177	0.40047	0.42224	550.1	640.9	1191.0	0.7507	0.6344	1.3851	1050.0
1100.0	556.28	0.02195	0.37863	0.40058	557.5	631.5	1189.1	0.7578	0.6216	1.3794	1100.0
1150.0	561.82	0.02214	0.35859	0.38073	564.8	622.2	1187.0	0.7647	0.6091	1.3738	1150.0
1200.0	567.19	0.02232	0.34013	0.36245	571.9	613.0	1184.8	0.7714	0.5969	1.3683	1200.0
1250.0	572.38	0.02250	0.32306	0.34556	578.8	603.8	1182.6	0.7780	0.5850	1.3630	1250.0
1300.0	577.42	0.02269	0.30722	0.32991	585.6	594.6	1180.2	0.7843	0.5733	1.3577	1300.0
1350.0	582.32	0.02288	0.29250	0.31537	592.3	585.4	1177.8	0.7906	0.5620	1.3525	1350.0
1400.0	587.07	0.02307	0.27871	0.30178	598.8	576.5	1175.3	0.7966	0.5507	1.3474	1400.0
1450.0	591.70	0.02327	0.26584	0.28911	605.3	567.4	1172.8	0.8026	0.5397	1.3423	1450.0
1500.0	596.20	0.02346	0.25372	0.27719	611.7	558.4	1170.1	0.8085	0.5288	1.3373	1500.0
1550.0	600.59	0.02366	0.24235	0.26601	618.0	549.4	1167.4	0.8142	0.5182	1.3324	1550.0
1600.0	604.87	0.02387	0.23159	0.25545	624.2	540.3	1164.5	0.8199	0.5076	1.3274	1600.0
1650.0	609.05	0.02407	0.22143	0.24551	630.4	531.3	1161.6	0.8254	0.4971	1.3225	1650.0
1700.0	613.13	0.02428	0.21178	0.23607	636.5	522.2	1158.6	0.8309	0.4867	1.3176	1700.0
1750.0	617.12	0.02450	0.20263	0.22713	642.5	513.1	1155.6	0.8363	0.4765	1.3128	1750.0
1800.0	621.02	0.02472	0.19390	0.21861	648.5	503.8	1152.3	0.8417	0.4662	1.3079	1800.0
1850.0	624.83	0.02495	0.18558	0.21052	654.5	494.6	1149.0	0.8470	0.4561	1.3030	1850.0
1900.0	628.56	0.02517	0.17761	0.20278	660.4	485.2	1145.6	0.8522	0.4459	1.2981	1900.0
1950.0	632.22	0.02541	0.16999	0.19540	666.3	475.8	1142.0	0.8574	0.4358	1.2931	1950.0
2000.0	635.80	0.02565	0.16266	0.18831	672.1	466.2	1138.3	0.8625	0.4256	1.2881	2000.0
2100.0	642.76	0.02615	0.14885	0.17501	683.8	446.7	1430.5	0.8727	0.4053	1.2780	2100.0
2200.0	649.45	0.02669	0.13603	0.16272	695.5	426.7	1122.2	0.8828	0.3848	1.2676	2200.0
2300.0	655.89	0.02727	0.12406	0.15133	707.2	406.0	1113.2	0.8929	0.3640	1.2569	2300.0
2400.0	662.11	0.02790	0.11287	0.14076	719.0	384.8	1103.7	0.9031	0.3430	1.2460	2400.0
2500.0	668.11	0.02859	0.10209	0.13068	731.7	361.6	1093.3	0.9139	0.3206	1.2345	2500.0
2600.0	673.91	0.02938	0.09172	0.12110	744.5	337.6	1082.0	0.9247	0.2977	1.2225	2600.0
2700.0	679.53	0.03029	0.08165	0.11194	757.3	312.3	1069.7	0.9356	0.2741	1.2097	2700.0
2800.0	684.96	0.03134	0.07171	0.10305	770.7	285.1	1055.8	0.9468	0.2491	1.1958	2800.0
2900.0	690.22	0.03262	0.06158	0.09420	785.1	254.7	1039.8	0.9588	0.2215	1.1803	2900.0
3000.0	695.33	0.03428	0.05073	0.08500	801.8	218.4	1020.3	0.9728	0.1891	1.1619	3000.0
3100.0	700.28	0.03681	0.03771	0.07452	824.0	169.3	993.3	0.9914	0.1460	1.1373	3100.0
3200.0	705.08	0.04472	0.01191	0.05663	875.5	56.1	931.6	1.0351	0.0482	1.0832	3200.0
3208.2*	705.47	0.05078	0.00000	0.05078	906.0	0.0	906.0	1.0612	0.0000	1.0612	3208.2*

*Critical pressure

Table A6.3 Superheated Steam (2, 4)

Abs Press. Lb/Sq In. (Sat. Temp)		Sat. Water	Sat. Steam	200	250	300	350	400	450	500	600	700	800	900	1000	1100	1200
1 (101.74)	Sh			98.26	148.26	198.26	248.26	298.26	348.26	398.26	498.26	598.26	698.26	798.26	898.26	998.26	1098.26
	v	0.01614	333.6	392.5	422.4	452.3	482.1	511.9	541.7	571.5	631.1	690.7	750.2	809.8	869.4	929.1	988.7
	h	69.73	1105.8	1150.2	1172.9	1195.7	1218.7	1241.8	1265.1	1288.6	1336.1	1384.5	1431.0	1480.8	1531.4	1583.0	1635.4
	s	0.1326	1.9781	2.0509	2.0841	2.1152	2.1445	2.1722	2.1985	2.2237	2.2708	2.3144	2.3512	2.3892	2.4251	2.4592	2.4918
5 (162.24)	Sh			37.76	87.76	137.76	187.76	237.76	287.76	337.76	437.76	537.76	637.76	737.76	837.76	937.76	1037.76
	v	0.01641	73.53	78.14	84.21	90.24	96.25	102.24	108.23	114.21	126.15	138.08	150.01	161.94	173.86	185.78	197.70
	h	130.20	1131.1	1148.6	1171.7	1194.8	1218.0	1241.3	1264.7	1288.2	1335.9	1384.3	1433.6	1483.7	1534.7	1586.7	1639.6
	s	0.2349	1.8443	1.8716	1.9054	1.9369	1.9664	1.9943	2.0208	2.0460	2.0932	2.1369	2.1776	2.2159	2.2521	2.2866	2.3194
10 (193.21)	Sh			6.79	56.79	106.79	156.79	206.79	256.79	306.79	406.79	506.79	606.79	706.79	806.79	906.79	1006.79
	v	0.01659	38.42	38.84	41.93	44.98	48.02	51.03	54.04	57.04	63.03	69.00	74.98	80.94	86.91	92.87	98.84
	h	161.26	1143.3	1146.6	1170.2	1193.7	1217.1	1240.6	1264.1	1287.8	1335.5	1384.0	1433.4	1483.5	1534.6	1586.6	1639.5
	s	0.2836	1.7879	1.7928	1.8273	1.8593	1.8892	1.9173	1.9439	1.9692	2.0166	2.0603	2.1011	2.1394	2.1757	2.2101	2.2430
* **14.696** (212.00)	Sh				38.00	88.00	138.00	188.00	238.00	288.00	388.00	488.00	588.00	688.00	788.00	888.00	988.00
	v	0.0167	26.828		28.44	30.52	32.61	34.65	36.73	38.75	42.83	46.91	50.97	55.03	59.09	63.19	67.25
	h	180.07	1150.4		1169.2	1192.0	1215.4	1238.9	1262.1	1285.4	1333.0	1381.4	1430.5	1480.4	1531.1	1582.7	1635.1
	s	0.3120	1.7566		1.7838	1.8148	1.8446	1.8727	1.8989	1.9238	1.9709	2.0145	2.0551	2.0932	2.1292	2.1634	2.1960
15 (213.03)	Sh				36.97	86.97	136.97	186.97	236.97	286.97	386.97	486.97	586.97	686.97	786.97	886.97	986.97
	v	0.01673	26.290		27.837	29.899	31.939	33.963	35.977	37.985	41.986	45.978	49.964	53.946	57.926	61.905	65.882
	h	181.21	1150.9		1168.7	1192.5	1216.2	1239.9	1263.6	1287.3	1335.2	1383.8	1433.2	1483.4	1534.5	1586.5	1639.4
	s	0.3137	1.7552		1.7809	1.8134	1.8437	1.8720	1.8988	1.9242	1.9717	2.0155	2.0563	2.0946	2.1309	2.1653	2.1982
20 (227.96)	Sh				22.04	72.04	122.04	172.04	222.04	272.04	372.04	472.04	572.04	672.04	772.04	872.04	972.04
	v	0.01683	20.087		20.788	22.356	23.900	25.428	26.946	28.457	31.466	34.465	37.458	40.447	43.435	46.420	49.405
	h	196.27	1156.3		1167.1	1191.4	1215.4	1239.2	1263.0	1286.9	1334.9	1383.5	1432.9	1483.2	1534.3	1586.3	1639.3
	s	0.3358	1.7320		1.7475	1.7805	1.8111	1.8397	1.8666	1.8921	1.9397	1.9836	2.0244	2.0628	2.0991	2.1336	2.1665
25 (240.07)	Sh				9.93	59.93	109.93	159.93	209.93	259.93	359.93	459.93	559.93	659.93	759.93	859.93	959.93
	v	0.01693	16.301		16.558	17.829	19.076	20.307	21.527	22.740	25.153	27.557	29.954	32.348	34.740	37.130	39.518
	h	208.52	1160.6		1165.6	1190.2	1214.5	1238.5	1262.5	1286.4	1334.6	1383.3	1432.7	1483.0	1534.2	1586.2	1639.2
	s	0.3535	1.7141		1.7212	1.7547	1.7856	1.8145	1.8415	1.8672	1.9149	1.9588	1.9997	2.0381	2.0744	2.1089	2.1418
30 (250.34)	Sh					49.66	99.66	149.66	199.66	249.66	349.66	449.66	549.66	649.66	749.66	849.66	949.66
	v	0.01701	13.744			14.810	15.859	16.892	17.914	18.929	20.945	22.951	24.952	26.949	28.943	30.936	32.927
	h	218.93	1164.1			1189.0	1213.6	1237.8	1261.9	1286.0	1334.2	1383.0	1432.5	1482.8	1534.0	1586.1	1639.0
	s	0.3682	1.6995			1.7334	1.7647	1.7937	1.8210	1.8467	1.8946	1.9386	1.9795	2.0179	2.0543	2.0888	2.1217
35 (259.29)	Sh					40.71	90.71	140.71	190.71	240.71	340.71	440.71	540.71	640.71	740.71	840.71	940.71
	v	0.01708	11.896			12.654	13.562	14.453	15.334	16.207	17.939	19.662	21.379	23.092	24.803	26.512	28.220
	h	228.03	1167.1			1187.8	1212.7	1237.1	1261.3	1285.5	1333.9	1382.8	1432.3	1482.7	1533.9	1586.0	1638.9
	s	0.3809	1.6872			1.7152	1.7468	1.7761	1.8035	1.8294	1.8774	1.9214	1.9624	2.0009	2.0372	2.0717	2.1046
40 (267.25)	Sh					32.75	82.75	132.75	182.75	232.75	332.75	432.75	532.75	632.75	732.75	832.75	932.75
	v	0.01715	10.497			11.036	11.838	12.624	13.398	14.165	15.685	17.195	18.699	20.199	21.697	23.194	24.689
	h	236.14	1169.8			1186.6	1211.7	1236.4	1260.8	1285.0	1333.6	1382.5	1432.1	1482.5	1533.7	1585.8	1638.8
	s	0.3921	1.6765			1.6992	1.7312	1.7608	1.7883	1.8143	1.8624	1.9065	1.9476	1.9860	2.0224	2.0569	2.0899
** **45** (274.43)	Sh					25.57	75.57	125.57	175.57	225.57	325.57	425.57	525.57	625.57	725.57	825.57	925.57
	v	0.01722	9.403			9.782	10.503	11.206	11.897	12.584	13.939	15.284	16.623	17.959	19.292	20.623	21.954
	h	243.47	1172.1			1185.4	1210.8	1235.7	1260.2	1284.6	1333.3	1382.3	1432.0	1482.4	1533.6	1585.7	1638.8
	s	0.4021	1.6671			1.6849	1.7174	1.7472	1.7749	1.8010	1.8492	1.8934	1.9345	1.9730	2.0094	2.0439	2.0769
50 (281.02)	Sh					18.98	68.98	118.98	168.98	218.98	318.98	418.98	518.98	618.98	718.98	818.98	918.98
	v	0.1727	8.514			8.769	9.424	10.062	10.688	11.306	12.529	13.741	14.947	16.150	17.350	18.549	19.746
	h	250.21	1174.1			1184.1	1209.9	1234.9	1259.6	1284.1	1332.9	1382.0	1431.7	1482.2	1533.4	1585.6	1638.6
	s	0.4112	1.6586			1.6720	1.7048	1.7349	1.7628	1.7890	1.8374	1.8816	1.9227	1.9613	1.9977	2.0322	2.0652
** **55** (287.07)	Sh					12.93	62.93	112.93	162.93	212.93	312.93	412.93	512.93	612.93	712.93	812.93	912.93
	v	0.01733	7.787			7.947	8.550	9.134	9.706	10.270	11.385	12.489	13.587	14.682	15.775	16.865	17.954
	h	256.42	1176.0			1182.9	1208.9	1234.3	1259.1	1283.6	1332.6	1381.8	1431.6	1482.0	1533.3	1585.5	1638.5
	s	0.4196	1.6510			1.6602	1.6934	1.7238	1.7518	1.7781	1.8267	1.8710	1.9123	1.9507	1.9871	2.0217	2.0546
60 (292.71)	Sh					7.29	57.29	107.29	157.29	207.29	307.29	407.29	507.29	607.29	707.29	807.29	907.29
	v	0.1738	7.174			7.257	7.815	8.354	8.881	9.400	10.425	11.438	12.446	13.450	14.452	15.452	16.450
	h	262.21	1177.6			1181.6	1208.0	1233.5	1258.5	1283.2	1332.3	1381.5	1431.3	1481.8	1533.2	1585.3	1638.4
	s	0.4273	1.6440			1.6492	1.6934	1.7134	1.7417	1.7681	1.8168	1.8612	1.9024	1.9410	1.9774	2.0120	2.0450
65 (297.98)	Sh					2.02	52.02	102.02	152.02	202.02	302.02	402.02	502.02	602.02	702.02	802.02	902.02
	v	0.01743	6.653			6.675	7.195	7.697	8.186	8.667	9.615	10.552	11.484	12.412	13.337	14.261	15.183
	h	267.63	1179.1			1180.3	1207.0	1232.7	1257.9	1282.7	1331.9	1381.3	1431.1	1481.6	1533.0	1585.2	1638.3
	s	0.4344	1.6375			1.6390	1.6731	1.7040	1.7324	1.7590	1.8077	1.8522	1.8935	1.9321	1.9685	2.0031	2.0361
70 (302.93)	Sh						47.07	97.07	147.07	197.07	297.07	397.07	497.07	597.07	697.07	797.07	897.07
	v	0.01748	6.205				6.664	7.133	7.590	8.039	8.922	9.793	10.659	11.522	12.382	13.240	14.097
	h	272.74	1180.6				1206.0	1232.0	1257.3	1282.2	1331.6	1381.0	1430.9	1481.5	1532.9	1585.1	1638.2
	s	0.4411	1.6316				1.6640	1.6951	1.7237	1.7504	1.7993	1.8439	1.8852	1.9238	1.9603	1.9949	2.0279
75 (307.61)	Sh						42.39	92.39	142.39	192.39	292.39	392.39	492.39	592.39	692.39	792.39	892.39
	v	0.01753	5.814				6.204	6.645	7.074	7.494	8.320	9.135	9.945	10.750	11.553	12.355	13.155
	h	277.56	1181.9				1205.0	1231.2	1256.7	1281.7	1331.3	1380.7	1430.7	1481.3	1532.7	1585.0	1638.1
	s	0.4474	1.6260				1.6554	1.6868	1.7156	1.7424	1.7915	1.8361	1.8774	1.9161	1.9526	1.9872	2.0202

Sh = superheat, F
v = specific volume, cu ft per lb
h = enthalpy, Btu per lb
s = entropy, Btu per F per lb

*Values from STEAM TABLES, Properties of Saturated and Superheated Steam
Published by COMBUSTION ENGINEERING, INC., Copyright 1940
**Values interpolated from ASME STEAM TABLES

Table A6.3 Superheated Steam (*cont.*)

Abs Press. Lb/Sq In. (Sat. Temp)		Sat. Water	Sat. Steam	350	400	450	500	550	600	700	800	900	1000	1100	1200	1300	1400
80 (312.04)	Sh			37.96	87.96	137.96	187.96	237.96	287.96	387.96	487.96	587.96	687.96	787.96	887.96	987.96	1087.96
	v	0.01757	5.471	5.801	6.218	6.622	7.018	7.408	7.794	8.560	9.319	10.075	10.829	11.581	12.331	13.081	13.829
	h	282.15	1183.1	1204.0	1230.5	1256.1	1281.3	1306.2	1330.9	1380.5	1430.5	1481.1	1532.6	1584.9	1638.0	1692.0	1746.8
	s	0.4534	1.6208	1.6473	1.6790	1.7080	1.7349	1.7602	1.7842	1.8289	1.8702	1.9089	1.9454	1.9800	2.0131	2.0446	2.0750
85 (316.26)	Sh			33.74	83.74	133.74	183.74	233.74	283.74	383.74	483.74	583.74	683.74	783.74	883.74	983.74	1083.74
	v	0.01762	5.167	5.445	5.840	6.223	6.597	6.966	7.330	8.052	8.768	9.480	10.190	10.898	11.604	12.310	13.014
	h	286.52	1184.2	1203.0	1229.7	1255.5	1280.8	1305.8	1330.6	1380.2	1430.3	1481.0	1532.4	1584.7	1637.9	1691.9	1746.8
	s	0.4590	1.6159	1.6396	1.6716	1.7008	1.7279	1.7532	1.7772	1.8220	1.8634	1.9021	1.9386	1.9733	2.0063	2.0379	2.0682
90 (320.28)	Sh			29.72	79.72	129.72	179.72	229.72	279.72	379.72	479.72	579.72	679.72	779.72	879.72	979.72	1079.72
	v	0.01766	4.895	5.128	5.505	5.869	6.223	6.572	6.917	7.600	8.277	8.950	9.621	10.290	10.958	11.625	12.290
	h	290.69	1185.3	1202.0	1228.9	1254.9	1280.3	1305.4	1330.2	1380.0	1430.1	1480.8	1532.3	1584.6	1637.8	1691.8	1746.7
	s	0.4643	1.6113	1.6323	1.6646	1.6940	1.7212	1.7467	1.7707	1.8156	1.8570	1.8957	1.9323	1.9669	2.0000	2.0316	2.0619
95 (324.13)	Sh			25.87	75.87	125.87	175.87	225.87	275.87	375.87	475.87	575.87	675.87	775.87	875.87	975.87	1075.87
	v	0.01770	4.651	4.845	5.205	5.551	5.889	6.221	6.548	7.196	7.838	8.477	9.113	9.747	10.380	11.012	11.643
	h	294.70	1186.2	1200.9	1228.1	1254.3	1279.8	1305.0	1329.9	1379.7	1429.9	1480.6	1532.1	1584.5	1637.7	1691.7	1746.6
	s	0.4694	1.6069	1.6253	1.6580	1.6876	1.7149	1.7404	1.7645	1.8094	1.8509	1.8897	1.9262	1.9609	1.9940	2.0256	2.0559
100 (327.82)	Sh			22.18	72.18	122.18	172.18	222.18	272.18	372.18	472.18	572.18	672.18	772.18	872.18	972.18	1072.18
	v	0.01774	4.431	4.590	4.935	5.266	5.588	5.904	6.216	6.833	7.443	8.050	8.655	9.258	9.860	10.460	11.060
	h	298.54	1187.2	1199.9	1227.4	1253.7	1279.3	1304.6	1329.6	1379.5	1429.7	1480.4	1532.0	1584.4	1637.6	1691.6	1746.5
	s	0.4743	1.6027	1.6187	1.6516	1.6814	1.7088	1.7344	1.7586	1.8036	1.8451	1.8839	1.9205	1.9552	1.9883	2.0199	2.0502
105 (331.37)	Sh			18.63	68.63	118.63	168.63	218.63	268.63	368.63	468.63	568.63	668.63	768.63	868.63	968.63	1068.63
	v	0.01778	4.231	4.359	4.690	5.007	5.315	5.617	5.915	6.504	7.086	7.665	8.241	8.816	9.389	9.961	10.532
	h	302.24	1188.0	1198.8	1226.6	1253.1	1278.8	1304.2	1329.2	1379.2	1429.4	1480.3	1531.8	1584.2	1637.5	1691.5	1746.4
	s	0.4790	1.5988	1.6122	1.6455	1.6755	1.7031	1.7288	1.7530	1.7981	1.8396	1.8785	1.9151	1.9498	1.9828	2.0145	2.0448
110 (334.79)	Sh			15.21	65.21	115.21	165.21	215.21	265.21	365.21	465.21	565.21	665.21	765.21	865.21	965.21	1065.21
	v	0.01782	4.048	4.149	4.468	4.772	5.068	5.357	5.642	6.205	6.761	7.314	7.865	8.413	8.961	9.507	10.053
	h	305.80	1188.9	1197.7	1225.8	1252.5	1278.3	1303.8	1328.9	1379.0	1429.2	1480.1	1531.7	1584.1	1637.4	1691.4	1746.4
	s	0.4834	1.5950	1.6061	1.6396	1.6698	1.6975	1.7233	1.7476	1.7928	1.8344	1.8732	1.9099	1.9446	1.9777	2.0093	2.0397
115 (338.08)	Sh			11.92	61.92	111.92	161.92	211.92	261.92	361.92	461.92	561.92	661.92	761.92	861.92	961.92	1061.92
	v	0.01785	3.881	3.957	4.265	4.558	4.841	5.119	5.392	5.932	6.465	6.994	7.521	8.046	8.570	9.093	9.615
	h	309.25	1189.6	1196.7	1225.0	1251.8	1277.9	1303.3	1328.6	1378.7	1429.0	1479.9	1531.6	1584.0	1637.2	1691.4	1746.3
	s	0.4877	1.5913	1.6001	1.6340	1.6644	1.6922	1.7181	1.7425	1.7877	1.8294	1.8682	1.9049	1.9396	1.9727	2.0044	2.0347
120 (341.27)	Sh			8.73	58.73	108.73	158.73	208.73	258.73	358.73	458.73	558.73	658.73	758.73	858.73	958.73	1058.73
	v	0.01789	3.7275	3.7815	4.0786	4.3610	4.6341	4.9009	5.1637	5.6813	6.1928	6.7006	7.2060	7.7096	8.2119	8.7130	9.2134
	h	312.58	1190.4	1195.6	1224.1	1251.2	1277.4	1302.9	1328.2	1378.4	1428.8	1479.8	1531.4	1583.9	1637.1	1691.3	1746.2
	s	0.4919	1.5879	1.5943	1.6286	1.6592	1.6872	1.7132	1.7376	1.7829	1.8246	1.8635	1.9001	1.9349	1.9680	1.9996	2.0300
130 (347.33)	Sh			2.67	52.67	102.67	152.67	202.67	252.67	352.67	452.67	552.67	652.67	752.67	852.67	952.67	1052.67
	v	0.01796	3.4544	3.4699	3.7489	4.0129	4.2672	4.5151	4.7589	5.2384	5.7118	6.1814	6.6486	7.1140	7.5781	8.0411	8.5033
	h	318.95	1191.7	1193.4	1222.5	1249.9	1276.4	1302.1	1327.5	1377.9	1428.4	1479.4	1531.1	1583.6	1636.9	1691.1	1746.1
	s	0.4998	1.5813	1.5833	1.6182	1.6493	1.6775	1.7037	1.7283	1.7737	1.8155	1.8545	1.8911	1.9259	1.9591	1.9907	2.0211
140 (353.04)	Sh				46.96	96.96	146.96	196.96	246.96	346.96	446.96	546.96	646.96	746.96	846.96	946.96	1046.96
	v	0.01803	3.2190		3.4661	3.7143	3.9526	4.1844	4.4119	4.8588	5.2995	5.7364	6.1709	6.6036	7.0349	7.4652	7.8946
	h	324.96	1193.0		1220.8	1248.7	1275.3	1301.3	1326.8	1377.4	1428.0	1479.1	1530.8	1583.4	1636.7	1690.9	1745.9
	s	0.5071	1.5752		1.6085	1.6400	1.6686	1.6949	1.7196	1.7652	1.8071	1.8461	1.8828	1.9176	1.9508	1.9825	2.0129
150 (358.43)	Sh				41.57	91.57	141.57	191.57	241.57	341.57	441.57	541.57	641.57	741.57	841.57	941.57	1041.57
	v	0.01809	3.0139		3.2208	3.4555	3.6799	3.8978	4.1112	4.5298	4.9421	5.3507	5.7568	6.1612	6.5642	6.9661	7.3671
	h	330.65	1194.1		1219.1	1247.4	1274.3	1300.5	1326.1	1376.9	1427.6	1478.7	1530.5	1583.1	1636.5	1690.7	1745.7
	s	0.5141	1.5695		1.5993	1.6313	1.6602	1.6867	1.7115	1.7573	1.7992	1.8383	1.8751	1.9099	1.9431	1.9748	2.0052
160 (363.55)	Sh				36.45	86.45	136.45	186.45	236.45	336.45	436.45	536.45	636.45	736.45	836.45	936.45	1036.45
	v	0.01815	2.8336		3.0060	3.2288	3.4413	3.6469	3.8480	4.2420	4.6295	5.0132	5.3945	5.7741	6.1522	6.5293	6.9055
	h	336.07	1195.1		1217.4	1246.0	1273.3	1299.6	1325.4	1376.4	1427.2	1478.4	1530.3	1582.9	1636.3	1690.5	1745.6
	s	0.5206	1.5641		1.5906	1.6231	1.6522	1.6790	1.7039	1.7499	1.7919	1.8310	1.8678	1.9027	1.9359	1.9676	1.9980
170 (368.42)	Sh				31.58	81.58	131.58	181.58	231.58	331.58	431.58	531.58	631.58	731.58	831.58	931.58	1031.58
	v	0.01821	2.6738		2.8162	3.0288	3.2306	3.4255	3.6158	3.9879	4.3536	4.7155	5.0749	5.4325	5.7888	6.1440	6.4983
	h	341.24	1196.0		1215.6	1244.7	1272.2	1298.8	1324.7	1375.8	1426.8	1478.0	1530.0	1582.6	1636.1	1690.4	1745.4
	s	0.5269	1.5591		1.5823	1.6152	1.6447	1.6717	1.6968	1.7428	1.7850	1.8241	1.8610	1.8959	1.9291	1.9608	1.9913
180 (373.08)	Sh				26.92	76.92	126.92	176.92	226.92	326.92	426.92	526.92	626.92	726.92	826.92	926.92	1026.92
	v	0.01827	2.5312		2.6674	2.8508	3.0433	3.2286	3.4093	3.7621	4.1084	4.4508	4.7907	5.1289	5.4657	5.8014	6.1363
	h	346.19	1196.9		1213.8	1243.4	1271.2	1297.9	1324.0	1375.3	1426.3	1477.7	1529.7	1582.4	1635.9	1690.2	1745.3
	s	0.5328	1.5543		1.5743	1.6078	1.6376	1.6647	1.6900	1.7362	1.7784	1.8176	1.8545	1.8894	1.9227	1.9545	1.9849
190 (377.53)	Sh				22.47	72.47	122.47	172.47	222.47	322.47	422.47	522.47	622.47	722.47	822.47	922.47	1022.47
	v	0.01833	2.4030		2.4961	2.6915	2.8756	3.0525	3.2246	3.5601	3.8889	4.2140	4.5365	4.8572	5.1766	5.4949	5.8124
	h	350.94	1197.6		1212.0	1242.0	1270.1	1297.1	1323.3	1374.8	1425.9	1477.4	1529.4	1582.1	1635.7	1690.0	1745.1
	s	0.5384	1.5498		1.5667	1.6006	1.6307	1.6581	1.6835	1.7299	1.7722	1.8115	1.8484	1.8834	1.9166	1.9484	1.9789
200 (381.80)	Sh				18.20	68.20	118.20	168.20	218.20	318.20	418.20	518.20	618.20	718.20	818.20	918.20	1018.20
	v	0.01839	2.2873		2.3598	2.5480	2.7247	2.8939	3.0583	3.3783	3.6915	4.0008	4.3077	4.6128	4.9165	5.2191	5.5209
	h	355.51	1198.3		1210.1	1240.6	1269.0	1296.2	1322.6	1374.3	1425.5	1477.0	1529.1	1581.9	1635.4	1689.8	1745.0
	s	0.5438	1.5454		1.5593	1.5938	1.6242	1.6518	1.6773	1.7239	1.7663	1.8057	1.8426	1.8776	1.9109	1.9427	1.9732

Sh = superheat, F
v = specific volume, cu ft per lb
h = enthalpy, Btu per lb
s = entropy, Btu per F per lb

Table A6.3 Superheated Steam (*cont.*)

Abs Press. Lb/Sq In. (Sat. Temp)		Sat. Water	Sat. Steam	400	450	500	550	600	700	800	900	1000	1100	1200	1300	1400	1500
210 (385.91)	Sh			14.09	64.09	114.09	164.09	214.09	314.09	414.09	514.09	614.09	714.09	814.09	914.09	1014.09	1114.09
	v	0.01844	2.1822	2.2364	2.4181	2.5880	2.7504	2.9078	3.2137	3.5128	3.8080	4.1007	4.3915	4.6811	4.9695	5.2571	5.5440
	h	359.91	1199.0	1208.02	1239.2	1268.0	1295.3	1321.9	1373.7	1425.1	1476.7	1528.8	1581.6	1635.2	1689.6	1744.8	1800.8
	s	0.5490	1.5413	1.5522	1.5872	1.6180	1.6458	1.6715	1.7182	1.7607	1.8001	1.8371	1.8721	1.9054	1.9372	1.9677	1.9970
220 (389.88)	Sh			10.12	60.12	110.12	160.12	210.12	310.12	410.12	510.12	610.12	710.12	810.12	910.12	1010.12	1110.12
	v	0.01850	2.0863	2.1240	2.2999	2.4638	2.6199	2.7710	3.0642	3.3504	3.6327	3.9125	4.1905	4.4671	4.7426	5.0173	5.2913
	h	364.17	1199.6	1206.3	1237.8	1266.9	1294.5	1321.2	1373.2	1424.7	1476.3	1528.5	1581.4	1635.0	1689.4	1744.7	1800.6
	s	0.5540	1.5374	1.5453	1.5808	1.6120	1.6400	1.6658	1.7128	1.7553	1.7948	1.8318	1.8668	1.9002	1.9320	1.9625	1.9919
230 (393.70)	Sh			6.30	56.30	106.30	156.30	206.30	306.30	406.30	506.30	606.30	706.30	806.30	906.30	1006.30	1106.30
	v	0.01855	1.9985	2.0212	2.1919	2.3503	2.5008	2.6461	2.9276	3.2020	3.4726	3.7406	4.0068	4.2717	4.5355	4.7984	5.0606
	h	368.28	1200.1	1204.4	1236.3	1265.7	1293.6	1320.4	1372.7	1424.2	1476.0	1528.2	1581.1	1634.8	1689.3	1744.5	1800.5
	s	0.5588	1.5336	1.5385	1.5747	1.6062	1.6344	1.6604	1.7075	1.7502	1.7897	1.8268	1.8618	1.8952	1.9270	1.9576	1.9869
240 (397.39)	Sh			2.61	52.61	102.61	152.61	202.61	302.61	402.61	502.61	602.61	702.61	802.61	902.61	1002.61	1102.61
	v	0.01860	1.9177	1.9268	2.0928	2.2462	2.3915	2.5316	2.8024	3.0661	3.3259	3.5831	3.8385	4.0926	4.3456	4.5977	4.8492
	h	372.27	1200.6	1202.4	1234.9	1264.6	1292.7	1319.7	1372.1	1423.8	1475.6	1527.9	1580.9	1634.6	1689.1	1744.3	1800.4
	s	0.5634	1.5299	1.5320	1.5687	1.6006	1.6291	1.6552	1.7025	1.7452	1.7848	1.8219	1.8570	1.8904	1.9223	1.9528	1.9822
250 (400.97)	Sh				49.03	99.03	149.03	199.03	299.03	399.03	499.03	599.03	699.03	799.03	899.03	999.03	1099.03
	v	0.01865	1.8432		2.0016	2.1504	2.2909	2.4262	2.6872	2.9410	3.1909	3.4382	3.6837	3.9278	4.1709	4.4131	4.6546
	h	376.14	1201.1		1233.4	1263.5	1291.8	1319.0	1371.6	1423.4	1475.3	1527.6	1580.6	1634.4	1688.9	1744.2	1800.2
	s	0.5679	1.5264		1.5629	1.5951	1.6239	1.6502	1.6976	1.7405	1.7801	1.8173	1.8524	1.8858	1.9177	1.9482	1.9776
260 (404.44)	Sh				45.56	95.56	145.56	195.56	295.56	395.56	495.56	595.56	695.56	795.56	895.56	995.56	1095.56
	v	0.01870	1.7742		1.9173	2.0619	2.1981	2.3289	2.5808	2.8256	3.0663	3.3044	3.5408	3.7758	4.0097	4.2427	4.4750
	h	379.90	1201.5		1231.9	1262.4	1290.9	1318.2	1371.1	1423.0	1474.9	1527.3	1580.4	1634.2	1688.7	1744.0	1800.1
	s	0.5722	1.5230		1.5573	1.5899	1.6189	1.6453	1.6930	1.7359	1.7756	1.8128	1.8480	1.8814	1.9133	1.9439	1.9732
270 (407.80)	Sh				42.20	92.20	142.20	192.20	292.20	392.20	492.20	592.20	692.20	792.20	892.20	992.20	1092.20
	v	0.01875	1.7101		1.8391	1.9799	2.1123	2.2388	2.4824	2.7186	2.9509	3.1806	3.4084	3.6349	3.8603	4.0849	4.3087
	h	383.56	1201.9		1230.4	1261.2	1290.0	1317.5	1370.5	1422.6	1474.6	1527.1	1580.1	1634.0	1688.5	1743.9	1800.0
	s	0.5764	1.5197		1.5518	1.5848	1.6140	1.6406	1.6885	1.7315	1.7713	1.8085	1.8437	1.8771	1.9090	1.9396	1.9690
280 (411.07)	Sh				38.93	88.93	138.93	188.93	288.93	388.93	488.93	588.93	688.93	788.93	888.93	988.93	1088.93
	v	0.01880	1.6505		1.7665	1.9037	2.0322	2.1551	2.3909	2.6194	2.8437	3.0655	3.2855	3.5042	3.7217	3.9384	4.1543
	h	387.12	1202.3		1228.8	1260.0	1289.1	1316.8	1370.0	1422.1	1474.2	1526.8	1579.9	1633.8	1688.4	1743.7	1799.8
	s	0.5805	1.5166		1.5464	1.5798	1.6093	1.6361	1.6841	1.7273	1.7671	1.8043	1.8395	1.8730	1.9050	1.9356	1.9649
290 (414.25)	Sh				35.75	85.75	135.75	185.75	285.75	385.75	485.75	585.75	685.75	785.75	885.75	985.75	1085.75
	v	0.01885	1.5948		1.6988	1.8327	1.9578	2.0772	2.3058	2.5269	2.7440	2.9585	3.1711	3.3824	3.5926	3.8019	4.0106
	h	390.60	1202.6		1227.3	1258.9	1288.1	1316.0	1369.5	1421.7	1473.9	1526.5	1579.6	1633.5	1688.2	1743.6	1799.7
	s	0.5844	1.5135		1.5412	1.5750	1.6048	1.6317	1.6799	1.7232	1.7630	1.8003	1.8356	1.8690	1.9010	1.9316	1.9610
300 (417.35)	Sh				32.65	82.65	132.65	182.65	282.65	382.65	482.65	582.65	682.65	782.65	882.65	982.65	1082.65
	v	0.01889	1.5427		1.6356	1.7665	1.8883	2.0044	2.2263	2.4407	2.6509	2.8585	3.0643	3.2688	3.4721	3.6746	3.8764
	h	393.99	1202.9		1225.7	1257.7	1287.2	1315.2	1368.9	1421.3	1473.6	1526.2	1579.4	1633.3	1688.0	1743.4	1799.6
	s	0.5882	1.5105		1.5361	1.5703	1.6003	1.6274	1.6758	1.7192	1.7591	1.7964	1.8317	1.8652	1.8972	*1.9278*	1.9572
310 (420.36)	Sh				29.64	79.64	129.64	179.64	279.64	379.64	479.64	579.64	679.64	779.64	879.64	979.64	1079.64
	v	0.01894	1.4939		1.5763	1.7044	1.8233	1.9363	2.1520	2.3600	2.5638	2.7650	2.9644	3.1625	3.3594	3.5555	3.7509
	h	397.30	1203.2		1224.1	1256.5	1286.3	1314.5	1368.4	1420.9	1473.2	1525.9	1579.2	1633.1	1687.8	1743.3	1799.4
	s	0.5920	1.5076		1.5311	1.5657	1.5960	1.6233	1.6719	1.7153	1.7553	1.7927	1.8280	1.8615	1.8935	1.9241	1.9536
320 (423.31)	Sh				26.69	76.69	126.69	176.69	276.69	376.69	476.69	576.69	676.69	776.69	876.69	976.69	1076.69
	v	0.01899	1.4480		1.5207	1.6462	1.7623	1.8725	2.0823	2.2843	2.4821	2.6774	2.8708	3.0628	3.2538	3.4438	3.6332
	h	400.53	1203.4		1222.5	1255.2	1285.3	1313.7	1367.8	1420.5	1472.9	1525.6	1578.9	1632.9	1687.6	1743.1	1799.3
	s	0.5956	1.5048		1.5261	1.5612	1.5918	1.6192	1.6680	1.7116	1.7516	1.7890	1.8243	1.8579	1.8899	1.9206	1.9500
330 (426.18)	Sh				23.82	73.82	123.82	173.82	273.82	373.82	473.82	573.82	673.82	773.82	873.82	973.82	1073.82
	v	0.01903	1.4048		1.4684	1.5915	1.7050	1.8125	2.0168	2.2132	2.4054	2.5950	2.7828	2.9692	3.1545	3.3389	3.5227
	h	403.70	1203.6		1220.9	1254.0	1284.4	1313.0	1367.3	1420.0	1472.5	1525.3	1578.7	1632.7	1687.5	1742.9	1799.2
	s	0.5991	1.5021		1.5213	1.5568	1.5876	1.6153	1.6643	1.7079	1.7480	1.7855	1.8208	1.8544	1.8864	1.9171	1.9466
340 (428.99)	Sh				21.01	71.01	121.01	171.01	271.01	371.01	471.01	571.01	671.01	771.01	871.01	971.01	1071.01
	v	0.01908	1.3640		1.4191	1.5399	1.6511	1.7561	1.9552	2.1463	2.3333	2.5175	2.7000	2.8811	3.0611	3.2402	3.4186
	h	406.80	1203.8		1219.2	1252.8	1283.4	1312.2	1366.7	1419.6	1472.2	1525.0	1578.4	1632.5	1687.3	1742.8	1799.0
	s	0.6026	1.4994		1.5165	1.5525	1.5836	1.6114	1.6606	1.7044	1.7445	1.7820	1.8174	1.8510	1.8831	1.9138	1.9432
350 (431.73)	Sh				18.27	68.27	118.27	168.27	268.27	368.27	468.27	568.27	668.27	768.27	868.27	968.27	1068.27
	v	0.01912	1.3255		1.3725	1.4913	1.6002	1.7028	1.8970	2.0832	2.2652	2.4445	2.6219	2.7980	2.9730	3.1471	3.3205
	h	409.83	1204.0		1217.5	1251.5	1282.4	1311.4	1366.2	1419.2	1471.8	1524.7	1578.2	1632.3	1687.1	1742.6	1798.9
	s	0.6059	1.4968		1.5119	1.5483	1.5797	1.6077	1.6571	1.7009	1.7411	1.7787	1.8141	1.8477	1.8798	1.9105	1.9400
360 (434.41)	Sh				15.59	65.59	115.59	165.59	265.59	365.59	465.59	565.59	665.59	765.59	865.59	965.59	1065.59
	v	0.01917	1.2891		1.3285	1.4454	1.5521	1.6525	1.8421	2.0237	2.2009	2.3755	2.5482	2.7196	2.8898	3.0592	3.2279
	h	412.81	1204.1		1215.8	1250.3	1281.5	1310.6	1365.6	1418.7	1471.5	1524.4	1577.9	1632.1	1686.9	1742.5	1798.8
	s	0.6092	1.4943		1.5073	1.5441	1.5758	1.6040	1.6536	1.6976	1.7379	1.7754	1.8109	1.8445	1.8766	1.9073	1.9368
380 (439.61)	Sh				10.39	60.39	110.39	160.39	260.39	360.39	460.39	560.39	660.39	760.39	860.39	960.39	1060.39
	v	0.01925	1.2218		1.2472	1.3606	1.4635	1.5598	1.7410	1.9139	2.0825	2.2484	2.4124	2.5750	2.7366	2.8973	3.0572
	h	418.59	1204.4		1212.4	1247.7	1279.5	1309.0	1364.5	1417.9	1470.8	1523.8	1577.4	1631.6	1686.5	1742.2	1798.5
	s	0.6156	1.4894		1.4982	1.5360	1.5683	1.5969	1.6470	1.6911	1.7315	1.7692	1.8047	1.8384	1.8705	1.9012	1.9307

Sh = superheat, F
v = specific volume, cu ft per lb
h = enthalpy, Btu per lb
s = entropy, Btu per F per lb

Table A6.3 Superheated Steam (*cont.*)

Abs Press. Lb/Sq In. (Sat. Temp)		Sat. Water	Sat. Steam	450	500	550	600	650	700	800	900	1000	1100	1200	1300	1400	1500
400 (444.60)	Sh			5.40	55.40	105.40	155.40	205.40	255.40	355.40	455.40	555.40	655.40	755.40	855.40	955.40	1055.40
	v	0.01934	116.10	1.1738	1.2841	1.3836	1.4763	1.5646	1.6499	1.8151	1.9759	2.1339	2.2901	2.4450	2.5987	2.7515	2.9037
	h	424.17	1204.6	1208.8	1245.1	1277.5	1307.4	1335.9	1363.4	1417.0	1470.1	1523.3	1576.9	1631.2	1686.2	1741.9	1798.2
	s	0.6217	1.4847	1.4894	1.5282	1.5611	1.5901	1.6163	1.6406	1.6850	1.7255	1.7632	1.7988	1.8325	1.8647	1.8955	1.9250
420 (449.40)	Sh			.60	50.60	100.60	150.60	200.60	250.60	350.60	450.60	550.60	650.60	750.60	850.60	950.60	1050.60
	v	0.01942	1.1057	1.1071	1.2148	1.3113	1.4007	1.4856	1.5676	1.7258	1.8795	2.0304	2.1795	2.3273	2.4739	2.6196	2.7647
	h	429.56	1204.7	1205.2	1242.4	1275.4	1305.8	1334.5	1362.3	1416.2	1469.4	1522.7	1576.4	1630.8	1685.8	1741.6	1798.0
	s	0.6276	1.4802	1.4808	1.5206	1.5542	1.5835	1.6100	1.6345	1.6791	1.7197	1.7575	1.7932	1.8269	1.8591	1.8899	1.9195
440 (454.03)	Sh				45.97	95.97	145.97	195.97	245.97	345.97	445.97	545.97	645.97	745.97	845.97	945.97	1045.97
	v	0.01950	1.0554		1.1517	1.2454	1.3319	1.4138	1.4926	1.6445	1.7918	1.9363	2.0790	2.2203	2.3605	2.4998	2.6384
	h	434.77	1204.8		1239.7	1273.4	1304.2	1333.2	1361.1	1415.3	1468.7	1522.1	1575.9	1630.4	1685.5	1741.2	1797.7
	s	0.6332	1.4759		1.5132	1.5474	1.5772	1.6040	1.6286	1.6734	1.7142	1.7521	1.7878	1.8216	1.8538	1.8847	1.9143
460 (458.50)	Sh				41.50	91.50	141.50	191.50	241.50	341.50	441.50	541.50	641.50	741.50	841.50	941.50	1041.50
	v	0.01959	1.0092		1.0939	1.1852	1.2691	1.3482	1.4242	1.5703	1.7117	1.8504	1.9872	2.1226	2.2569	2.3903	2.5230
	h	439.83	1204.8		1236.9	1271.3	1302.5	1331.8	1360.0	1414.4	1468.0	1521.5	1575.4	1629.9	1685.1	1740.9	1797.4
	s	0.6387	1.4718		1.5060	1.5409	1.5711	1.5982	1.6230	1.6680	1.7089	1.7469	1.7826	1.8165	1.8488	1.8797	1.9093
480 (462.82)	Sh				37.18	87.18	137.18	187.18	237.18	337.18	437.18	537.18	637.18	737.18	837.18	937.18	1037.18
	v	0.01967	0.9668		1.0409	1.1300	1.2115	1.2881	1.3615	1.5023	1.6384	1.7716	1.9030	2.0330	2.1619	2.2900	2.4173
	h	444.75	1204.8		1234.1	1269.1	1300.8	1330.5	1358.8	1413.6	1467.3	1520.9	1574.9	1629.5	1684.7	1740.6	1797.2
	s	0.6439	1.4677		1.4990	1.5346	1.5652	1.5925	1.6176	1.6628	1.7038	1.7419	1.7777	1.8116	1.8439	1.8748	1.9045
500 (467.01)	Sh				32.99	82.99	132.99	182.99	232.99	332.99	432.99	532.99	632.99	732.99	832.99	932.99	1032.99
	v	0.01975	0.9276		0.9919	1.0791	1.1584	1.2327	1.3037	1.4397	1.5708	1.6992	1.8256	1.9507	2.0746	2.1977	2.3200
	h	449.52	1204.7		1231.2	1267.0	1299.1	1329.1	1357.7	1412.7	1466.6	1520.3	1574.4	1629.1	1684.4	1740.3	1796.9
	s	0.6490	1.4639		1.4921	1.5284	1.5595	1.5871	1.6123	1.6578	1.6990	1.7371	1.7730	1.8069	1.8393	1.8702	1.8998
520 (471.07)	Sh				28.93	78.93	128.93	178.93	228.93	328.93	428.93	528.93	628.93	728.93	828.93	928.93	1028.93
	v	0.01982	0.8914		0.9466	1.0321	1.1094	1.1816	1.2504	1.3819	1.5085	1.6323	1.7542	1.8746	1.9940	2.1125	2.2302
	h	454.18	1204.5		1228.3	1264.8	1297.4	1327.7	1356.5	1411.8	1465.9	1519.7	1573.9	1628.7	1684.0	1740.0	1796.7
	s	0.6540	1.4601		1.4853	1.5223	1.5539	1.5818	1.6072	1.6530	1.6943	1.7325	1.7684	1.8024	1.8348	1.8657	1.8954
540 (475.01)	Sh				24.99	74.99	124.99	174.99	224.99	324.99	424.99	524.99	624.99	724.99	824.99	924.99	1024.99
	v	0.01990	0.8577		0.9045	0.9884	1.0640	1.1342	1.2010	1.3284	1.4508	1.5704	1.6880	1.8042	1.9193	2.0336	2.1471
	h	458.71	1204.4		1225.3	1262.5	1295.7	1326.3	1355.3	1410.9	1465.1	1519.1	1573.4	1628.2	1683.6	1739.7	1796.4
	s	0.6587	1.4565		1.4786	1.5164	1.5485	1.5767	1.6023	1.6483	1.6897	1.7280	1.7640	1.7981	1.8305	1.8615	1.8911
560 (478.84)	Sh				21.16	71.16	121.16	171.16	221.16	321.16	421.16	521.16	621.16	721.16	821.16	921.16	1021.16
	v	0.01998	0.8264		0.8653	0.9479	1.0217	1.0902	1.1552	1.2787	1.3972	1.5129	1.6266	1.7388	1.8500	1.9603	2.0699
	h	463.14	1204.2		1222.2	1260.3	1293.9	1324.9	1354.2	1410.0	1464.4	1518.6	1572.9	1627.8	1683.3	1739.4	1796.1
	s	0.6634	1.4529		1.4720	1.5106	1.5431	1.5717	1.5975	1.6438	1.6853	1.7237	1.7598	1.7939	1.8263	1.8573	1.8870
580 (482.57)	Sh				17.43	67.43	117.43	167.43	217.43	317.43	417.43	517.43	617.43	717.43	817.43	917.43	1017.43
	v	0.02006	0.7971		0.8287	0.9100	0.9824	1.0492	1.1125	1.2324	1.3473	1.4593	1.5693	1.6780	1.7855	1.8921	1.9980
	h	467.47	1203.9		1219.1	1258.0	1292.1	1323.4	1353.0	1409.2	1463.7	1518.0	1572.4	1627.4	1682.9	1739.1	1795.9
	s	0.6679	1.4495		1.4654	1.5049	1.5380	1.5668	1.5929	1.6394	1.6811	1.7196	1.7556	1.7898	1.8223	1.8533	1.8831
600 (486.20)	Sh				13.80	63.80	113.80	163.80	213.80	313.80	413.80	513.80	613.80	713.80	813.80	913.80	1013.80
	v	0.02013	0.7697		0.7944	0.8746	0.9456	1.0109	1.0726	1.1892	1.3008	1.4093	1.5160	1.6211	1.7252	1.8284	1.9309
	h	471.70	1203.7		1215.9	1255.6	1290.3	1322.0	1351.8	1408.3	1463.0	1517.4	1571.9	1627.0	1682.6	1738.8	1795.6
	s	0.6723	1.4461		1.4590	1.4993	1.5329	1.5621	1.5884	1.6351	1.6769	1.7155	1.7517	1.7859	1.8184	1.8494	1.8792
650 (494.89)	Sh				5.11	55.11	105.11	155.11	205.11	305.11	405.11	505.11	605.11	705.11	805.11	905.11	1005.11
	v	0.02032	0.7084		0.7173	0.7954	0.8634	0.9254	0.9835	1.0929	1.1969	1.2979	1.3969	1.4944	1.5909	1.6864	1.7813
	h	481.89	1202.8		1207.6	1249.6	1285.7	1318.3	1348.7	1406.0	1461.2	1515.9	1570.7	1625.9	1681.8	1738.0	1794.9
	s	0.6828	1.4381		1.4430	1.4858	1.5207	1.5507	1.5775	1.6249	1.6671	1.7059	1.7422	1.7765	1.8092	1.8403	1.8701
700 (503.08)	Sh					46.92	96.92	146.92	196.92	296.92	396.92	496.92	596.92	696.92	796.92	896.92	996.92
	v	0.02050	0.6556			0.7271	0.7928	0.8520	0.9072	1.0102	1.1078	1.2023	1.2948	1.3858	1.4757	1.5647	1.6530
	h	491.60	1201.8			1243.4	1281.0	1314.6	1345.6	1403.7	1459.4	1514.4	1569.4	1624.8	1680.7	1737.2	1794.3
	s	0.6928	1.4304			1.4726	1.5090	1.5399	1.5673	1.6154	1.6580	1.6970	1.7335	1.7679	1.8006	1.8318	1.8617
750 (510.84)	Sh					39.16	89.16	139.16	189.16	289.16	389.16	489.16	589.16	689.16	789.16	889.16	989.16
	v	0.02069	0.6095			0.6676	0.7313	0.7882	0.8409	0.9386	1.0306	1.1195	1.2063	1.2916	1.3759	1.4592	1.5419
	h	500.89	1200.7			1236.9	1276.1	1310.7	1342.5	1401.5	1457.6	1512.9	1568.2	1623.8	1679.8	1736.4	1793.6
	s	0.7022	1.4232			1.4598	1.4977	1.5296	1.5577	1.6065	1.6494	1.6886	1.7252	1.7598	1.7926	1.8239	1.8538
800 (518.21)	Sh					31.79	81.79	131.79	181.79	281.79	381.79	481.79	581.79	681.79	781.79	881.79	981.79
	v	0.02087	0.5690			0.6151	0.6774	0.7323	0.7828	0.8759	0.9631	1.0470	1.1289	1.2093	1.2885	1.3669	1.4446
	h	509.81	1199.4			1230.1	1271.1	1306.8	1339.3	1399.1	1455.8	1511.4	1566.9	1622.7	1678.9	1735.7	1792.9
	s	0.7111	1.4163			1.4472	1.4869	1.5198	1.5484	1.5980	1.6413	1.6807	1.7175	1.7522	1.7851	1.8164	1.8464
850 (525.24)	Sh					24.76	74.76	124.76	174.76	274.76	374.76	474.76	574.76	674.76	774.76	874.76	974.76
	v	0.02105	0.5330			0.5683	0.6296	0.6829	0.7315	0.8205	0.9034	0.9830	1.0606	1.1366	1.2115	1.2855	1.3588
	h	518.40	1198.0			1223.0	1265.9	1302.8	1336.0	1396.8	1454.0	1510.0	1565.7	1621.6	1678.0	1735.0	1792.3
	s	0.7197	1.4096			1.4347	1.4763	1.5102	1.5396	1.5899	1.6336	1.6733	1.7102	1.7450	1.7780	1.8094	1.8395
900 (531.95)	Sh					18.05	68.05	118.05	168.05	268.05	368.05	468.05	568.05	668.05	768.05	868.05	968.05
	v	0.02123	0.5009			0.5263	0.5869	0.6388	0.6858	0.7713	0.8504	0.9262	0.9998	1.0720	1.1430	1.2131	1.2825
	h	526.70	1196.4			1215.5	1260.6	1298.6	1332.7	1394.4	1452.2	1508.5	1564.6	1620.6	1677.1	1734.1	1791.6
	s	0.7279	1.4032			1.4223	1.4659	1.5010	1.5311	1.5822	1.6263	1.6662	1.7033	1.7382	1.7713	1.8028	1.8329

Sh = superheat, F
v = specific volume, cu ft per lb
h = enthalpy, Btu per lb
s = entropy, Btu per F per lb

7. APPENDIX

Critical Constants and Constants *a* and *b* of van der Waals Equation

Table A7.1 Critical Constants and Constants *a* and *b* of van der Waals Equation* (5)

(Units of a and b: atm, cu. ft, °K, and lb-moles)

Substance	T, °K	p, atm	Critical volume cu. ft/ lb-mole	$\dfrac{p_c v_c}{RT_c}$	van der Waals constants†	
					a	b
Acetylene	309.1	61.7	1.81	0.2755	1,129.	0.8232
Air	132.4	37.2	1.32‡	0.284	343.5	0.585
			1.49§	0.321		
Allylene	401.					
Ammonia	405.5	111.5	1.16	0.2425	1,076.	0.598
Argon	151.	48.	1.21	0.293	346.	0.517
Benzene	561.6	47.7	4.11		4,820.	1.935
Boron trifluoride	260.8	49.2			1,009.	0.871
n-Butane	426.0	36.0	4.01		3,675.	1.944
Carbon dioxide	304.1	72.9	1.54	0.280	925.	0.686
Carbon monoxide	134.4	34.6	1.44	0.282	381.	0.639
Carbon oxysulfide	378.	61.			1,708.	1.02
Chlorine	417.	76.	1.99	0.275	1,668.	0.90
Cyanogen	401.	59.			1,544.	1.12
Cyclohexane	554.1	40.6	4.95		5,513.	2.242
Dichlorodifluoromethane	384.6	39.56	3.55	0.276	2,726.	1.595
Dichloromethane	489.	51.4			3,392.	1.564
Diethyl amine	496.4	36.58			4,923.	2.229
Difluorotetrachloroethane	551.1					
Diisobutyl	549.9	24.5	7.72		8,997.	3.688
Diisopropyl	500.5	30.6	5.72		5,966.	2.688
Dimethyl amine	437.7	52.4			2,665.	1.372
Ethane	305.2	48.8	2.20	0.279	1,391.	1.028
Ethyl chloride	460.3	52.			2,970.	1.455
Ethylene	282.8	50.7	2.14	0.33	1,150.	0.9165

414

Table A7.1   Critical Constants and Constants *a* and *b* of van der Waals Equation* (*cont.*)

Substance	T, °K	p, atm	Critical volume cu. ft/ lb-mole	$\dfrac{p_c v_c}{RT_c}$	van der Waals constants†	
					a	b
Fluorine	144.	55.			302.7	0.418
Helium	5.2	2.3	0.97	0.328	8.57	0.372
n-Heptane	540.0	26.8	6.84		7,931.	3.311
n-Hexane	507.9	29.5	5.88		6,374.	2.829
Hydrocyanic acid	458.6	56.9	2.22	0.209	2,693.	1.323
Hydrogen	33.2	12.8	1.03	0.306	62.8	0.426
Hydrogen bromide	363.	84.			1,144.	0.71
Hydrogen chloride	324.5	81.6			942.	0.654
Hydrogen iodide	424.	82.			1,598.	0.85
Hydrogen sulfide	373.5	88.9			1,145.	0.691
Isobutane	407.1	37.0	3.99		3,265.	1.808
Isopentane	460.9	32.92	4.93		4,704.	2.300
Krypton	210. ?	54. ?	1.70 ?		596. ?	0.64 ?
Mercury	1,172.	180.			5,100.	1.070
Methane	191.1	45.8	1.59	0.289	581.2	0.6855
Methyl chloride	416.2	65.8	2.19 ?		1,920.	1.041
Methyl fluoride	317.6	58.0			1,268.	0.899
Monoethyl amine	456.3	55.54			2,735.	1.351
Monomethyl amine	430.0	73.6			1,832.	0.960
Monopropyl amine	496.9	46.76			3,853.	1.747
Neon	44.4	25.9	0.66	0.297	55.4	0.282
Nitric oxide	179. ?	65. ?			359.	0.45 ?
Nitrogen	126.0	33.5	1.44	0.292	346.	0.618
Nitrous oxide	309.6	71.7	1.57 ?		974.	0.709
n-Octane	569.3	24.6	7.85		9,604.	3.803
Oxygen	154.3	49.7	1.19	0.292	349.5	0.510
Ozone	268. ?	92. ?			569.	0.479
n-Pentane	470.3	33.0	4.98		4,886.	2.342
Phosgene	456. ?					
Phosphine	325.	65.			1,185.	0.82
Phosphorus	948.1	80.			8,200.	1.945
Propane	369.9	42.01	3.12		2,374.	1.446
Propyl chloride	503.2	45.18			4,187.	1.828
Propylene	364.8	45.0	2.91		2,155.	1.332
Silicon tetrafluoride	272.	50.			1,079.	0.89
Sulfur dioxide	430.3	77.7	1.97		1,737.	0.910
Sulfur trioxide	491.4	83.8	2.02	0.262	2,105.	0.964
Trifluorotrichloroethane	460.7					
Water	647.3	218.2	0.91	0.232	1,400.	0.488
Xenon	290.	58.		0.276	1,057.	0.82

* Most of the data taken from *Bur. Standards Circ.* 279. Hydrocarbon data from Edmister, *Ind. Eng. Chem.*, 30, 353 (1938).
† Calculated from the critical pressure and temperature by

$$a = \frac{27}{64} \frac{R^2 T_c^2}{p_c} \qquad b = \frac{RT_c}{8 p_c} \qquad R = 1.3145$$

‡ Critical point.
§ Cricondentherm point.
? Indicates doubtful values.

Table A7.2 Conversion Factors for *a* and *b* of van der Waals Equation (5)

(Original units: atm., cu. ft, °K, lb-moles)

To change to	Multiply *a* by	Multiply *b* by
(1) atm, liters, °K, g-moles	0.003896	0.0624
(2) atm, cc, °K, g-moles	3896.0	62.4
(3) atm, cu. ft, °R, lb-moles	1.0	1.0
(4) lb/sq. in., cu. ft, °R, lb-moles	14.7	1.0

APPENDIX 8.

Specific Heats
of Liquids
and Gases

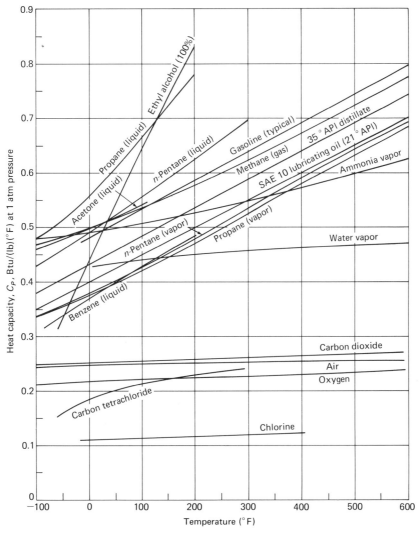

Figure A8.1 Specific heats of various liquids and gases at 1 atm pressure as a function of temperature (3)

417

Specific heat = Btu/(lb)(°F) = Pcu/(lb)(°C)

No.	Liquid	Range (°C)
29	Acetic acid (100%)	0–80
32	Acetone	20–50
52	Ammonia	−70–50
37	Amyl alcohol	−50–25
26	Amyl acetate	0–100
30	Aniline	0–130
23	Benzene	10–80
27	Benzyl alcohol	−20–30
10	Benzyl chloride	−30–30
49	Brine (25% CaCl$_2$)	−40–20
51	Brine (25% NaCl)	−40–20
44	Butyl alcohol	0–100
2	Carbon disulphide	−100–25
3	Carbon tetrachloride	10–60
8	Chlorobenzene	0–100
4	Chloroform	0–50
21	Decane	−80–25
6A	Dichloroethane	−30–60
5	Dichloromethane	−40–50
15	Diphenyl	80–120
22	Diphenylmethane	30–100
16	Diphenyl oxide	0–200
16	Dowtherm A	0–200
24	Ethyl acetate	−50–25
42	Ethyl alcohol (100%)	30–80
46	Ethyl alcohol (95%)	20–80
50	Ethyl alcohol (50%)	20–80
25	Ethyl benzene	0–100
1	Ethyl bromide	5–25
13	Ethyl chloride	−30–40
36	Ethyl ether	−100–25
7	Ethyl iodide	0–100
39	Ethylene glycol	−40–200
2A	Freon-11(CCl$_3$F)	−20–70
6	Freon-12(CCl$_2$F$_2$)	−40–15
4A	Freon-21(CHCl$_2$F)	−20–70
7A	Freon-22(CHClF$_2$)	−20–60
3A	Freon-113(CCl$_2$F-CClF$_2$)	−20–70
38	Glycerol	−40–20
28	Heptane	0–60
35	Hexane	−80–20
48	Hydrochloric acid (30%)	20–100
41	Isoamyl alcohol	10–100
43	Isobutyl alcohol	0–100
47	Isopropyl alcohol	−20–50
31	Isopropyl ether	−80–20
40	Methyl alcohol	−40–20
13A	Methyl chloride	−80–20
14	Naphthalene	90–200
12	Nitrobenzene	0–100
34	Nonane	−50–25
33	Octane	−50–25
3	Perchlorethylene	−30–140
45	Propyl alcohol	−20–100
20	Pyridine	−50–25
9	Sulphuric acid (98%)	10–45
11	Sulphur dioxide	−20–100
23	Toluene	0–60
53	Water	10–200
18	Xylene meta	0–100
19	Xylene ortho	0–100
17	Xylene para	0–100

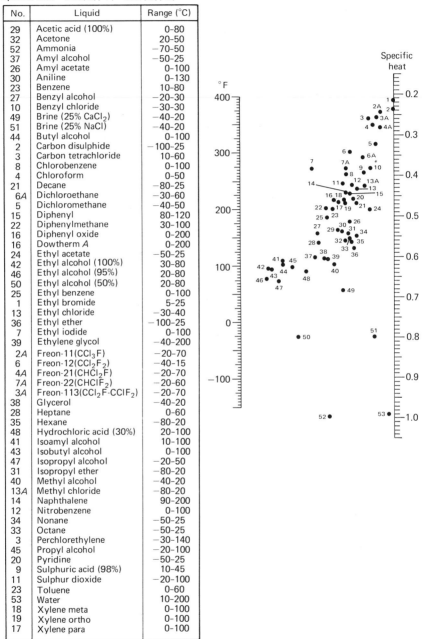

Figure A8.2 Specific heats of liquids (7)

Thermal Conductivities of Liquids and Gases, Metals and Nonmetals

Table A9.1 Thermal Conductivities of Gases and Vapors, $k = $ Btu/hr-ft²-°F/ft (7, 10)

Substance	Temperature, °F	k
Acetone	32	0.0057
	115	0.0074
Air	−148	0.0091
	32	0.0140
	212	0.0184
	392	0.0224
Ammonia	32	0.0126
	212	0.0192
Carbon dioxide	32	0.0084
	212	0.0128
Carbon monoxide	32	0.0134
	212	0.0176
Chlorine	32	0.0043
Hydrogen	32	0.1000
	212	0.1300
Methane	32	0.0180
	212	0.0255
Nitrogen	32	0.0139
	212	0.0181
Oxygen	−148	0.0091
	122	0.0166
Sulfur dioxide	32	0.0050
	212	0.0069
Water vapor	212	0.0136
	752	0.0279

Table A9.2 Thermal Conductivities of Liquids, $k = $ Btu/hr-ft²-°F/ft (7, 10)

Substance	°F	k
Acetic acid 100%	68	0.099
Acetic acid 50%	68	0.200
Acetone	86	0.102
	167	0.095
Benzene	86	0.092
	140	0.087
Ethyl alcohol 100%	68	0.105
	122	0.087
Ethyl alcohol 40%	68	0.224
Ethylene glycol	32	0.153
Glycerol 100%	68	0.164
	212	0.164
Glycerol 40%	68	0.259
n-Hexane	86	0.081
Kerosene	68	0.086
Methyl alcohol 100%	68	0.124
	122	0.114
Methyl alcohol 40%	68	0.234
n-Octane	86	0.083
NaCl 25%	86	0.330
Oil (light, MW = 284, μ = 62 cp at 68° F)	86	0.077
Olive oil	68	0.097
	212	0.095
Sulfuric acid 90%	86	0.210
Sulfuric acid 30%	86	0.300
Toluene	86	0.086
Water	32	0.320
	200	0.392

Table A9.3   Thermal Conductivities of Nonmetallic Substances,
$k =$ Btu/hr-ft^2-°F/ft (7, 9, 10)

Substance	°F	k
Asbestos-cement board	68	0.43
Brick		
Building	68	0.40
Fire clay	392	0.58
	1832	0.95
Calcium carbonate (natural)	86	1.30
Calcium sulfate (building material)	77	0.15
Celluloid	86	0.12
Concrete		0.54
Cork board	86	0.025
Felt (wool)	86	0.03
Glass (window)		0.3–0.6
Rubber (hard)	32	0.087
Silk	32	0.025
	100	0.028
Wood (across grain)		
Oak	59	0.12
Maple	122	0.11
Pine	59	0.087
Wool (animal)	32	0.022
	100	0.027

Table A9.4 Thermal Conductivities of Metals, $k = Btu/hr\text{-}ft^2\text{-}°F/ft$ (10)

Substance	Thermal conductivity, k							Melting point, °F
	32°F 0°C	212 100	392 200	572 300	752 400	932 500	1112 600	
Aluminum	117	119	124	133	144	155	—	1220
Brass (70% copper, 30% zinc)	56	60	63	66	67	—	—	1724
Cast iron	32	30	28	26	25	—	—	2192
Copper, pure	224	218	215	212	210	207	204	1976
Graphite (longitudinal)	97	87	76	66	58	53	48	—
Lead	20	19	18	18	—	—	—	621
Nickel	36	34	33	32	—	—	—	2642
Silver	242	238	—	—	—	—	—	1760
Steel, mild	—	26	26	25	23	22	21	2507
Steel, stainless								
301, 302, 303, 304, 305	9.4	—	—	—	—	12.4	—	—
321, 347	9.3	—	—	—	—	12.8	—	—
403, 404, 410, 416	14.4	—	—	—	—	16.6	—	—
501, 502	21.2	—	—	—	—	19.5	—	—
Tin	36	34	33	—	—	—	—	450
Wrought iron, Swedish	—	32	30	28	26	23	—	2741
Zinc	65	64	62	59	54	—	—	786

Viscosities

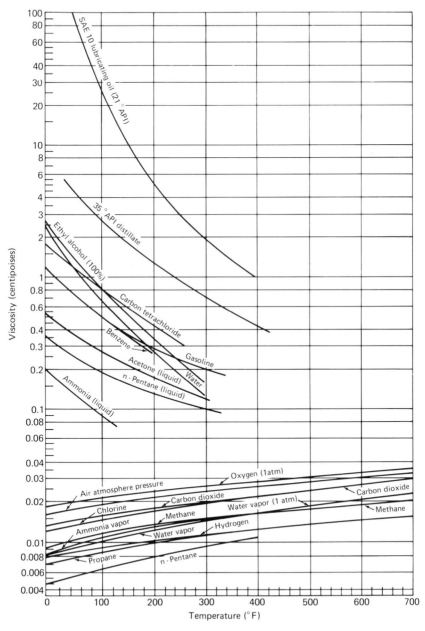

Figure A10.1   Viscosities of various liquids and gases as a function of temperature at 1 atm (3)

11. APPENDIX

Dimensions, Capacities, and Weights of Standard Steel Pipes

Table A11.1   Dimensions, Capacities, and
Weights of Standard Steel Pipes (8)

Nominal pipe size, in.	Outside diameter, in.	Schedule No.	Wall thickness, in.	Inside diameter, in.	Cross-sectional area of metal, in.²
⅛	0.405	40	0.068	0.269	0.072
		80	0.095	0.215	0.093
¼	0.540	40	0.088	0.364	0.125
		80	0.119	0.302	0.157
⅜	0.675	40	0.091	0.493	0.167
		80	0.126	0.423	0.217
½	0.840	40	0.109	0.622	0.250
		80	0.147	0.546	0.320
¾	1.050	40	0.113	0.824	0.333
		80	0.154	0.742	0.433
1	1.315	40	0.133	1.049	0.494
		80	0.179	0.957	0.639
1¼	1.660	40	0.140	1.380	0.668
		80	0.191	1.278	0.881
1½	1.900	40	0.145	1.610	0.800
		80	0.200	1.500	1.069
2	2.375	40	0.154	2.067	1.075
		80	0.218	1.939	1.477
2½	2.875	40	0.203	2.469	1.704
		80	0.276	2.323	2.254
3	3.500	40	0.216	3.068	2.228
		80	0.300	2.900	3.016
3½	4.000	40	0.226	3.548	2.680
		80	0.318	3.364	3.678
4	4.500	40	0.237	4.026	3.17
		80	0.337	3.826	4.41
5	5.563	40	0.258	5.047	4.30
		80	0.375	4.813	6.11
6	6.625	40	0.280	6.065	5.58
		80	0.432	5.761	8.40
8	8.625	40	0.322	7.981	8.396
		80	0.500	7.625	12.76
10	10.75	40	0.365	10.020	11.91
		80	0.594	9.562	18.95
12	12.75	40	0.406	11.938	15.74
		80	0.688	11.374	26.07

† Based on USAS B 16.10.

Inside sectional area, ft²	Circumference, ft, or surface, ft²/ft of length		Capacity at 1 ft/sec velocity		Pipe weight, lb/ft
	Outside	Inside	U.S. gal/min	Water, lb/hr	
0.00040	0.106	0.0705	0.179	89.5	0.24
0.00025	0.106	0.0563	0.113	56.5	0.31
0.00072	0.141	0.095	0.323	161.5	0.42
0.00050	0.141	0.079	0.224	112.0	0.54
0.00133	0.177	0.129	0.596	298.0	0.57
0.00098	0.177	0.111	0.440	220.0	0.74
0.00211	0.220	0.163	0.945	472.0	0.85
0.00163	0.220	0.143	0.730	365.0	1.09
0.00371	0.275	0.216	1.665	832.5	1.13
0.00300	0.275	0.194	1.345	672.5	1.47
0.00600	0.344	0.275	2.690	1,345	1.68
0.00499	0.344	0.250	2.240	1,120	2.17
0.01040	0.435	0.361	4.57	2,285	2.27
0.00891	0.435	0.335	3.99	1,995	3.00
0.01414	0.497	0.421	6.34	3,170	2.72
0.01225	0.497	0.393	5.49	2,745	3.63
0.02330	0.622	0.541	10.45	5,225	3.65
0.02050	0.622	0.508	9.20	4,600	5.02
0.03322	0.753	0.647	14.92	7,460	5.79
0.02942	0.753	0.608	13.20	6,600	7.66
0.05130	0.916	0.803	23.00	11,500	7.58
0.04587	0.916	0.759	20.55	10,275	10.25
0.06870	1.047	0.929	30.80	15,400	9.11
0.06170	1.047	0.881	27.70	13,850	12.51
0.08840	1.178	1.054	39.6	19,800	10.79
0.07986	1.178	1.002	35.8	17,900	14.98
0.1390	1.456	1.321	62.3	31,150	14.62
0.1263	1.456	1.260	57.7	28,850	20.78
0.2006	1.734	1.588	90.0	45,000	18.97
0.1810	1.734	1.508	81.1	40,550	28.57
0.3474	2.258	2.089	155.7	77,850	28.55
0.3171	2.258	1.996	142.3	71,150	43.39
0.5475	2.814	2.620	246.0	123,000	40.48
0.4987	2.814	2.503	223.4	111,700	64.40
0.7773	3.338	3.13	349.0	174,500	53.56
0.7056	3.338	2.98	316.7	158,350	88.57

12. APPENDIX
Friction and Surfaces

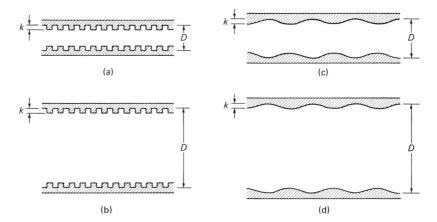

Figure A12.1 Types of roughness (8)

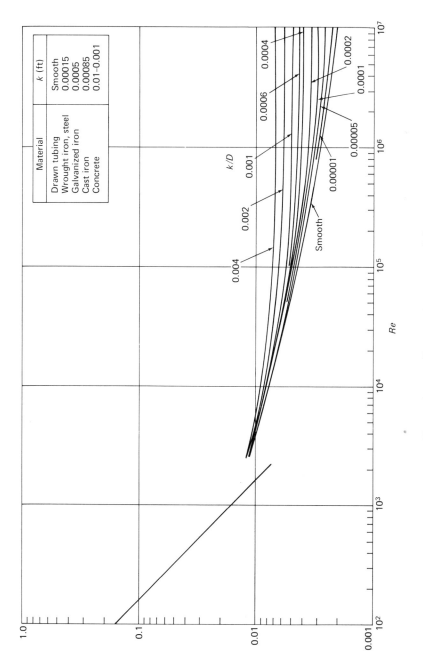

Figure A12.2 Friction-factor chart (8)

13. APPENDIX

Standard Heats
of Formation

Table A13.1   Standard Heats of Formation (9)

ΔH_f is the heat in kilocalories which would be absorbed were one gram-mole of the indicated compound to be formed from its constituent elements at a constant temperature of 25° C, reactants and product being pure (unmixed) substances at a pressure of one atmosphere.

Compound	Formula	State	ΔH_f kcal/g-mole
Acetaldehyde	CH_3CHO	gas	-39.72
Acetic acid	CH_3COOH	liquid	-116.2
Acetone	CH_3COCH_3	liquid	-59.32
Acetylene	C_2H_2	gas	54.194
Ammonia	NH_3	gas	-10.96
Benzene	C_6H_6	gas	19.82
Carbon dioxide	CO_2	gas	-94.052
Carbon disulfide	CS_2	gas	28.11
Carbon monoxide	CO	gas	-26.416
Ethane	C_2H_6	gas	-20.236
Ethyl alcohol	C_2H_5OH	gas	-52.23
Ethylene	C_2H_4	gas	12.496
Ethylene oxide	C_2H_4O	gas	-16.1
Ethylene glycol	$C_2H_6O_2$	gas	-92.53
Formaldehyde	CH_2O	gas	-28.29
Hydrogen chloride	HCl	gas	-22.063
Hydrogen cyanide	HCN	gas	31.1
Hydrogen sulfide	H_2S	gas	-4.77
Methane	CH_4	gas	-17.889
Methyl alcohol	CH_3OH	gas	-48.08
Nitric acid	HNO_3	liquid	-41.35
Nitric oxide	NO	gas	21.600
Nitrogen dioxide	NO_2	gas	7.96

Table A13.1   Standard Heats of Formation (*cont.*)

Compound	Formula	State	ΔH_f kcal/g-mole
Nitrous oxide	N_2O	gas	19.55
Phenol	C_6H_5OH	liquid	-37.80
Propane	C_3H_8	gas	-24.820
Propylene	C_3H_6	gas	4.879
Sulfur dioxide	SO_2	gas	-70.94
Sulfuric acid	H_2SO_4	liquid	-193.69
Sulfur trioxide	SO_3	gas	-94.39
Toluene	$C_6H_5CH_3$	liquid	2.867
Urea	NH_2CONH_2	liquid	-77.55
Water	H_2O	liquid	-68.317
Water	H_2O	gas	-57.798

14. APPENDIX

Standard Heats
of Combustion

Table A14.1 Standard Heats of Combustion (6)

ΔH_c is the heat in kilocalories which would be absorbed were one gram-mole of the indicated compound to react with oxygen at a constant temperature of 25° C and a constant pressure of one atmosphere to form $CO_2(g)$, $H_2O(l)$, $SO_2(g)$, and free N_2, to the extent that these products are pertinent.

Compound	Formula	State	ΔH_c kcal/g-mole
Acetic anhydride	$C_6H_4O_3$	liquid	-426.00
Aniline	$C_6H_5NH_2$	liquid	$-812.$
Benzene	C_6H_6	liquid	-780.98
Camphor	$C_{10}H_{16}O$	solid	$-1411.$
Carbon disulfide	CS_2	liquid	-256.97
Carbonyl sulfide	COS	gas	-132.21
Cyanogen	C_2N_2	gas	-261.70
Cyclopentane	C_5H_{10}	liquid	-786.54
Dimethyl sulfide	C_2H_6S	liquid	-450.42
Ethyl alcohol	C_2H_5OH	liquid	-326.70
Ethyl mercaptan	C_2H_6S	liquid	-448.0
Ethylene glycol	$C_2H_6O_2$	liquid	-284.48
Formic acid	$CHOOH$	liquid	-64.57
Glycerol	$C_3H_8O_3$	liquid	-396.27
Methyl alcohol	CH_3OH	liquid	-173.65
Methyl mercaptan	CH_4S	gas	-298.68
Naphthalene	$C_{10}H_8$	solid	-1231.6
Nitrobenzene	$C_6H_5NO_2$	liquid	$-739.$
Phenol	C_6H_5OH	gas	-747.55
Phthalic anhydride	$C_8H_4O_3$	solid	-781.4
Trinitrotoluene	$C_7H_5N_3O_6$	solid	$-821.$
Urea	NH_2CONH_2	solid	-151.05

Appendix
References

1. American Chemical Society. 1970. Table of the Elements. *Chemical & Engineering News,* January 26.

2. American Society of Mechanical Engineers. 1967. "1967 ASME Steam Tables."

3. Brown, G. G., *et al.,* 1956. *Unit operations.* New York: John Wiley.

4. Combustion Engineering, Inc. "Steam Tables." Windsor, Conn.: Combustion Engineering, Inc.

5. Dodge, B. F. 1944. *Chemical engineering thermodynamics.* New York: McGraw-Hill.

6. Hougen, O. A., Watson, K. M., and Ragatz, R. A. 1954. *Chemical process principles: Part I, Material and energy balances.* New York: John Wiley.

7. McAdams, W. H. 1954. *Heat transmission.* New York: McGraw-Hill.

8. McCabe, W. L., and Smith, J. C. 1967. *Unit operations of chemical engineering,* 2d ed. New York: McGraw-Hill.

9. Perry, J. H., *et al.,* 1963. *Chemical engineers' handbook,* 4th ed. New York: McGraw-Hill.

10. Peters, M. S. 1954. *Elementary chemical engineering.* New York: McGraw-Hill.

11. Thatcher, C. M. 1962. *Fundamentals of chemical engineering.* Columbus, Ohio: Charles E. Merril Books.

Credits

Appendix 4

From American Chemical Society, Table of the elements. *Chemical & Engineering News,* January 26, 1970.

Appendix 6

From Combustion Engineering, Inc., *Steam Tables.* Windsor, Conn., 1967, pp. 6–21.

Appendix 7

From *Chemical Engineering Thermodynamics* by B. F. Dodge. Copyright © 1944 by McGraw-Hill, Inc. Used with permission of McGraw-Hill Book Company, Tables IV, V, pp. 662, 663.

Appendix 8

From Brown, G. G., et al. *Unit Operations.* New York: John Wiley, 1956, Fig. 545, p. 586. And from *Heat Transmission* by W. H. McAdams. Copyright © 1954 by McGraw-Hill, Inc. Used with permission of McGraw-Hill Book Company.

Appendix 9

From *Heat Transmission by* W. H. McAdams. Copyright © 1954 by McGraw-Hill, Inc. Used with permission of McGraw-Hill Book Company. And from *Chemical Engineers' Handbook,* 4th ed. by J. H. Perry. Copyright © 1963 by McGraw-Hill, Inc. Used with permission of McGraw-Hill Book Company.

Appendix 10

Reprinted with permission from Brown, G. G., et al., *Unit Operations.* New York: John Wiley, 1956, Fig. 546, p. 587.

Appendix 11

From *Unit Operations of Chemical Engineering* by W. L. McCabe and J. C. Smith. Copyright © 1967 by McGraw-Hill, Inc. Used with permission of McGraw-Hill Book Company, Fig. 5–9, p. 104.

Appendix 12

From *Unit Operations of Chemical Engineering* by W. L. McCabe and J. C. Smith. Copyright © 1967 by McGraw-Hill, Inc. Used with permission of McGraw-Hill Book Company, Fig. 5–10, p. 105.

Appendix 13

From *Chemical Engineers' Handbook,* 4th ed. by J. H. Perry. Copyright © 1963 by McGraw-Hill, Inc. Used with permission of McGraw-Hill Book Company.

Appendix 14

Reprinted with permission from Hougen, O. A., Watson, K. M., and Ragatz, R. A., *Chemical Process Principles:* Part I, *Material and Energy Balances.* New York: John Wiley, 1954.

Index